C000163894

Building site works, substructure and plant

General editor: Colin Bassett B.Sc., F.C.I.O.B., F.F.B.

Publisher's note
The contents of this book were originally published in the author's larger four-volume work entitled *Construction Technology* (1973, 1974, 1976 and 1977), (second edition of all four volumes 1987). These chapters have been reproduced in a single volume reference book to meet the well-established need for such a volume.

Note regarding Building Regulations
The reader's attention is drawn to the fact that the Building Regulations, British Standards, Codes of Practice and similar documents are constantly under review and are therefore often revised or amended. It is therefore important that all the Building Regulations, British Standards, Codes of Practice and similar documents quoted in this book are checked by the reader to ensure that the current regulations or recommendations are known and used in practice. Changes in regulations and recommendations often change specific data but the basic principles embodied within them often remain unchanged.

Building site works, substructure and plant

Second edition

R. Chudley M.C.I.O.B.
Chartered Builder

Illustrated by the author

Longman Scientific & Technical

Longman Scientific & Technical,
Longman Group UK Limited,
Longman House, Burnt Mill, Harlow,
Essex CM20 2JE, England
and Associated Companies throughout the world.

© Construction Press 1982
This edition © Longman Group UK Limited 1988

All rights reserved; no part of this publication may be reproduced, stored in a retrieval system, or transmitted in any form or by an means, electronic, mechanical, photo-copying, recording, or otherwise without either the prior written permission of the Publishers or a licence permitting restricted copying in the United Kingdom issued by the Copyright Licensing Agency Ltd, 33−34 Alfred Place, London, WC1E 7DP.

First published 1982 by Construction Press
Reprinted 1985
Second impression 1990

British Library Cataloguing in Publication Data
Chudley, R. (Roy)
   Building site works, substructure and
   plant. — 2nd ed.
   1. Buildings. Construction. Sites.
   Organisation
   I. Title
   690
ISBN 0-582-01974-5

Produced by Longman Group (FE) Limited
Printed in Hong Kong

Contents

Preface to the first edition

The compilation of this book has been carried out with the main objective of providing a reference book for the practical and practising builder. It may also be a useful reference work for building students of all levels engaged in assignment and project work. The contents have been arranged to cover the basic site organisation processes including plant selection together with typical temporary and permanent works up to ground level.

The contents of this book are based on typical construction technology concepts. Technology can be defined as the science of mechanical and industrial arts, as contrasted with fine arts. Similarly science can be defined as an ordered arrangement of facts under classes or headings, theoretical knowledge as distinguished from practical knowledge and knowledge of principles and rules. The information contained within this book is therefore based on the principles and techniques of construction and not on actual case studies of works in progress, however, if experience and practical knowledge are added to the technological concepts the result should provide buildings and construction techniques of a high and therefore acceptable standard.

The reader's attention is particularly drawn to the note at the beginning of the text regarding current Building Regulations.

R. Chudley
Guildford 1982

Acknowledgements

We are grateful to the following for permission to reproduce copyright material:

British Standards Institution for reference to British Standards Codes of Practice; Building Research Station for extracts from *Building Research Station Digests*; Her Majesty's Stationery Office for extracts from Acts, Regulations and Statutory Instruments; the Electricity Council for extracts from their publication *Lighting for Building Sites*.

Introduction

There are, in general, two aspects of building technology:

1. Conventional or traditional methods.
2. Modern or industrialised methods.

The first is covered by the syllabus of the first two years of most building technology courses, whereas the second is an extension of the first and is covered by advanced building technology courses. This does not mean that there is no overlapping or reference to modern techniques in elementary courses. The first two years of a building technology course concentrates on the smaller type of structure such as a domestic dwelling of one or two storeys built by traditional methods. Generally it is cheaper to construct this type of building by these methods unless large numbers of similar types are being erected at the same time.

By industrial methods we mean those which are mainly composed of factory produced components to a module or standard increment such as 300 mm.

It is a fact that over half of the building contractors in this country employ only a few operatives and are therefore small firms. These firms are mainly engaged on maintenance work, extensions and one-off jobs, in the main using traditional methods and materials. It is essential that all students of building have a good knowledge of these methods and materials. For those that make their careers in the industrialised building side of the industry they will find that the majority of these systems have been developed from traditional building techniques.

The building team

Building is essentially a team effort in which each member has an important role to play. Figure 1 shows the organisation structure of a typical team and the role of each member is defined below:

Building owner: the client; the person who commissions the work and directly or indirectly employs everybody.

Architect: engaged by the building owner as his agent to design, advise and ensure that the project is kept within cost and complies with the design.

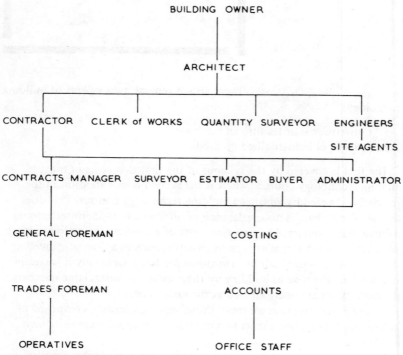

Fig. 1. The building team

Clerk of works: employed on large contracts as the architect's on-site representative. He has only liaison powers and cannot issue instructions on his own behalf; he can only offer advice.

Quantity surveyor: engaged to prepare bills of quantities, check tenders, prepare interim valuations and advise the architect on the cost of variations.

Engineers: specialists such as a structural engineer employed to work with the architect on that particular aspect of the design.

Site agent: on large contracts the engineer's on-site representative.

Contractor: employed by the building owner, on the architect's advice, to carry out the constructional works. He takes his instructions from the architect.

Surveyor: employed by the contractor to check and assist the quantity surveyor in the preparation of interim valuations and final accounts. He may also measure work done for bonus and sub-contractor payments.

Estimator: prepares unit rates for the pricing of tenders and carries out pre-tender investigations into the cost aspects of the proposed contract.

Buyer: orders materials, obtains quotations for the supply of materials and services.

Accountant: prepares and submits accounts to clients and makes payments to suppliers and sub-contractors. He may also have a costing department which would allocate the labour and material costs to each contract to assist with the preparation of future tenders and with the preparation of accounts.

Administrator: organises the general clerical duties of the contractor's office for the payment of wages, insurances and all necessary correspondence.

Contracts manager: liaises between the office and the site and has overall responsibility for the site operations.

General foreman (sometimes called the agent): the contractor's on-site representative, responsible for the day-to-day running of the site.

Trades foreman: in charge of a trade gang.

Operatives: the main work force on-site, including tradesmen, apprentices and labourers.

The size of the building firm or the size of the contract will determine the composition of any team. For the medium sized contract some of the above jobs may be combined: the surveyor may also fulfil the function of estimator.

Statutory Instruments

These are rules which are made under an Act of Parliament and are therefore legally binding on the builder and the architect. The main ones with which the builder is concerned are:

The Construction Regulations: these are for the health, safety and welfare of operatives and deal with such things as excavations, scaffolds, site accommodation and lifting equipment.

The Building Regulations 1985: these are designed to set minimum standards for buildings in the context of functional requirements to achieve acceptable health, safety and energy conservation objectives. They are made under the consolidating statute The Building Act 1984 and apply throughout England and Wales.

The Building Regulations are supported by a series of Approved Documents (AD's) which are not mandatory but give practical guidance on how to comply with the requirements of the regulations. There is also a set of mandatory rules on means of escape in case of fire.

Generally the control of the Building Regulations is vested in the local authority but a developer can opt for private certification whereby the developer and an approved inspector jointly serve an initial notice on the local authority describing the proposed works which the local authority can reject within ten days. In this option the responsibility for inspecting plans, work, site supervision and certification of satisfactory completion rests with the approved inspector as set out in The Building (Approved Inspectors) Regulations 1985.

British Standards

These are issued by the British Standards Institution, British Standards House, 2 Park Street, London W1Y 4AA. The standards are presented in two forms:

Codes of practice: these are codes of good practice in particular fields of activity such as drainage and structural steelwork.

Standard specifications: these are specifications which deal with materials and components such as bricks and windows.

Draft for development: these are issued instead of a Code of Practice or Standard Specification where there is insufficient data or information to make a firm or positive recommendation.

Published document: these are publications which cannot be placed into any of the above categories.

Codes of practice and standard specifications are compiled by specialist committees of interested parties in the particular subject of the code or specification. It must be remembered that these codes and specifications are only recommendations. Generally British Standard Specifications and British Standard Codes of Practice will satisfy the requirements of the building regulations. Copies of the codes and specifications can be obtained from the British Standards Institution, Sales Branch, 101 Pentonville Road, London N1 9ND.

Metrication

The building industry has changed to the metric system of measurement and during any period of change there is bound to be a great deal of modification and rationalisation as the designers and manufacturers adapt themselves to the new units, particularly with the recommendation for coordinated planning based on the preferred dimension of 300 mm.

Although the metric system has been adopted it should be remembered that a large proportion of the nation's building stock was designed and constructed using imperial units of measurement which are not always compatible with their metric equivalents. It can be assumed therefore that many building materials and components will be continued to be produced to imperial sizes for the purpose of maintenance, replacement and/or refurbishment.

Part I
Site works and accommodation

1
Site works and setting out

When a builder is given possession of a building site he will have been provided with a site lay-out plan and the drawings necessary for him to erect the building. Under most forms of building contract it is the builder's responsibility to see that the setting out is accurate.

The site having been taken over, the task of preparing for and setting out the building can be commenced. These operations can be grouped under three headings:

1. Clearing the site.
2. Setting out the building.
3. Establishing a datum level.

Clearing the site

This may involve the demolition of existing buildings, the grubbing out of bushes and trees and the removal of soil to reduce levels. Demolition is a skilled occupation and should only be tackled by a skilled demolition contractor. The removal of trees can be carried out by manual or mechanical means. The removal of large trees should be left to the expert.

Building Regulation C1 'The ground to be covered by the building shall be reasonably free from vegetable matter.' This is in effect to sterilise the ground since the top 300 mm or so will contain plant life and decaying vegetation. This means that the top soil is easily compressed and would

3

be unsuitable for foundations. Top soil is valuable as a top dressing for gardens and may be disposed of in this manner. The method chosen for carrying out the site clearance work will be determined by overall economics.

Setting out the site

The first task is to establish a base line from which the whole of the building can be set out. The position of this line must be clearly marked on-site so that it can be re-established at any time. For on-site measuring a steel tape should be used (30 metres would be a suitable length). Linen and plastic coated tapes are also available. The disadvantage with linen tapes is that they are liable to stretch.

After the base line has been set out, marked and checked the main lines of the building can be set out, each corner being marked with a stout peg. A check should now be made of the setting-out lines for right-angles and correct lengths. There are several methods of checking if a right-angle has been established and in fact the setting out would have been carried out by one of these methods. A check must still be made and it is advisable to check by a different method to that used for the setting out. The setting-out procedure and the methods of checking the right-angles are illustrated in Fig. I.1.

After the setting out of the main building lines has been completed and checked, profile boards are set up as shown in Fig. I.2. These are set up clear of the foundation trench positions to locate the trench, foundations and walls. Profile boards are required at all trench and wall intersections.

Establishing a datum level

It is important that all levels in a building are taken from a fixed point called a 'datum'. This point should now be established, wherever possible this should be related to an ordnance bench-mark. This is an arrow with a horizontal mark above the arrow, the centre line of the horizontal being the actual level indicated on an ordnance survey map. Bench-marks are found cut or let into the sides of walls and buildings. Where there are no bench-marks on or near the site a suitable permanent datum must be established. A site datum or temporary bench-mark could be a post set in concrete or a concrete plinth set up on site.

SLOPING SITES

Very few sites are level and therefore before any building work can be commenced the area covered by the building must be levelled. In building

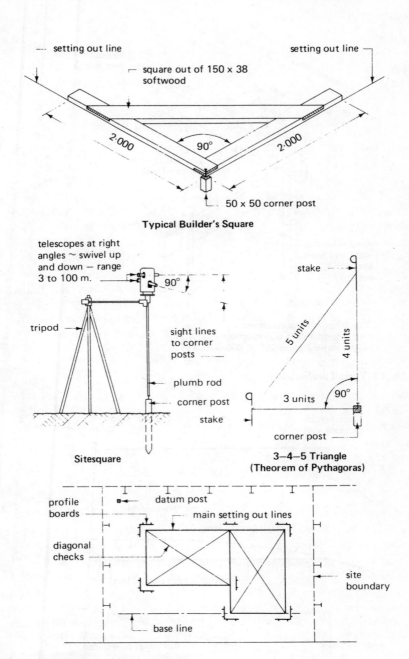

setting out line

setting out line

square out of 150 × 38 softwood

2·000

90°

2·000

50 × 50 corner post

Typical Builder's Square

telescopes at right angles ~ swivel up and down — range 3 to 100 m.

90°

tripod

sight lines to corner posts

plumb rod

corner post

stake

Sitesquare

stake

5 units

4 units

3 units

90°

corner post

3–4–5 Triangle (Theorem of Pythagoras)

profile boards

datum post

main setting out lines

diagonal checks

site boundary

base line

Fig. I.1 Setting out and checking methods

5

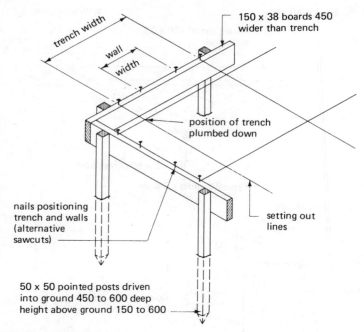

150 x 38 boards 450 wider than trench

trench width

wall width

position of trench plumbed down

nails positioning trench and walls (alternative sawcuts)

setting out lines

50 x 50 pointed posts driven into ground 450 to 600 deep height above ground 150 to 600

Fig. I.2 Typical profile board

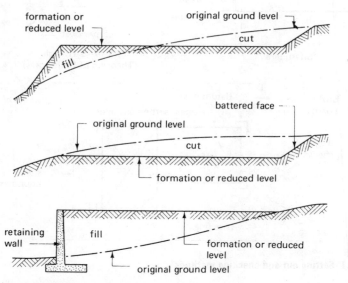

formation or reduced level

original ground level

cut

fill

battered face

original ground level

cut

formation or reduced level

retaining wall

fill

formation or reduced level

original ground level

Fig. I.3 Sloping sites

6

terms this operation is called reducing levels. Three methods can be used and it is the most economical which is usually employed.

1. **Cut and fill:** the usual method because, if properly carried out, the amount of cut will equal the amount of fill.
2. **Cut:** this method has the advantage of giving undisturbed soil over the whole of the site but has the disadvantage of the cost of removing the spoil from the site.
3. **Fill:** a method not to be recommended because, if the building is sited on the filled area, either deep foundations would be needed or the risk of settlement at a later stage would have to be accepted.

The principles of the above methods are shown in Fig. I.3.

2
Accommodation, storage and security

The activities and the temporary nature of a building site do not generally justify the provision of permanent buildings for staff accommodation or for the storage of materials. It is, however, within the builder's interest to provide the best facilities which are economically possible for any particular contract; this should promote good relationships between management and staff, it should also reduce the loss of materials due to theft, accidental damage and vandalism. The better the facilities and amenities provided on a building site the greater will be the contentment of the site staff which will ultimately lead to higher productivity.

ACCOMMODATION

The Construction (Health and Welfare) Regulations 1966 is a statutory instrument which sets out the legal requirements for the minimum accommodation and facilities for site staff to be provided on sites throughout the construction industry having regard to the number of employees on site and in some cases the anticipated duration of the contract. The main requirements of this document are shown in Table I.4.

Units of staff accommodation usually come in one of two forms:
1. Sectional timber huts.
2. Mobile caravans or cabins.

No. of persons employed by contractor on site		0 5 10 20 25 40 50 100
FIRST AID	Box to be clearly marked and in charge of named person	First-Aid boxes. — First-Aid boxes and person trained in First Aid.
STRETCHER AMBULANCE		Stretcher provided. Local Health Authority informed of site, work and completion date. If no 'phone or radio, ambulance kept ready.
FIRST-AID ROOM	To be used only for treatment and in charge of trained person.	Where number of persons on site exceeds 250 each employer of more than 40 persons must provide First-Aid room.
SHELTER AND CLOTHING	All persons to have shelter and place for depositing clothing.	Adequate means of warming themselves and drying wet clothing. — Where possible, means of warming themselves and drying wet clothing.
MEALS ROOM	All persons to have drinking water provided and facilities for boiling water and eating meals.	Facilities for heating food if hot meals are not available on site.
WASHING FACILITIES	All persons on site for more than 4 hours to have washing facilities.	Where work is likely to last 6 weeks / h. and c. or warm water, soap and towel provided. — Where work is likely to last 12 months / 4 wash places plus 1 for every 35 persons more than 100.
SANITARY FACILITIES	To be maintained and kept clean—provision to be made for lighting.	1 convenience for every 25 persons. — 1 convenience for every 35 persons.

NOTES: Washing facilities to be close to meals room;
Protective clothing to be provided where person is required to work in inclement weather.
Sub-contractors may use the facilities provided by another contractor and for the purpose of these regulations their work force on site is included in the total work force on site.

THE CONSTRUCTION (HEALTH AND WELFARE) REGULATIONS 1966

TABLE 1.1

Sectional timber huts are prefabricated to allow for ease of dismantling and assembly to facilitate the re-use on other sites. Huts of this nature should be designed, constructed and maintained with the same care as permanent buildings to ensure their use for many years on a number of different contracts. A well-designed sectional hut should permit the addition of more bays to increase the modular size by length and/or width.

The anticipated use of each hut will govern the construction and facilities required. Offices need to be weatherproof, heated, insulated to conserve the heat, some form of artificial lighting, equipped with furniture such as desks, work tops, plan chests and chairs to suit the office activities; a typical timber sectional site office detail is shown in Fig. I.4. The same basic construction can be used for all other units of accommodation such as meals rooms and toilets equipped with the facilities shown in Table I.4.

Caravans and mobile cabins are available in a wide variety of sizes, styles and applications. The construction is generally of a ply clad timber frame suitably insulated and decorated; they are made to a modular system so that by using special connection units any reasonable plan size and shape is possible. The caravans and cabins are fully equipped with all the necessary furniture, lights and heating units. The toilets are supplied with all the necessary sanitary fittings and plumbing which can be connected to site services or be self contained. Transportation of caravans or cabins can be on any suitable vehicle; caravans can be towed whereas special transporter trailers are available for cabins. Whichever method is used the time taken to load, offload and position on site is considerably shorter than the time required to dismantle, transport and reassemble a sectional timber hut, but the initial capital outlay is higher. Typical examples of units of accommodation are shown in Fig. I.5.

STORAGE

The type of storage facilities required of any particular material will depend upon the following factors:

1. Durability — will it need protection from the elements?
2. Vulnerability to damage.
3. Vulnerability to theft.

Cement, plaster and lime supplied in bag form require a dry store free from draughts which can bring in moist air and may cause an air set of material. These materials should not be stored for long periods on site,

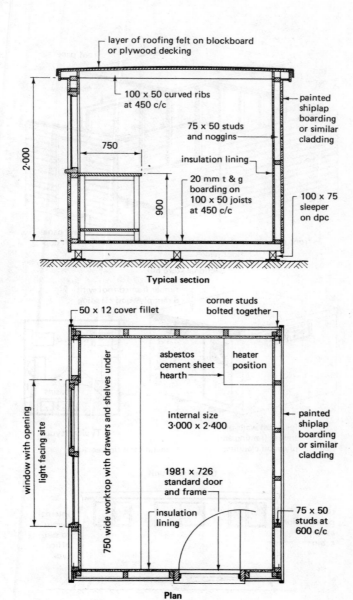

layer of roofing felt on blockboard or plywood decking

100 x 50 curved ribs at 450 c/c

painted shiplap boarding or similar cladding

75 x 50 studs and noggins

insulation lining

20 mm t & g boarding on 100 x 50 joists at 450 c/c

100 x 75 sleeper on dpc

2·000

750

900

Typical section

corner studs bolted together

50 x 12 cover fillet

asbestos cement sheet hearth

heater position

window with opening

light facing site

750 wide worktop with drawers and shelves under

internal size 3·000 x 2·400

painted shiplap boarding or similar cladding

1981 x 726 standard door and frame

insulation lining

75 x 50 studs at 600 c/c

Plan

Fig. I.4 Typical prefabricated timber site office

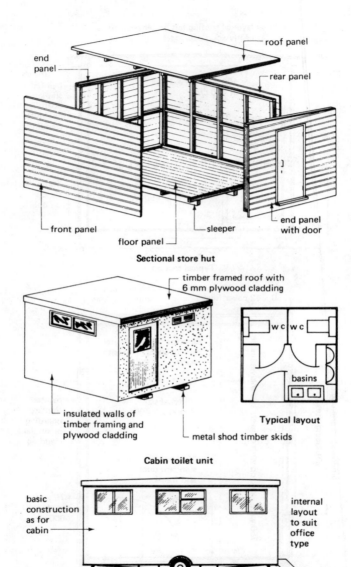

Sectional store hut

roof panel

end panel

rear panel

end panel with door

front panel

sleeper

floor panel

timber framed roof with 6 mm plywood cladding

w c   w c

basins

Typical layout

insulated walls of timber framing and plywood cladding

metal shod timber skids

Cabin toilet unit

basic construction as for cabin

internal layout to suit office type

Mobile office

Fig. I.5 Typical site accommodation units

12

therefore provision should be made for rotational use so that the material being used comes from the older stock.

Aggregates such as sand and ballast require a clean firm base to ensure that foreign matter is not included when extracting materials from the base of the stock pile. Different materials and grades must be kept separated so that the ultimate mix batches are consistent in quality and texture. Care must be taken, by careful supervision, to ensure that the stock piles are not used as a rubbish tip. If the storage piles are exposed to the elements a careful watch should be kept on the moisture content; if this rises it must be allowed to drain after heavy rain or alternatively the water/cement ratio of the mix can be adjusted.

Bricks and blocks should be stacked in stable piles on a level and well-drained surface in a position where double handling is reduced to a minimum. Facing bricks and light-coloured bricks can become discoloured by atmospheric pollution and/or adverse weather conditions; in these situations the brick stacks should be covered with tarpaulin or polythene sheeting adequately secured to prevent dislodgement. Blocks, being less dense than bricks, should be stacked to allow air movement around them and should always be covered with a suitable sheet material.

Roof tiles have a greater resistance to load when it is imposed on the edge; for this reason tiles should be stacked on edge and in pairs, head to tail, to give protection to the nibs. An ideal tile stack would be five to seven rows high with end tiles laid flat to provide an abutment. Tile fittings such as ridge and hip tiles should be kept separate and if possible placed on end.

Drainage goods, like tiles, may be stored in an open compound; they should be stacked with their barrels horizontal and laid with spigots and sockets alternately reversed or placed in layers with the spigots and sockets reversed in alternate layers. Fittings should be kept separate and those like gullies, which can hold water, should be placed upside down.

Timber is a hygroscopic material and therefore to prevent undue moisture movement it should be stored in such a manner that its moisture content remains fairly constant. A rack of scaffold tubulars with a sheet roof covering makes an ideal timber store. The various section sizes allow good air flow around the timber and the roof provides protection from the rain and snow.

Ironmongery, hand tools and paint are some of the most vulnerable items on a building site. Small items such as locks, power drills and cans of paint should be kept in a locked hut and only issued against an authorised stores requisition. Large items like baths can be kept in the compound and suitably protected; it is also good practice only to issue materials from the compound against a requisition order.

SECURITY AND PROTECTION
Fencing
A building site and the compound can be given a degree of protection by surrounding with a fence. The fence fulfils two functions:
1. Defines the limit of the site or compound.
2. Acts as a deterrent to the would-be trespasser or thief.

A fence can be constructed to provide a physical barrier of solid construction or a visual barrier of open work construction. If the site is to be fenced as part of the contract it may be advantageous to carry out this work at the beginning of the site operations. The type of fencing chosen will depend upon the degree of security required, cost implications, type of neighbourhood and duration of contract.

A security fence around the site or compound should be at least 1.800 m high above the ground and include the minimum number of access points which should have a lockable barrier or gate. Standard fences are made in accordance with the recommendations of BS 1722 which covers ten forms of fencing giving suitable methods for both visual and physical barriers; typical examples are shown in Fig. I.6.

Hoardings
These are close boarded fences or barriers erected adjacent to a highway or public footpath to prevent unauthorised persons obtaining access to the site and to provide a degree of protection for the public from the dust and noise associated with building operations. Under Sections 147 and 148 of the Highways Act 1959 it is necessary to obtain written permission from the Local Authority to erect a hoarding. The permission, which is in the form of a licence, sets out the conditions and gives details of duration, provision of footway for the public and the need for lighting during the hours of darkness.

Two forms of hoarding are in common use:
1. Vertical hoardings.
2. Fan hoardings.

The vertical hoardings consist of a series of closed boarded panels securely fixed to resist wind loads and accidental impact loads. It can be free standing or fixed by stays to the external walls of an existing building (see Fig. I.7).

Regulation 46 of the Construction (General Provisions) Regulations 1961 requires protection to be given to persons from falling objects. A fan hoarding fulfils this function by being placed at a level above the normal traffic height and arranged in such a manner that any falling débris is directed back towards the building or scaffold (see Fig. I.7).

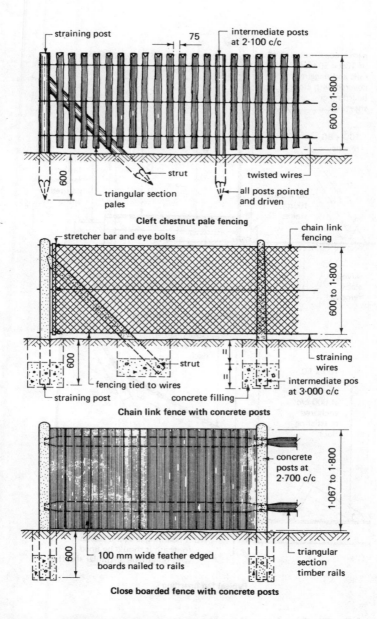

Cleft chestnut pale fencing

straining post

intermediate posts at 2·100 c/c

75

600 to 1·800

600

strut

triangular section pales

twisted wires

all posts pointed and driven

Chain link fence with concrete posts

stretcher bar and eye bolts

chain link fencing

600 to 1·800

600

straining wires

strut

fencing tied to wires

straining post

concrete filling

intermediate pos at 3·000 c/c

Close boarded fence with concrete posts

concrete posts at 2·700 c/c

1·067 to 1·800

600

100 mm wide feather edged boards nailed to rails

triangular section timber rails

Fig. I.6 Typical fencing details

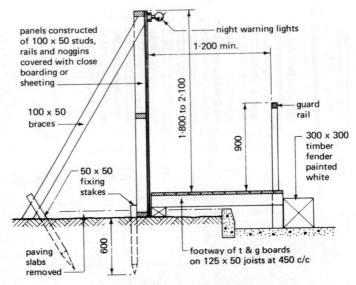

panels constructed of 100 x 50 studs, rails and noggins covered with close boarding or sheeting

100 x 50 braces

50 x 50 fixing stakes

paving slabs removed

600

1·800 to 2·100

night warning lights

1·200 min.

guard rail

300 x 300 timber fender painted white

900

footway of t & g boards on 125 x 50 joists at 450 c/c

Typical freestanding vertical hoarding

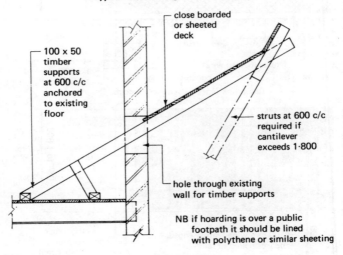

100 x 50 timber supports at 600 c/c anchored to existing floor

close boarded or sheeted deck

struts at 600 c/c required if cantilever exceeds 1·800

hole through existing wall for timber supports

NB if hoarding is over a public footpath it should be lined with polythene or similar sheeting

Typical fan hoarding

Fig. I.7   Timber hoardings

16

3

General site works: site layouts

The construction of a building can be considered as the product being produced with a temporary factory, the building site being the 'factory' in which the building contractor will make the product. To enable this activity to take place the builder requires men, materials and plant, all of which have to be carefully controlled so that the men have the right machines in the most advantageous position, the materials stored so that they are readily available and not interfering with the general site circulation, and adequate storage space and site accommodation.

There is no standard size ratio between the free site space required to construct a building and the total size of the site on which the building is to be erected; therefore each site must be considered as a separate problem in terms of allocating space for men, materials and plant. To obtain maximum efficiency there is an optimum way of laying out the site and also a correct amount of expenditure to support the proposed site layout. Any planned layout should be reviewed periodically and adjusted to suit the changing needs of the site activities. If this aspect of building construction is carefully considered, planned and controlled it will be reflected in the progress and profitability of the contract.

Before any initial planning of the site layout can take place certain preliminary work must be carried out, preferably at the pre-tender stage. The decision to tender will usually be taken by the managing director or for small works by the senior estimator up to a contract value laid down by the managing director. With given designs and specifications the best opportunity for the contractor to prepare a competitive and economic tender is in the programming and planning of the construction activities. A thorough study of the bill of quantities will give an indication of the amount and quality of the materials required and also of the various labour resources needed to carry out the contract. A similar study of the drawings, together with the bill of quantities and the specification will enable the builder to make a preliminary assessment of the size and complexity of the contract, the plant required and the amount of money which can reasonably be expended on labour-saving items such as concrete mixing and placing alternatives, handling and transporting equipment and off-site fabrication of such items as formwork and reinforcement.

Before the estimator can make a start on calculating his unit rates a site investigation should be carried out, preferably by the site agent who will supervise the contract should the tender be successful. His report should include the following information:

1. *Access to site* — on- and off-site access, road and rail facilities, distances involved, rights of way restrictions, local authority or police restrictions and bridge weight or height limitations on approach routes.
2. *Services* — available power and water supplies together with rates of payment, nuisance or value of services already on site, diversions required and the time element involved in carrying out any necessary diversions together with cost implications.
3. *Layout* — general site conditions such as nature of soil, height of water table, flooding risks, tidal waters, neighbouring properties and any demolition problems.
4. *Labour* — travel distances, local or own labour resources to be used, availability of local labour and prevailing rates of pay, lodging and local catering facilities.
5. *Security* — local vandalism and pilfering record, security patrol facilities, need for night security, fencing and hoarding requirements.

With the knowledge and data gained from contract documents, site investigations and any information gained from the police and local authority sources the following pre-tender work can now be carried out:

1. *Pre-tender programme* — usually in a bar chart form showing the proposed time allowances for the major activities.
2. *Cost implications* — several programmes for comparison should be made to establish possible break-even points giving an indication of required overdraft, possible cash inflow and anticipated profit.
3. *Plant schedule* — can be prepared in the form of a bar chart showing requirements and utilisation which will help in deciding whether

there is a need for a site workshop and the necessary maintenance staff and equipment required on site. The problem of whether the plant should be purchased or hired, or if a balance of buying and hiring is most economical, will have to be considered at this stage.

4. *Materials schedule* — basic data can be obtained from the bill of quantities. The buyer's knowledge of the prevailing market conditions and future trends will enable usage and delivery periods and the amount of site space and/or accommodation required to be predicted.

5. *Labour summary* — basic data obtained from the bill of quantities, site investigation report and pre-tender bar chart programme to establish number and trades of staff required for future staff job allocation and also the amount and type of site accommodation required. Approximate labour requirements can be calculated as in the typical example below:

Item — excavate by hand foundation trenches in ordinary ground commencing at oversite level and not exceeding 1.5 m deep.

Assumed labour constant 2.5 hours per m^3.
Total excavation quantity 525 m^3.
Time allowed on pre-tender bar chart programme 1 month = 20 working days.
Total man hours = 525 x 2.5 = 1 312.5
Man hours per day = 1 312.5 ÷ 20 = 65.655
Therefore assuming an 8-hour working day
Number of men = 65.655 ÷ 8 = 8.2
Say 9-man gang.

6. *Site organisation structure* — this is a 'family tree' chart showing the relationships and inter-relationships between the various members of the site team and is normally only required on large sites where the areas of responsibility and accountability must be clearly defined.

7. *Site layout* — site space allocation for materials storage, working areas, units of accommodation, plant positions and general circulation areas.

PLANNING SITE LAYOUTS

When planning site layouts the following must be taken into account:

1. Site activities.
2. Efficiency.
3. Movement.
4. Control.
5. Accommodation for staff and storage of materials.

Site activities: the time needed for carrying out the principal activities can be estimated from the data obtained previously for preparing the material and labour requirements. With repetitive activities estimates will be required to determine the most economical balance of units which will allow simultaneous construction processes; this in turn will help to establish staff numbers, work areas and material storage requirements. A similar argument can be presented for overlapping activities. If a particular process presents a choice in the way the result can be achieved the alternatives must be considered; for example, the rate of placing concrete will be determined by the output of the mixer and the speed of transporting the mix to the appropriate position. Alternatives which can be considered are:

1. More than one mixer.
2. Regulated supply of ready mixed concrete.
3. On large contracts, pumping the concrete to the placing position.

All alternative methods for any activity will give different requirements for staff numbers, material storage, access facilities and possibly plant types and numbers.

Efficiency: to achieve maximum efficiency the site layout must aim at maintaining the desired output of the planned activities throughout the working day and this will depend largely upon the following factors:

1. Avoidance, as far as practicable, of double handling materials.
2. Proper store-keeping arrangements to ensure that the materials are of the correct type, in the correct quantity and are available when required.
3. Walking distances are kept to a minimum to reduce the non-productive time spent in covering the distances between working, rest and storage areas without interrupting the general circulation pattern.
4. Avoidance of loss by the elements by providing adequate protection for unfixed materials on site, thereby preventing time loss and cost of replacing damaged materials.
5. Avoidance of loss by theft and vandalism by providing security arrangements in keeping with the value of the materials being protected and by making the task difficult for the would-be thief or vandal by having adequate hoardings and fences. Also to be avoided is the loss of materials due to pilfering by site staff who may consider this to be a perquisite of the industry. Such losses can be reduced by having an adequate system of stores' requisition and material checking procedures.
6. Minimising on-site traffic congestion by planning delivery arrivals,

having adequate parking facilities for site staff cars and mobile machinery when not in use, and by having sufficient turning circle room for the types of delivery vehicles likely to enter the site.

Movement: apart from the circulation problems mentioned above the biggest problem is one of access. Vehicles delivering materials to the site should be able to do so without difficulty or delay. Many of the contractors' vehicles will be lightweight and will therefore present few or no problems, but the weight and length of suppliers' vehicles should be taken into account. For example, a fully laden ready-mix concrete lorry can weigh 20 tonnes and lorries used for delivering structural steel can be 18.000 metres long, weighing up to 40 tonnes and requiring a large turning circle. If it is anticipated that heavy vehicles will be operating on site it will be necessary to consider the road surface required. If the roads and paved areas are part of the contract and will have adequate strength for the weight of the anticipated vehicles it may be advantageous to lay the roads at a very early stage in the contract, but if the specification for the roads is for light traffic it would be advisable to lay only the base hoggin or hardcore layer at the initial stages because of the risk of damage to the completed roads by the heavy vehicles. As an alternative it may be considered a better policy to provide only temporary roadways composed of railway sleepers, metal tracks or mats until a later stage in the contract, especially if such roads will only be required for a short period.

Control: this is mainly concerned with the overall supervision of the contract, including men, materials and the movement of both around the site. This control should form the hub of the activities which logically develops into areas or zones of control radiating from this hub or centre. Which zone is selected for storage, accommodation or specific activities is a matter of conjecture and the conditions prevailing on a particular site but as a rule the final layout will be one of compromise with storage and accommodation areas generally receiving priority.

Accommodation: as previously stated this must be considered for each individual site but certain factors will be common to all sites. Accommodation for staff is covered by the Construction (Health and Welfare) Regulations 1966, the main contents of which should have been studied in the second year. This document sets out the minimum amount and type of accommodation which must legally be provided for the number of persons employed on the site and the anticipated duration of the contract. Apart from these minimum requirements the main areas of concern will be sizing, equipping and siting the various units of accommodation.

Mess huts: covered by Regulation No. 11 and are for the purposes of preparing, heating and consuming food which may require the following services: drainage, light, power, hot and cold water supply. To provide a reasonable degree of comfort a floor area of 2.0 to 2.5 m^2 per person should be allowed. This will provide sufficient circulation space and room for tables, seating and space for the storage of any utensils. Consideration can also be given to introducing a system of staggered meal-breaks thus reducing space requirements. On large sites where full canteen facilities are being provided it may be prudent to place this in the hands of a catering firm. Mess huts should be sited so that they do not interfere with the development of the site but in such a position that travel time is kept to a minimum. On sites which by their very nature are large, it is worth while considering a system whereby tea-breaks can be taken in the vicinity of the work areas. Siting mess huts next to the main site circulation and access roads is not of major importance.

Drying rooms: used for the purposes of depositing and drying wet clothes are covered by Regulation No. 11. Drying rooms generally require a lighting and power supply with lockers or racks for deposited clothes. A floor area of 0.6 m^2 per person should provide sufficient space for equipment and circulation. Drying rooms should be sited near or adjacent to the mess room.

Toilets: contractors are required to provide at least the necessary minimum washing and sanitary facilities as set out in Regulations Nos. 12, 13 and 14. All these facilities will require light, water and drainage services. If it is not possible or practicable to make a permanent or temporary connection to a drainage system the use of chemical methods of disposal should be considered. Sizing of toilet units is governed by the facilities being provided and if female staff are employed on site separate toilet facilities must be provided. Toilets should be located in a position which is convenient to both offices and mess rooms, which may mean providing more than one location on large sites.

First-aid rooms: only required on large sites where the number of persons employed exceeds 250, but any contractor who has more than 40 persons in his employment on that site must provide this facility in accordance with the requirements of Regulation No. 9. The first-aid room should be sited in a position which is conveniently accessible from the working areas and must be of such a size as to allow for the necessary equipment and adequate circulation which would indicate a minimum floor area of 6 m^2.

Before the proposed site layout is planned and drawn the contracts manager and the proposed site agent should visit the site to familiarise themselves with the prevailing conditions. During this visit the position and condition of any existing roads should be noted and the siting of any temporary roads considered necessary should be planned. Information regarding the soil conditions, height of water table, and local weather patterns should be obtained by observation, site investigation, soil investigation, local knowledge or from the local authority. The amount of money which can be expended on this exercise will depend upon the size of the proposed contract and possibly upon how competitive the tenders are likely to be for the contract under consideration.

Figure I.8 shows a typical small-scale general arrangement drawing and needs to be read in conjunction with Fig. I.9 which shows the proposed site layout. The following data has been collected from a study of the contract documents and by carrying out a site investigation:

1. Site is in a typical urban district within easy reach of the contractor's main yard and therefore will present no transport or labour availability problems.
2. Subsoil is a firm sandy clay with a water table at a depth which should give no constructional problems.
3. Possession of site is to be at the end of April and the contract period is 18 months. The work can be programmed to enable the foundation and substructure work to be completed before adverse winter weather conditions prevail.
4. Development consists of a single five-storey office block with an *in situ* reinforced concrete structural frame, *in situ* reinforced concrete floors and roof, precast concrete stairs and infill brick panels to the structural frame with large hardwood timber frames fixed into openings formed by the bricklayers. Reduced level dig is not excessive but the top soil is to be retained for landscaping upon completion of the building contract by a separate contractor; the paved area in front of the office block, however, forms part of the main contract. The existing oak trees in the north-east corner of the site are to be retained and are to be protected during the contract period.
5. Estimated maximum number of staff on site at any one time is 40 in the ratio of 1 supervisory staff to 10 operatives plus a resident Clerk of Works.
6. Main site requirements are as follows:
   1 office for 3 supervisory staff.
   1 office for resident Clerk of Works.
   1 office for timekeeper and materials checker.
   1 hutment as lock-up store.

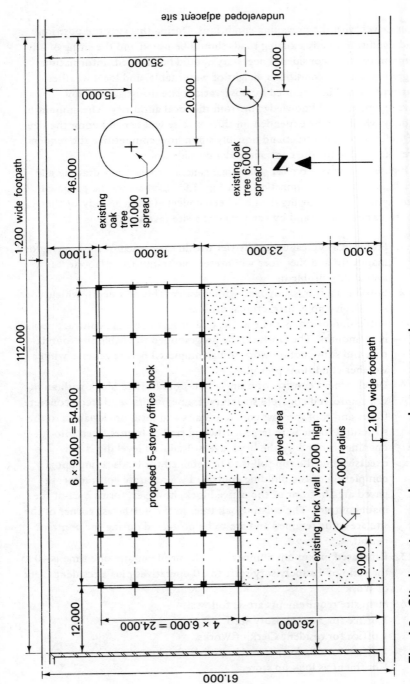

Fig. I.8 Site layout example — general arrangement

undeveloped adjacent site

1.200 wide footpath

35.000
15.000
10.000
20.000
46.000

existing oak tree 10.000 spread

existing oak tree 6.000 spread

N

11.000
18.000
23.000
9.000

112.000

proposed 5-storey office block

6 × 9.000 = 54.000

paved area

2.100 wide footpath

existing brick wall 2.000 high

4.000 radius

9.000

12.000

4 × 6.000 = 24.000

26.000

61.000

24

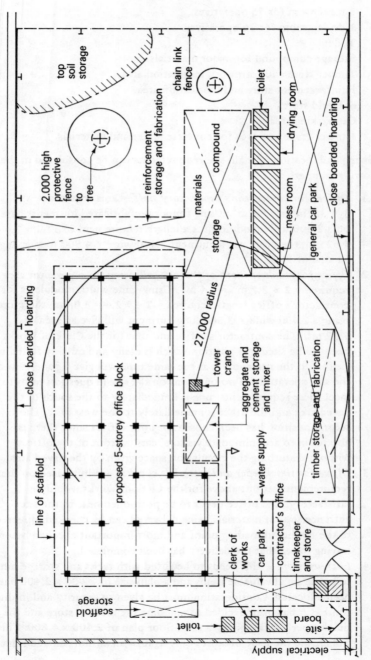

Fig. 1.9 Site layout example — proposed layout of accommodation and storage

25

1 mess room for 36 operatives.
1 drying room for 36 operatives.
Toilets.
Storage compound for major materials.
Timber store and formwork fabrication area.
Reinforcement store and fabrication area.
Scaffold store.
Car parking areas.
1 tower crane and area for concrete mixer and materials.

Sizing and location of main site requirements can be considered in the following manner:

1. *Offices for contractor's supervisory staff* — area required = $3 \times 3.7 \text{ m}^2 = 11.1 \text{ m}^2$. Using timber prefabricated hutments based on a 2.400 wide module gives a length requirement of $11.1 \div 2.4 = 4.625$ m, therefore use a hutment 2.400 wide $\times$ 4.800 long giving an area of 11.52 m^2.

2. *Office for resident Clerk of Works* — allowing for one visitor area required = $2 \times 3.7 \text{ m}^2 = 7.4 \text{ m}^2$. Using same width module as for contractor's office length required = $7.4 \div 2.4 = 3.08$ m, therefore using a 2.400 wide $\times$ 3.300 long hutment will give an area of 7.92 m^2. The contractor's office and that for the Clerk of Works needs to be sited in a position which is easily and quickly found by visitors to the site and yet at the same time will give a good view of the site operations. Two positions on the site in question seem to meet these requirements: one is immediately to the south of the paved area and the other is immediately to the west of it. The second position has been chosen for both offices since there is also room to accommodate visitors' cars in front of the offices without disturbing the circulation space given by the paved area.

3. *Office for timekeeper and materials checker* — a hut based on the requirements set out above for the Clerk of Works would be satisfactory. The office needs to be positioned near to the site entrance so that materials being delivered can be checked, directed to the correct unloading point and most important checked before leaving to see that the delivery has been completed.

4. *Lock-up store* — this needs to be fitted with racks and storage bins to house small valuable items and a plan size of 2.400 x 2.400 has been allocated. Consideration must be given to security and in this context it has been decided to combine the lock-up store and the timekeeper's office giving a total floor plan of 2.400 x 4.800. This will enable the issue of stores only against an authorised and signed

requisition to be carefully controlled, the timekeeper fulfilling the function of storekeeper.

5. *Mess room* — area required = 36 x 2.5 m^2 = 90 m^2, using a width module of 4.800, length required = 90 ÷ 4.8 = 18.75 m; therefore using a length of 7.5 modules of 2.400 actual length = 18.000 giving an area of 4.8 x 18.0 = 86.4 m^2 which is considered satisfactory. The mess room needs to be sited in a fairly central position to all the areas of activity and the east end of the paved area has been selected.

6. *Drying room* — area required = 36 x 0.6 m^2 = 21.6 m^2, using a width module of 4.800, length required = 21.6 ÷ 4.8 = 4.5 m; therefore using a length of 2 modules of 2.400 actual length = 4.800, giving an area of 4.8 x 4.8 = 23.04 m^2. The drying room needs to be in close proximity to the mess room and has therefore been placed at the east end of the mess room. Consideration could be given to combining the mess room and drying room into one unit.

7. *Toilets* — a decision was made during the site investigation to hire and use self-contained chemical toilets to eliminate the need for temporary drains thus giving complete freedom in the programming of drainage works. Two such units are considered to be adequate, one to be sited near to the mess room and the other to be sited near to the office complex. The minimum number of sanitary conveniences is laid down in Regulation No. 13 in the Construction (Health and Welfare) Regulations 1966. For the mess toilet unit catering for 36 operatives, two conveniences are required as a minimum but a three-convenience toilet unit will be used having a plan size of 2.400 x 3.600. Similarly although only one convenience is required for the office toilet unit a two-convenience unit will be used with a plan size of 2.400 x 2.400.

8. *Materials storage compound* — area to be defined by a temporary timber fence 1.800 high and sited at the east end of the paved area giving good access for deliveries and within reach of the crane. Plan size to be allocated 12.000 wide x 30.000 long.

9. *Timber storage* — timber is to be stored in top-covered but open-sided racks made from framed standard scaffold tubulars. Maximum length of timber to be ordered is unlikely to exceed 6.000 in length; therefore, allowing for removal, cutting and fabricating into formwork units, a total plan size of 6.000 wide x 36.000 long has been allocated. This area has been sited to the south of the paved area, giving good access for delivery and within the reach of the crane.

10. *Reinforcement storage* — the bars are to be delivered cut to length,

bent and labelled and will be stored in racks as described above for timber storage. Maximum bar length to be ordered assumed not to exceed 12.000; therefore a storage and fabrication plan size of 6.000 wide x 30.000 long has been allocated. This area has been sited to the north of the storage compound, giving reasonable delivery access and within reach of the crane.

11. *Scaffold storage* — tube lengths to be stored in racks as described for timber storage with bins provided for the various types of couplers. Assuming a maximum tube length of 6.000 a plan size of 3.000 wide x 12.000 long. This storage area has been positioned alongside the west face of the proposed structure, giving reasonable delivery access and within reach of the crane if needed. The scaffold to be erected will be of an independent type around the entire perimeter positioned 200 mm clear of the building face and of five-board width, giving a total minimum width of 200+ (5 x 225) = 1.325, say 1.400 total width.

12. *Tower crane* — to be sited on the paved area in front of the proposed building alongside the mixer and aggregate storage position. A crane with a jib length of 27.000, having a lifting capacity of 1.25 tonnes at its extreme position, has been chosen so that the crane's maximum radius will cover all the storage areas thus making maximum utilisation of the crane possible.

13. *Car parking* — assume 20 car parking spaces are required for opera-tives needing a space per car of 2.300 wide x 5.500 long, giving a total length of 2.3 x 20 = 46.000 and, allowing 6.000 clearance for manoeuvring, a width of 5.5 + 6.0 = 11.500 will be required. This area can be provided to the south of the mess room and drying room complex. Staff car parking space can be sited in front of the office hutments giving space for the parking of seven cars which will require a total width of 7 x 2.3 = 16.100.

14. *Fencing* — the north and south sides of the site both face onto public footpaths and highways. Therefore a close-boarded hoarding in accordance with the licence issued by the local authority will be provided. A lockable double-gate is to be included in the south side hoarding to give access to the site. The east side of the site faces an undeveloped site and the contract calls for a 2.000 high concrete post and chain-link fence to this boundary. This fence will be erected at an early stage in the contract to act as a security fence during the construction period as well as providing the permanent fencing. The west side of the site has a 2.000 high brick wall which is in a good structural condition and therefore no action is needed on this boundary.

15. *Services* — it has been decided that temporary connections to the foul drains will not be made thus giving complete freedom in planning the drain-laying activities. The permanent water supply to the proposed office block is to be laid at an early stage and this run is to be tapped to provide the supplies required to the mixer position and the office complex. A temporary connection is to be made to supply the water service to the mess room complex since a temporary supply from the permanent service would mean running the temporary supply for an unacceptable distance. An electrical supply is to be taken onto site with a supply incoming unit housed in the timekeeper's office along with the main distribution unit. The subject of electrical supplies to building sites is dealt with in Chapter 2. Telephones will be required to the contractor's and Clerk of Works' offices. It has been decided that a gas supply is not required.

16. *Site identification* — a V-shaped board bearing the contractor's name and company symbol is to be erected in the south-west corner of the site in such a manner that it can be clearly seen above the hoarding by traffic travelling in both directions enabling the site to be clearly identified. The board will also advertise the company's name and possibly provide some revenue by including on it the names of participating sub-contractors. As a further public relations exercise it might be worth while considering the possibility of including public viewing panels in the hoarding on the north and south sides of the site.

The extent to which the above exercise in planning a site layout would be carried out in practice will depend upon a number of factors such as the time and money which can reasonably be expended and the benefits which could accrue in terms of maximum efficiency compared with the amount of the capital outlay. The need for careful site layout and site organisation planning becomes more relevant as the size and complexity of the operation increases. This is particularly true for contracts where spare site space is very limited.

4

Electricity on building sites

A supply of electricity is usually required on construction sites to provide lighting to the various units of accommodation and may also be needed to provide the power to drive small and large items of plant. Two sources of electrical supply to the site are possible, namely:

1. Portable self-powered generators.
2. Metered supply from the local area electricity board.

Since a supply of electricity is invariably required in the final structure the second source is usually adopted because it is generally possible to tap off the permanent supply cable to the proposed development for construction operations, thus saving the cost of laying a temporary supply cable to the site.

To obtain a metered temporary supply of electricity a contract must be signed between the contractor and the local area electricity board who will require the following information:

1. Address of site.
2. Site location plan.
3. Maximum anticipated load demand in kW for the construction period. A reasonable method of estimating this demand is to allow for a loading of 10 W/m^2 for the total floor area of the finished structure and to add for any high load equipment such as cranes, pumps and drying out heaters which are to be used.

4. Final load demand of the completed building to ensure that the correct rating of cable is laid for the permanent supply.
5. Date on which temporary supply will be required.
6. Name, address and telephone number of the building owner and the contractor.

To ensure that the supply and installation is available when required by the builder it is essential that an application for a temporary supply of electricity is made at the earliest possible date.

On any construction site it is possible that there may be existing electricity cables which can be advantageous or constitute a hazard or nuisance. Overhead cables will be visible whereas the routes and depths of underground cables can only be ascertained from the records and maps kept by the local area supply board. Overhead cable voltages should be checked with the local area supply board since these cables are usually uninsulated and are therefore classed as a hazard due mainly to their ability to arc over a distance of several metres. High voltage cables of over 11 kV rating will need special care and any of the following actions could be taken to reduce or eliminate the danger:

1. Apply to the local area supply board to have the cables re-routed at a safe distance or height.
2. Apply to have the cable taken out of service.
3. Erect warning barriers to keep men and machines at a safe distance. These barriers must be clearly identified as to their intention and they may be required to indicate the safe distance in both the horizontal and vertical directions. The local area supply board will advise on suitable safe distances according to the type of cable and the load it is transmitting.

The position and depth of underground cables given by the local area board must be treated as being only approximate since their records show only the data regarding the condition as laid and since when changes in site levels may have taken place. When excavating in the locality of an underground cable extreme caution must be taken, which may even involve careful hand excavation to expose the cable. Exposed cables should be adequately supported and suitable barriers with warning notices should be erected. Any damage, however minor, must be reported to the local area supply board who will take the necessary remedial action. It is worth noting that if a contractor damages an underground electric cable, which he knew to be present, and possibly causing a loss of supply to surrounding properties he can be sued for negligence and trespass to goods, the remedy for both torts is an action for damages.

SUPPLY AND INSTALLATION

In Great Britain electrical installations on construction sites are subject to the requirements of the Electricity (Factories Act) Special Regulations 1908 and 1944. Requirements concerning precautions to be taken against contact with overhead lines and underground cables encountered on site are contained in the Construction (General Provisions) Regulations 1961 Part XI Regulation 44. The installation should follow the rules given in the Regulations for Electrical Equipment of Buildings issued by the Institute of Electrical Engineers and in particular Part H which deals with temporary installations and installations on construction sites. The supply distribution units used in the installation should comply with the recommendations of BS 4363 which covers the equipment suitable for the control and distribution of electricity from a three-phase four-wire a.c. system up to a voltage of 415 V with a maximum capacity of 300 A per phase.

The appliances and wiring used in temporary installations on construction sites may be subject to extreme abuse and adverse conditions; therefore correct circuit protection, earthing and frequent inspection are most important and this work, including the initial installation, should be entrusted to a qualified electrician or to a specialist electrical contractor.

Electrical distribution cables contain three line wires and one neutral which can give either a 415 V three-phase supply or a 240 V single-phase supply. Records of accidents involving electricity show that the highest risk is encountered when electrical power is used in wet or damp conditions, which are often present on construction sites. It is therefore generally recommended that wherever possible the distribution voltage on building sites should be 110 V. This is a compromise between safety and efficiency but it cannot be over stressed that a supply of this pressure can still be dangerous and lethal.

The recommended voltages for use on construction sites are as follows:

Mains voltage

415 V three-phase	supply to transformer unit, heavy plant such as cranes and movable plant fed via a trailing cable
	hoists and plant powered by electric motors in excess of a 2 kW rating
240 V single-phase	supply to transformer unit
	supply to distribution unit
	installations in site accommodation buildings
	fixed floodlighting
	small static machines

Reduced voltage

110 V three-phase	portable and hand held tools
110 V single-phase	portable and hand held tools
	small items of plant
	site floodlighting other than fixed floodlighting
	portable hand-lamps
50 V single-phase ⎫	as listed for 110 V single-phase but being used in
25 V single-phase ⎭	damp situations

It is worth considering the use of 50 or 25 V battery supplied hand-lamps if damp situations are present on site. All supply cables must be earthed and in particular 110 V supplies should be centre point earthed so that the nominal voltage to earth is not more than 65 V on a three-phase circuit and not more than 55 V on a single-phase circuit.

Protection to a circuit can be given by using bridge fuses, cartridge fuses and circuit breakers. Adequate protection should be given to all main and sub-circuits against any short-circuit current, overload current and earth faults.

Protection through earthing may be attained in two distinct ways:

1. Provision of a path of low impedence to ensure over-current device will operate in a short space of time.
2. Insertion in the supply of a circuit breaker with an operating coil which trips the breaker when the current due to earth leakage exceeds a predetermined value.

BS 4363 recommends that plug and socket outlets are identified by a colour coding as an additional safety precaution to prevent incorrect connections being made, the recommended colours are:

    25 V — violet
    50 V — white
    110 V — yellow
    240 V — blue
    415 V — red

The equipment which can be used to distribute an electrical supply around a construction site is as follows:

1. *Supply incoming unit* (SIU) — supply, control and distribution of mains supply on site — accommodates supply board's equipment and has one outgoing circuit.
2. *Main distribution unit* (MDU) — control and distribution of mains supply for circuits of 415 V three-phase and 240 V single-phase.
3. *Supply incoming and distribution unit* (SIDU) — a combined SIU

and MDU for use on sites where it is possible to locate these units together.

4. *Transformer unit* — transforms and distributes electricity at a reduced voltage and can be for single-phase, three-phase or both phases and is abbreviated TU/1, TU/3 or TU/1/3 accordingly.
5. *Outlet unit* (OU/1 or OU/3) — connection, protection and distribution of final sub-circuits at a voltage lower than the incoming supply.
6. *Extension outlet unit* (EOU/1 or EOU/3) — similar to outlet unit except outlets are not protected.
7. *Earth monitor unit* (EMU) — flexible cables supplying power at mains voltage from the MDU to movable plant incorporate a separate pilot conductor in addition to the main earth continuity conductor. A very low-voltage current passes along these conductors between the portable plant and the fixed EMU. A failure of the earth continuity conductor will interrupt the current flow which will be detected by the EMU and this device will automatically isolate the main circuit.

The cubicles or units must be of robust construction, strong, durable, rain resistant and rigid to resist any damage which could be caused by transportation, site handling or impact shocks likely to be encountered on a construction site. All access doors or panels must have adequate weather seals. Figure I.10 shows a typical supply and distribution system for a construction site.

The routing of the supply and distribution cables around the construction site should be carefully planned. Cables should not be allowed to trail along the ground unless suitably encased in a tube or conduit, and even this method should only be used for short periods of time. Overhead cables should be supported by hangers attached to a straining wire and suitably marked with 'flags' or similar visual warning. Recommended minimum height clearances for overhead cables are:

1. 5.200 in positions inaccessible to vehicles.
2. 5.800 where cable crosses an access road or any part of the site accessible to vehicles.

Cables which are likely to be in position for a long time, such as the supply to a crane, should preferably be sited underground at a minimum depth of 500 mm and protected by tiles or alternatively housed in clayware or similar pipes.

In the interest of safety and to enable first-aid treatment to be given in cases of accident, all contractors using a supply of electricity on a construction site for any purpose must display in a prominent position the

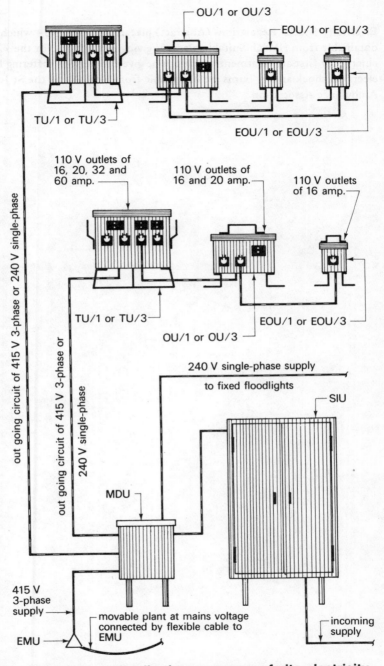

Fig. I.10 Typical distribution sequence of site electricity

OU/1 or OU/3

EOU/1 or EOU/3

TU/1 or TU/3

EOU/1 or EOU/3

110 V outlets of 16, 20, 32 and 60 amp.

110 V outlets of 16 and 20 amp.

110 V outlets of 16 amp.

TU/1 or TU/3

EOU/1 or EOU/3

OU/1 or OU/3

240 V single-phase supply to fixed floodlights

SIU

out going circuit of 415 V 3-phase or 240 V single-phase

out going circuit of 415 V 3-phase or 240 V single-phase

MDU

415 V 3-phase supply

movable plant at mains voltage connected by flexible cable to EMU

EMU

incoming supply

Electricity Special Regulations (Abstract) placard number F954 which is obtainable from HMSO. Suitable placards giving instructions for the emergency first-aid treatment which can be given to persons suffering from electrical shock and/or burns are obtainable from RoSPA and the St John Ambulance Association.

5
Lighting building sites

Inadequate light accounts for more than 50% of the loss of production on construction sites between the months of November and February. Inadequate lighting also increases the risks of accidents and lowers the security of the site. The initial costs of installing a system of artificial lighting for both internal and external activities can usually be offset by higher output, better quality work, a more secure site and apportioning the costs over a number of contracts on a use and re-use basis.

The reasons for installing a system of artificial lighting on a construction site can be listed as follows:

1. Inclement weather, particularly in winter when a reduction of natural daylight is such that the carrying out of work becomes impracticable.
2. Without adequate light all activities on construction sites carry an increased risk of accident and injury.
3. By enabling work to proceed losses in productivity can be reduced.
4. Reduce the wastage of labour and materials which often results from working in poor light.
5. Avoid short-time working due to the inability to see clearly enough for accurate and safe working.
6. Improve the general security of the site.

The following benefits may be obtained by installing and using a system of artificial lighting on a construction site:

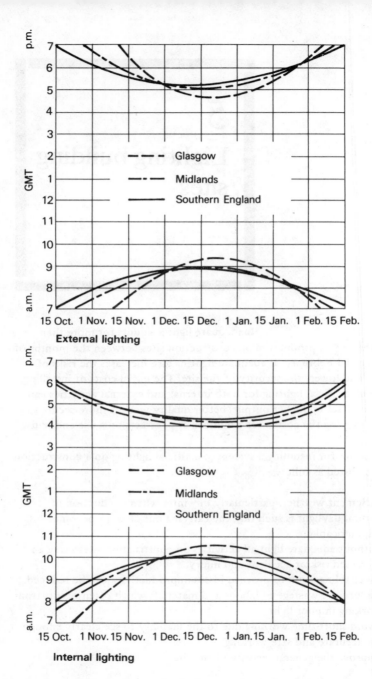

Fig. I.11 Approximate times for site lighting

1. Site activities will be independent of the availability of natural daylight and therefore the activities can be arranged to suit the needs of the contract, the availability of materials and the personnel involved.
2. Overtime and extra shifts can be worked to overcome delays that might occur from any cause.
3. Deliveries and collection of materials or plant can be made outside normal site working hours thus helping to avoid delays and/or congestion.
4. Reduction in the amount of spoilt material and the consequent rectification caused by working under inadequate light.
5. An effective deterrent to the would-be trespasser or pilferer.
6. Improved labour relationships by ensuring regular working hours and thus regular earnings.

Planning the lighting requirements depends on site layout, size of site, shape of site, geographical location, availability of an electrical supply and the planned activities for the winter period. Figure I.11 shows two charts covering various regions of the country giving an indication of the periods when external and internal artificial lighting may be required on a construction site under normal conditions. Any form of temporary artificial site lighting should be easy to install and modify as needs change and be easy to remove whilst works are still in progress.

The supply and distribution of an electrical service to a construction site has already been covered in the previous chapter and it is therefore only necessary to stress again the need for a safe, reliable installation preferably designed and installed by a specialist contractor.

ILLUMINATION

Illumination is measured in lux (lx) which is one lumen of light falling on 1 m^2 of surface and this can be measured with a small portable lightmeter which consists of a light-sensitive cell generating a small current proportional to the light falling on it. The level of illumination at which an operative can work in safety and carry out his tasks to an acceptable standard, both in terms of speed and quality, is quite low since the human eye is very adaptable and efficient. Although the amount of illumination required to enable a particular activity to be carried out is a subjective measure depending largely upon the task, age and state of health of the operative concerned, the following average service values of illumination are generally recommended:

Activities	Illumination (lx)
External lighting	
Materials handling	10
Open circulation areas	10
Internal lighting	
Circulation	5
Working areas	15
Reinforcing and concreting	50
Joinery, bricklaying and plastering	100
Painting and decorating	200
Fine craft work	200
Site offices	200
Drawing board positions	300

The above service values of illumination do not allow for deterioration, dirt, bad conditions or shadow effects. Therefore in calculating the illumination required for any particular situation a target value of twice the service value should be used.

When deciding on the type of installation to be used two factors need to be considered:

1. Type of lamp to be used.
2. Nature and type of area under consideration.

The properties of the various types of lamps available should be examined to establish the most appropriate for any particular site requirement.

LAMPS

Tungsten filament lamp — ideal for short periods such as a total of 200 hours during the winter period; main recommended uses are for general interior lighting and low-level external movement. They are cheap to buy but are relatively expensive to run.

Tungsten halogen lamp — compact fitting with high light output and is suitable for all general area floodlighting. They are easy to mount and have a more effective focused beam than the filament lamp. These lamps generally have a life of twice that of filament lamps and quartz lamps have a higher degree of resistance to thermal shock than glass filament lamps. They are dearer than filament lamps and are still relatively expensive to run but should be considered if the running time is in the region of 1 500 hours annually.

Mercury tungsten lamps — compact, efficient with a good lamp life and they do not need the expensive starting gear of the vapour discharge lamps. They can be used for internal and external area lighting where lamps are not mounted above 9.000 high. These are a high-cost lamp but are cheap to run.

Mercury discharge lamps — high efficiency lamps with a long life and can be used for area lighting where lamps are mounted above 9.000 high. Costs for lamps and control gear are high but the running costs are low.

Tubular fluorescent lamps — uniformly bright in all directions, used when a great concentration of light is not required, efficient with a range of colour values. These lamps have a long life and are cheap to run.

High-pressure sodium discharge lamps — compact, efficient with a long life and for the best coverage without glare they should be mounted above 13.500 high. Cost for lamp and control gear is high but running costs are low which makes them suitable for area lighting.

Apart from the cost of the lamps and the running charges, consideration must be given to the cost of cables, controlling equipment, mounting poles, masts or towers. A single high tower may well give an overall saving against using a number of individual poles or masts in spite of the high initial cost for the tower. Consideration can also be given to using the scaffold, incomplete structure or the mast of a tower crane for lamp-mounting purposes.

SITE LIGHTING INSTALLATIONS
When deciding upon the type and installation layout for construction site lighting, consideration must be given to the nature of area and work to be lit, and also to the type or types of lamp to be used. These aspects can be considered under the following headings:

1. External and large circulation areas.
2. Beam floodlighting.
3. Walkway lighting.
4. Local lighting.

External and large circulation areas
These areas may be illuminated by using mounted lamps situated around the perimeter of the site, in the corners

of the site or, alternatively, overhead illumination using dispersive fittings can be used. The main objectives of area lighting are to enable man and machinery to move around the site in safety and to give greater security to the site. Areas of local danger such as excavations and obstructions should however be marked separately with red warning lights or amber flashing lamps. Tungsten filament, mercury vapour or tungsten halogen lamps can be used and these should be mounted on poles, masts or towers according to the lamp type and wattage. Typical mounting heights for various lamps and wattages are:

Lamp type	Watts	Minimum height (m)
Tungsten filament	200	4.500
	300	6.000
	750	9.000
Mercury vapour	400	9.000
	1 000	15.000
	2 000	18.000
Tungsten halogen	500	7.500
	1 000	9.000
	2 000	15.000

Large areas are generally illuminated by using large high-mounted lamps whereas small areas and narrow sites use a greater number of smaller fittings. By mounting the lamps as high as practicable above the working level, glare is reduced and by lighting the site from at least two directions the formation of dense shadows is also reduced. The spacing of the lamps is also important if under-lit and over-lit areas are to be avoided. Figures I.12 and I.13 show typical lamps and the recommended spacing ratios.

Dispersive lighting is similar to an ordinary internal overhead lighting system and is suitable for both exterior and interior area lighting where overhead suspension is possible. Ordinary industrial fittings should not be used because of the adverse conditions which normally prevail on construction sites. The fittings selected should therefore be protected against rust, corrosion and water penetration. To obtain a reasonable spread of light the lamps should be suspended evenly over the area to be illuminated as shown diagrammatically in Fig. I.14. Tungsten filament, mercury vapour and fluorescent trough fittings are suitable and should be suspended at a minimum height according to their type and wattage. Typical suspension heights are:

Lamp type	Watts	Minimum height (m)
Tungsten filament	200	2.500
	300	3.000
	750	6.000
Mercury vapour	250	6.000
	400	7.500
	700	9.000
Fluorescent trough	40 to 125	2.500

Most manufacturers provide guidance as to the choice of lamps or combination of lamps but a simple method of calculating lamp requirements is as follows:

1. Decide upon the service illumination required and double this figure to obtain target value.
2. Calculate total lumens required $= \dfrac{\text{area (m}^2) \times \text{target value (lx)}}{0.23}$
3. Choose lamp type

   Number of lamps required $= \dfrac{\text{total lumens required}}{\text{lumen output of chosen lamp}}$
4. Repeat stage (3) for different lamp types to obtain most practicable and economic arrangement.
5. Consider possible arrangements remembering that:
   (a) Larger lamps give more lumens per watt and are generally more economic to run.
   (b) Fewer supports simplify wiring and aid overall economy.
   (c) Corner siting arrangements are possible.
   (d) Clusters of lamps are possible.

The calculations when using dispersive lighting are similar to those given above for mounted area lighting except for the formula in stage (2) which has a utilisation factor of 0.27 instead of 0.23.

Beam floodlighting

Tungsten filament or mercury vapour lamps can be used but the use of this technique is limited in application on construction sites to supplementing other forms of lighting. Beam floodlights are used to illuminate areas from a great distance. The beam of light is intense producing high glare and should therefore be installed to point downwards towards the working areas. Generally the lamps are selected direct from the manufacturers' catalogue without calculations.

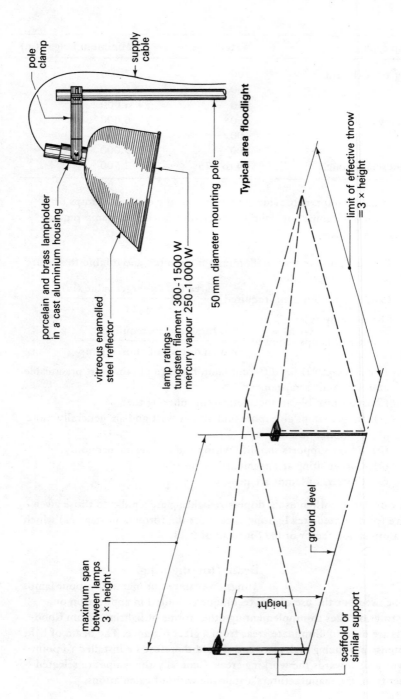

pole clamp

supply cable

porcelain and brass lampholder
in a cast aluminium housing

vitreous enamelled
steel reflector

lamp ratings-
tungsten filament 300-1 500 W
mercury vapour 250-1 000 W

50 mm diameter mounting pole

Typical area floodlight

limit of effective throw
= 3 × height

maximum span
between lamps
3 × height

height

ground level

scaffold or
similar support

Fig. I.12 Area lighting — lamps and spacing ratios 1

44

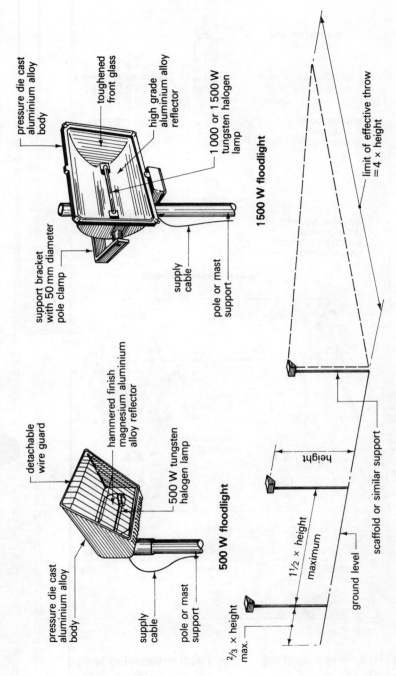

pressure die cast aluminium alloy body

toughened front glass

high grade aluminium alloy reflector

1 000 or 1 500 W tungsten halogen lamp

support bracket with 50 mm diameter pole clamp

supply cable

pole or mast support

1 500 W floodlight

limit of effective throw = 4 × height

detachable wire guard

hammered finish magnesium aluminium alloy reflector

500 W tungsten halogen lamp

500 W floodlight

pressure die cast aluminium alloy body

supply cable

pole or mast support

height

1½ × height maximum

⅔ × height max.

scaffold or similar support

ground level

Fig. I.13   Area lighting — lamps and spacing ratios 2

45

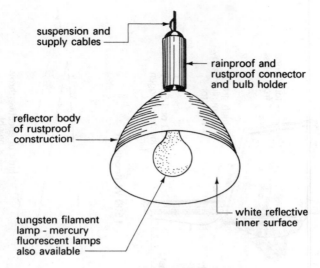

suspension and supply cables

rainproof and rustproof connector and bulb holder

reflector body of rustproof construction

white reflective inner surface

tungsten filament lamp - mercury fluorescent lamps also available

Typical dispersive lamp

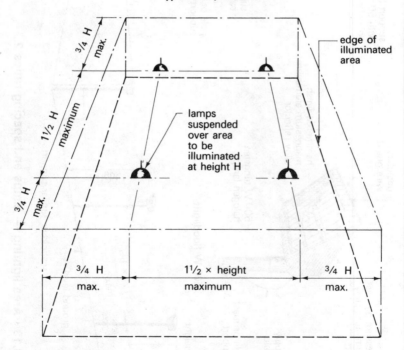

3/4 H max.

1½ H maximum

3/4 H max.

edge of illuminated area

lamps suspended over area to be illuminated at height H

3/4 H max.

1½ × height maximum

3/4 H max.

Fig. I.14   Area lighting — overhead dispersive lamps

Walkway lighting

Tungsten filament and fluorescent lamps can be used to illuminate access routes such as stairs, corridors and scaffolds. Bulkhead fittings which can be safely installed with adequate protection to the wiring can be run off a mains voltage of 240 V single-phase but if they are in a position where they can be handled a reduced voltage of 110 V single-phase should be used. Festoon lighting in which the ready-wired lampholders are moulded to the cable itself can also be used. A standard festoon cable would be 100 m long with rain-proof lampholders and protective shades or guards at 3.000 or 5.000 centres using 40 W or 60 W tungsten filament bulbs for the respective centres. See Fig. I.15. For lighting to scaffolds of 4 or 5 board width 60 W lamps placed at not more than 6.000 centres and preferably at least 2.400 to 3.000 above the working platform either to the wall side or centrally over the scaffold.

Local lighting

Clusters of pressed glass reflector flood-lamps, tungsten filament lamps, festoons and adjustable fluorescent can be used to increase the surface illumination at local points, particularly where finishing trades are involved. These fittings must be portable so that shadow casting can be reduced or eliminated from the working plane; therefore it is imperative that these lights are operated off a reduced voltage of 110 V single-phase. Fluorescent tubes do not usually work at a reduced voltage so special fittings working off a 110 V single-phase supply which internally increase the voltage are used. Typical examples of suitable lamps are shown in Fig. I.16.

As an alternative to a system of static site lighting connected to the site mains electrical supply mobile lighting sets are available. These consist of a diesel engine driven generator and a telescopic tower with a cluster of tungsten iodine lamps. These are generally cheaper to run than lamps operating off a mains supply. Small two-stroke generator sets with a single lamp attachment suitable for small isolated positions are also available.

Another system which can be used for local lighting is flame lamps which normally use propane gas as the fuel. The 'bulb' consists of a mantle and a reflector completes the lamp fitting which is attached to the fuel bottle by a flexible tube. These lamps produce a great deal of local heat and water vapour; the latter may have the effect of slowing down the drying out of the building. An alternative fuel to propane gas is butane gas but this fuel will not usually vaporise at temperatures below $-1°C$.

Whichever method of illumination is used on a construction site it is always advisable to remember the axiom 'a workman can only be safe and work well when he can see where he is going and what he is doing'.

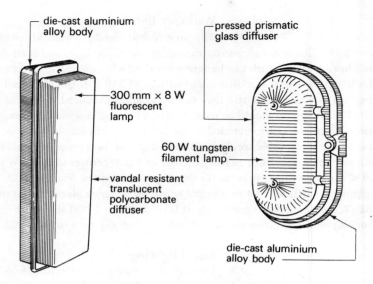

die-cast aluminium alloy body

pressed prismatic glass diffuser

300 mm × 8 W fluorescent lamp

60 W tungsten filament lamp

vandal resistant translucent polycarbonate diffuser

die-cast aluminium alloy body

Ceiling or wall mounted bulkhead lamp fittings

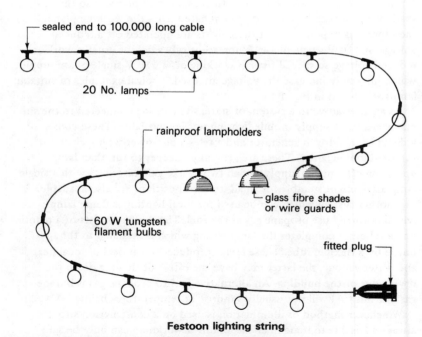

sealed end to 100.000 long cable

20 No. lamps

rainproof lampholders

glass fibre shades or wire guards

60 W tungsten filament bulbs

fitted plug

Festoon lighting string

Fig. I.15 Typical walkway lighting fittings

48

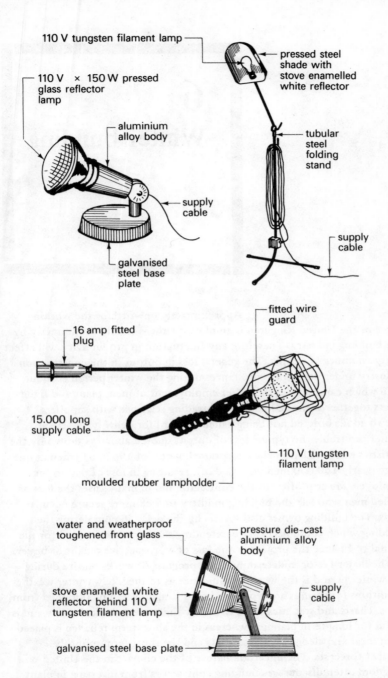

110 V tungsten filament lamp

pressed steel shade with stove enamelled white reflector

110 V × 150 W pressed glass reflector lamp

aluminium alloy body

tubular steel folding stand

supply cable

galvanised steel base plate

supply cable

fitted wire guard

16 amp fitted plug

15.000 long supply cable

110 V tungsten filament lamp

moulded rubber lampholder

water and weatherproof toughened front glass

pressure die-cast aluminium alloy body

stove enamelled white reflector behind 110 V tungsten filament lamp

supply cable

galvanised steel base plate

Fig. I.16 Local lighting — suitable lamps and fittings

6
Winter building

Approximately one-fifth of the working force of the United Kingdom is employed either directly or indirectly by the building industry. Therefore any fluctuation in productivity will affect a large number of people. The general loss in output in the construction industry under normal circumstances during the winter period is about 10% which can result in the under-employment of men, plant and fixed assets together with the loss of good trading relations with suppliers due to goods ordered not being called forward for delivery. A severe winter can treble the typical loss of output quoted above as shown by the statistics published after the exceptional winter of 1962—63 when at one stage nearly 160 000 men were laid off, resulting in loss of pay to the employee, lower profits for the contractor and in many cases the loss of skilled men who left the building industry to seek more secure occupations. The building owner also suffers by the delay in completing the building which could necessitate extending the borrowing period for the capital to finance the project or the loss of a prospective tenant or buyer.

The major factor in determining the progress of works on site during the winter period is the weather. Guidance as to the likely winter weather conditions for various areas of the United Kingdom can be obtained from maps, charts and statistical data issued by the meteorological office and is useful for long-term planning whereas in the short term reliance is placed upon local knowledge, daily forecasts and the short-term monthly weather forecasts. The uncertain nature of the climate in the United Kingdom often discourages building contractors from investing in plant and equipment for winter building techniques and protective measures which may prove to be unnecessary. The contractor must therefore assess the total cost of possible delays against the capital outlay required for plant and equipment to enable him to maintain full or near full production during the winter period.

EFFECTS OF WEATHER

Weather conditions which can have a delaying effect on building activities are rain, high winds, low temperatures, snow and poor daylight levels; the worst effects obviously occur when more than one of the above conditions occur at the same time.

Rain: affects site access and movement which in turn increases site hazards, particularly those associated with excavations and earth moving works. It also causes discomfort to operatives thus reducing their productivity rate. Delays with most external operations such as bricklaying and concreting are usually experienced particularly during periods of heavy rainfall. Damage can be caused to unprotected materials stored on site and in many cases to newly fixed materials or finished surfaces. The higher moisture content of the atmosphere will also delay the drying out of buildings. If high winds and rain occur together, rain penetration and site hazards are considerably increased.

High winds: apart from the discomfort felt by operatives, high winds can also make activities such as frame erection and sheet cladding fixing very hazardous. They can also limit the operations that can be carried out by certain items of plant such as tower cranes and suspended cradles. Positive and negative wind pressures can also cause damage to partially fixed claddings, incomplete structures and materials stored on site.

Low temperatures: as the air temperature approaches freezing point many site activities are slowed down. These include excavating, bricklaying, concreting, plastering and painting, until they cease altogether at sub-zero temperatures; also mechanical plant can be difficult to start, while stockpiles of materials can become frozen and difficult to move. General movement and circulation around the site becomes hazardous, creating with the low temperatures general discomfort and danger for site personnel. When high winds are experienced with low temperatures they will aggravate the above-mentioned effects.

Snow: this is one of the most variable factors in British weather ranging from an average of five days a year on which snow falls on low ground in the extreme south-west to 35 days in the north-east of Scotland. Snow will impair the movement of labour, plant and materials as well as create uncomfortable working conditions. Externally stored materials will become covered with a layer of snow, making identification difficult in some cases. This blanket of snow will also add to the load to be carried by all horizontal surfaces. High winds encountered with falling snow can cause drifting which could increase the site hazards, personal discomfort and decrease general movement around the site.

It should be appreciated that the adverse conditions described above could have an adverse effect on site productivity even though they are not present on the actual site by delaying the movement of materials to the site from suppliers outside the immediate vicinity.

WINTER BUILDING TECHNIQUES

The major aim of any winter building method or technique is to maintain an acceptable rate of productivity. Inclement weather conditions can have a very quick reaction on the transportation aspect of site operations, movement of vehicles around the site and, indeed, off the site, which will be impaired or even brought to a complete standstill unless firm access roads or routes are provided, maintained and kept free of snow. These access roads should extend right up to the discharge points to avoid the need for unnecessary double handling of materials. If the access roads and hardstandings form part of the contract and are suitable, these could be constructed at an early stage in the contract before the winter period. If the permanent road system is not suitable in layout for contractural purposes, temporary roads of bulk timbers, timber or concrete sleepers, compacted hardcore or proprietary metal tracks could be laid.

Frozen ground can present problems with all excavating activities. Most excavating plant can operate in frozen ground up to a depth of 300 mm but at a reduced rate of output; this is particularly true when using machines having a small bucket capacity. Prevention is always better than cure. Therefore if frost is anticipated it is a wise precaution to protect the areas to be excavated by covering with straw mats enclosed in a polythene envelope, insulating quilts of mineral wool or glass fibre incorporating steam lines for severe conditions. Similar precautions can be taken in the case of newly excavated areas to prevent them freezing and giving rise to frost-heave conditions. If it is necessary to defrost ground to enable excavating works to be carried out, this can usually be achieved by using flame throwers, steam jet pipes or coils. Care must be taken to ensure that defrosting is complete and that precautions are taken to avoid subsequent re-freezing.

Water supplies should be laid below ground at such a depth so as to avoid the possibility of freezing, the actual depth will vary according to the locality of the site with a minimum depth of 750 mm for any area. If the water supply is temporary and above ground the pipes should be well lagged and laid to falls so that they can be drained at the end of the day through a drain cock incorporated into the service.

Electrical supplies can fail in adverse weather conditions due to the vulnerable parts such as contacts becoming affected by moisture, frost or ice. These components should be fully protected in a manner advised by an electrical contractor.

Items of plant which are normally kept uncovered on site — such as mixers, dumper trucks, bulldozers and generators — should be protected as recommended by the manufacturer to avoid morning starting problems. These precautions will include selecting and using the correct grades of oils, lubricants and antifreeze, also the covering of engines and electrical systems, draining radiators where necessary and parking wheeled or tracked vehicles on timber runners to prevent them freezing to the ground.

Men and materials will also need protection from adverse winter conditions if an acceptable level of production is to be maintained. Such protection can be of one or more of the following types:

1. Temporary shelters.
2. Framed enclosures.
3. Air-supported structures.
4. Protective clothing.

Temporary shelters: are the cheapest and simplest form of giving protection to the working areas consisting of a screen of reinforced or unreinforced polythene sheeting of suitable gauge fixed to the outside of the scaffold to form a windbreak. The sheeting must be attached firmly to the scaffold standards so that it does not flap or tear, a suitable method is shown in Fig. I.18. To gain the maximum amount of use and re-use out of the sheeting used to form the windbreaks the edges should be reinforced with a suitable adhesive tape incorporating metal eyelets at the tying positions. Eyelets can be made on site using a special kit or alternatively the sheet can be supplied with prepared edges.

Framed enclosures: consist of a purpose-made frame having a curved roof clad with a corrugated material and polythene sheeted sides or alternatively a frame enclosing the whole of the proposed structure can be constructed from standard tubular scaffolding components, see Fig. I.17. Framed enclosures should be clad from the windward end to avoid a build-up of pressure inside the enclosure. It is also advantageous to load the working platform before sheeting in the sides of the enclosure since loading at a later stage is more difficult. The frame must be rigid enough to take the extra loading of the coverings and any imposed loading such as

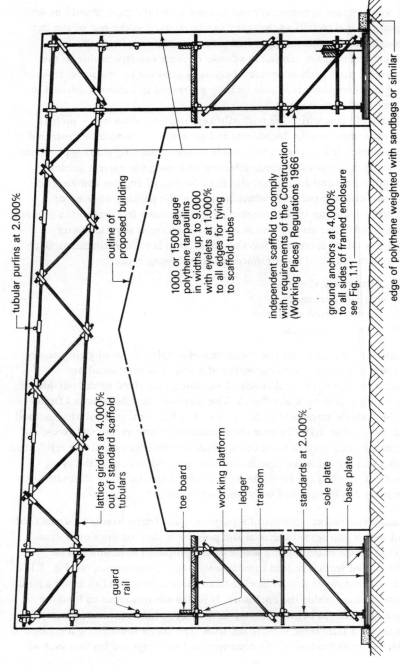

tubular purlins at 2.000%

outline of proposed building

1000 or 1500 gauge polythene tarpaulins in widths up to 9.000 with eyelets at 1.000% to all edges for tying to scaffold tubes

independent scaffold to comply with requirements of the Construction (Working Places) Regulations 1966

ground anchors at 4.000% to all sides of framed enclosure see Fig. 1.11

edge of polythene weighted with sandbags or similar

lattice girders at 4.000% out of standard scaffold tubulars

toe board

working platform

ledger

transom

standards at 2.000%

sole plate

base plate

guard rail

Fig. I.17 Protective screens and enclosures — typical framed enclosure

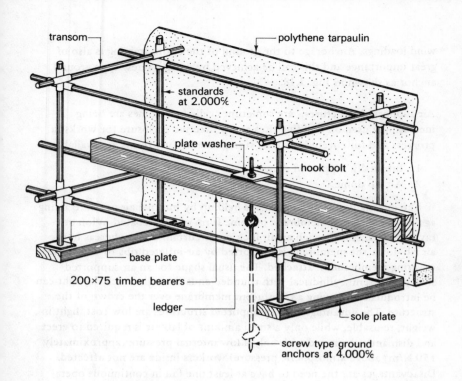

Ground anchor for framed enclosure

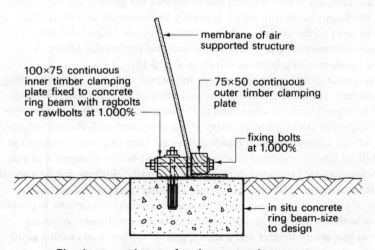

Ring beam anchorage for air supported structure

Fig. I.18 Protective screens and enclosures — anchorages

wind loadings. Anchorage to the ground of the entire framing is also of great importance and this can be achieved by using a screw-type ground anchor as shown in Fig. I.18.

Air-supported structures: are sometimes called air domes are being increasingly used on building sites as a protective enclosure for works in progress and for covered material storage areas. Two forms are available:

1. Internally supported dome.
2. Air rib dome.

The internally supported dome is held up by internal air pressure acting against the covering membrane of some form of PVC coated nylon or rayon with access through an air lock or air curtain door, whereas in the air rib dome the membrane is supported by air-inflated ribs to which the covering membrane is attached. The usual shape for an air-supported structure is semi-cylindrical with rounded ends through which daylight can be introduced by having a translucent membrane over the crown of the structure. The advantages of air-supported structures are low cost, light in weight, re-usable, while only a small amount of labour is required to erect and dismantle them and with only a low internal pressure (approximately 150 N/m^2 above atmospheric pressure) workers inside are not affected. Disadvantages are the need to have at least one fan in continuous operation to maintain the internal air pressure, provision of an air lock or curtain entrance which will impede or restrict the general site circulation and the height limitation which is usually in the region of 45% of the overall span of the structure. The anchorage and sealing of the air-supported structure is also very important and this can be achieved by using a concrete ring beam as shown in Fig. I.18.

Protective clothing is another very important aspect of winter building techniques. Statistics show that the incidence of ailments usually associated with inclement weather such as rheumatism and bronchitis are some 20% higher in the building industry when compared with British industry as a whole. Labour costs on building sites are such that maximum utilisation of all labour resources in all weathers must be the ultimate aim and therefore capital expended in providing protective clothing can be a worthwhile investment. The ideal protective clothing consists of a suit in the form of jacket and trousers made from a lightweight polyurethane proofed nylon with a removable jacket liner for extreme conditions. A strong lightweight safety helmet and a strong pair of rubber boots with a good grip tread would complete the protective clothing outfit.

Heating equipment may be needed on a building site to offset the effects of cold weather on building operations, particularly where wet trades are involved when the materials used could become frozen at an early stage in the curing process producing an unacceptable component or member. The main types of heater in use are convectors, radiant heaters, salamanders and forced-air heaters using solid fuel, electricity, gas or oil as fuel. Solid fuel is generally considered to be impracticable because of its bulk and the problem of disposal of the ash residue. Electricity is usually too expensive in the context of building operations except for the operation of pumps and fans included in many of the heating appliances using in the main other fuels. Gas and oil are therefore the most used fuels and these must be considered in the context of capital and running costs.

Convector heaters using propane, paraffin or a light fuel with an output of 3 to 7 kW are only suitable for small volumes such as site huts and drying rooms where a suitable flue to conduct the fumes to the outside air can be installed.

Radiant heaters using propane are an alternative to the convector heater with the advantage of being mobile, making them suitable for site hut heating or for local heating where personnel are working.

Salamanders work on a similar principle to the convector heater using air currents but have a larger heating area giving outputs of 20 to 40 kW burning propane, paraffin or light fuel oil. They are suitable for heating enclosed areas where the heat output is contained and have the advantages of low capital costs, low running costs and that no flue is required.

Forced-air heaters have high outputs of 30 to 70 kW, are efficient, versatile and mobile. Two forms of heater are available: the direct forced-hot-air heater which discharges water vapour into the space being heated, and the vented forced-air heater where the combustion gases are discharged through a flue to the outside air. Both forms of heater require a fan operated by electricity, propane or a petrol engine. The usual fuels for the heater are propane, paraffin or light fuel oil which produces sufficient heat for general area heating of buildings under construction and for providing heat to several parts of a building using plastic ducting to distribute the hot air. When using a ducted distribution system it is essential that the air velocity at the nozzle is sufficient to distribute the hot air throughout the system.

The natural drying out of buildings after the wet trades is considerably slower in the winter months and therefore to meet production targets this drying out process needs the aid of suitable plant. The heaters described above are often used for this purpose but they are generally very inefficient. Effective drying out or the removal of excess moisture from a building requires the use of a de-humidifier and a vented space heater. Direct fired heaters are generally unsuitable since moisture is contained in the combustion gases discharged into the space being dried out. The de-humidifier is used in conjunction with a heater to eliminate the need of heating the cold air which would replace the warm moist air discharged to the outside if only a vented heater is employed. Two basic types of de-humidifier are available:

1. Refrigeration types where the air is drawn over refrigeration coils which lower the dewpoint causing the excess moisture in the air to condense and discharge into a container. According to the model used the extraction rate can be from 10 to 150 litres per day.

2. Chemical desiccant types where the moist air is drawn over trays or drums containing hygroscopic chemicals which attract the moisture from the air, the extracted moisture being transferred to a bucket or other suitable container. The advantages of these types are low capital and running costs and their overall efficiency with an extraction rate between 45 and 110 litres per day according to the model being used. The only real disadvantage is the need periodically to replenish the chemicals in the de-humidifier trays or drums.

The use of steam boilers and generators for defrosting plant and materials or heating water is also a possible winter building technique. The steam generator can be connected to steam coils which can be inserted into stockpiles of materials or alternatively the steam generator can be connected to a hand held lance.

The use of artificial lighting on sites to aid production and increase safety on building sites during the winter period when natural daylighting is often inadequate has been fully covered in the previous chapter.

WORKING WITH TRADITIONAL MATERIALS

Concrete: can be damaged by rain, sleet, snow, freezing temperatures and cooling winds before it has matured by slowing down the rate at which concrete hardens or by increasing the rate at which the water evaporates to an unacceptable level. The following precautions should ensure that no detrimental effects occur when mixing and placing in winter conditions:

1. Storage of cement under cover and in perfectly dry conditions to prevent air setting.
2. Defrosting of aggregates.
3. Minimum of delay between mixing and placing.
4. Minimum temperature of concrete when placed ideally should be 10°C.
5. Newly placed concrete to be kept at a temperature of more than 5°C for at least three days since the rate at which concrete sets

below this temperature is almost negligible. It may be necessary to employ the use of covers and/or heating to maintain this minimum temperature.

6. If special cements or additives such as calcium chloride in mass concrete are used the manufacturers' specifications should be strictly observed. It must be noted that calcium chloride should not be used in concrete mixes containing metal such as reinforcing bars.
7. Do not use antifreeze solutions.
8. Follow the recommendations of BS 8110 with regard to the stripping of formwork.

Brickwork: can be affected by the same climatic conditions as given above for concrete resulting in damage to the mortar joints and possibly spalling of the bricks. The following precautions should be taken when bricklaying under winter weather conditions:

1. Bricks to be kept reasonably dry.
2. Use a 1:1:6 mortar or a 1:5—6 cement:sand mortar with an air-entraining plasticiser to form microscopic air spaces which can act as expansion chambers for the minute ice particles which may form at low temperatures.
3. Cover up the brickwork upon completion with a protective insulating quilt or similar covering for at least three days.
4. During periods of heavy frost use a heated mortar by mixing with heated water (approximately 50°C) to form a mortar with a temperature of between 15° and 25°C.
5. Do not use additives such as calcium chloride since part of the solution could be absorbed by the absorbent bricks resulting in damage to the finished work.

Plastering: precautions which can be taken when plastering internally during cold periods are simple and consist of closing windows and doors or covering the openings with polythene or similar sheeting, maintaining an internal temperature above freezing and if necessary using heated (maximum 50°C) mixing water. Lightweight plasters and aggregates are less susceptible to damage by frost than ordinary gypsum plasters and should be specified whenever possible. External plastering or rendering should only be carried out in dry weather when the air temperature is above freezing.

Timber: if the correct storage procedure of a covered but ventilated rack has been followed and the moisture content of the fixed joinery is maintained at the correct level few or no problems should be encountered when using this material during winter weather conditions.

If a contractor's output falls below his planned target figures then his fixed charges for overheads, site on-costs and plant costs are being wasted to a proportionate extent. His profit will also be less owing to the loss in turnover, therefore it is usually worth while expending an equivalent amount on winter building precautions and techniques to restore full production. In general terms a decrease of about 10% in productivity is experienced by builders during the winter period and by allocating 10% of his fixed charges and profit to winter building techniques a builder can bring his production back to normal. Cost analysis will show that the more exceptional the inclement weather becomes the greater is the financial reward for expended money on winter building techniques and precautions.

7
Demolition

This is a skilled and sometimes dangerous operation and unless of a very small nature should be entrusted to a specialist contractor. Demolition of a building or structure can be considered under two headings:

1. *Taking down* — partial demolition of a structure.
2. *Demolition* — complete removal of a structure.

Before any taking down or demolition is commenced it is usual to remove carefully all saleable items such as copper, lead, steel fittings, domestic fittings, windows, doors and frames.

Taking down requires a good comprehensive knowledge of building construction and design so that load bearing members and walls can be correctly identified and adequately supported by struts, props and suitable shoring. Most partial demolition works will need to be carried out manually using hand tools such as picks and hammers.

SURVEY

Before any works of demolition are started a detailed survey and examination of the building or structure and its curtilage should be made. Photographs of any existing defects on adjacent properties should be taken, witnessed and stored in a safe place. The relationship as well as the condition of adjoining properties which may be affected by the demolition should also be considered and noted, taking into account the existence of easements, wayleaves, party rights and boundary walls.

Roofs and framed structures: check whether proposed order of demolition will cause unbalanced thrusts to occur.

Walls: check whether these are load bearing, party or crosswalls. Examine condition and thickness of walls to be demolished and those to be retained.

Basements: careful examination required to determine if these extend under public footpaths or beyond boundary of site.

Cantilevers: check nature of support to balconies, heavy cornices and stairs.

Services these may have to be sealed off, protected or removed and could include any or all of the following:

1. Drainage runs.
2. Electricity cables.
3. Gas mains and service pipes.
4. Water mains and service pipes.
5. Telephone cables above and below ground level.
6. Radio and television relay cables.
7. District heating mains.

A careful survey of the whole site is advisable to ensure that any flammable or explosive materials such as oil drums and gas cylinders are removed before the demolition work commences. If the method of construction of the existing structure is at all uncertain all available drawings should be carefully studied and analysed or alternatively a detailed survey of the building should be conducted under the guidance of an experienced surveyor.

Adequate insurance should be taken out by the contractor to cover all claims from workmen, any third party and claims for loss or damage to property including roads, pavings and services.

STATUTORY NOTICES

Under the Public Health Act 1961 the local authority for the area in England or Wales must be notified before any demolition work can be started by the building owner or his agent. In the inner London area the notification is made to the district surveyor and in Scotland a warrant is required from the building authority of the burgh or county in which the proposed demolition work is to take place. It is also necessary in Great Britain to inform HM District Construction Inspector of Factories of any demolition works likely to take more than 6 weeks before such demolition commences.

Prior to the commencement of any demolition work the building owner or his agent must notify the Gas, Electricity and Water Area Boards, the Post Office telephone or telecommunication service and the companies responsible for other installations such as radio and television relay lines. It must be noted that it is the contractor's responsibility to ensure that all the services and other installations have been rendered safe or removed by the authority or company concerned.

SUPERVISION AND SAFETY

Part X of The Construction (General Provisions) Regulations 1961 covers all aspects of supervision and safety in respect of demolition works. The demolition contractor is required, under these regulations, to appoint a competent person to supervise the work. He must be experienced in the type of demolition work concerned and where more than one contractor is involved each must appoint a competent supervisor.

METHODS OF DEMOLITION

There are several methods of demolition and the choice is usually determined by:

1. *Type of structure* — for example, 2-storey framed structure, reinforced concrete chimney.
2. *Type of construction* — such as masonry wall, prestressed concrete, structural steelwork.
3. *Location of site* — a detached building on an isolated site which is defined as a building on a site where the minimum distance to the boundary is greater than twice the height of the building to be demolished. A confined site is where not all the boundaries are at a distance exceeding twice the height of the building to be demolished.

Hand demolition: involves the progressive demolition of a structure by operatives using hand-held tools; lifting appliances may be used to hoist and lower members or materials once they have been released. Buildings are usually demolished, by this method, in the reverse order to that of their construction storey by storey. Debris should only be allowed to fall freely where the horizontal distance from the point of fall to the public highway or an adjoining property is greater than 6.000 m or half the height from which the debris is dropped whichever is the greater. In all other cases a chute or skip should be used.

Pusher arm demolition: a method of progressive demolition using a machine fitted with a steel pusher arm exerting a horizontal thrust on to the building fabric. This method should only be used when the machine can be operated from a firm level base with a clear operating base of at least 6.000 m. The height of the building should be reduced by hand demolition if necessary to ensure that the height above the pusher arm does not exceed 600 mm. The pusher arm should not be overloaded and generally should be operated from outside the building. An experienced operator is required and he should work from within a robust cab capable of withstanding the impact of flying debris and be fitted with shatter proof glass cab windows. Where this method of demolition is adopted in connection with attached buildings, the structure to be demolished should first be detached from the adjoining structure by hand demolition techniques.

Deliberate collapse demolition: involves the removal of key structural members causing complete collapse of the whole or part of the building. Expert engineering advice should be obtained before this method is used. It should only be used on detached isolated buildings on reasonably level sites so that the safety to personnel can be carefully controlled.

Demolition ball techniques: a method of progressive demolition carried out by swinging a weight or demolition ball, suspended from a lifting appliance such as a crane, against the fabric of the structure. Three techniques can be used:

1. Vertical drop.
2. Swinging in line with the jib.
3. Slewing jib.

Whichever method is used a skilled operator is essential.

The use of a demolition ball from a normal duty mobile crane should be confined to the vertical drop technique only. A heavy duty machine such as a convertible dragline excavator should be used for the other techniques but in all cases an anti-spin device should be attached to the hoist rope. It is advisable to reduce the length of the crane jib as the demolition work proceeds but at no time should the jib head be less than 3.000 m above the part of the building being demolished.

Pitched roofs should be removed by hand demolition down to wall plate level and at least 50% to 70% of the internal flooring removed to allow for the free fall of debris within the building enclosure. Demolition should then proceed progressively storey by storey.

Demolition ball techniques should not be used on buildings over 30.000 m high since the fall of debris is uncontrollable. Attached buildings should be separated from the adjoining structure by hand demolition to leave a space of at least 6.000 m or half the height of the building, whichever is the greater; a similar clear space is required around the perimeter of the building to give the machine operating space.

Wire rope pulling demolition: only steel wire ropes should be used and the size should be adequate for the purpose but in no case less than 38 mm circumference. The rope should be firmly attached at both ends and the pulling tension gradually applied. No person should be forward of the winch or on either side of the rope within a distance of three quarters of the length between the winch and the building being demolished.

If after several pulls the method does not cause collapse of the structure it may have been weakened and should not therefore be approached but demolished by an alternative means such as a demolition ball or a pusher arm. A well-anchored winch or heavy vehicle should be used to apply the pulling force, great care being taken to ensure that the winch or the vehicle does not lift off its mounting, wheels or tracks.

Demolition by explosives: this is a specialist method where charges of explosives are placed within the fabric of the structure and detonated to cause partial or complete collapse. It should never be attempted by a building contractor without the advice and supervision of an expert.

Other methods: where site conditions are not suitable for the use of explosives the following specialist's methods can be considered:

1. *Gas expansion burster* — a steel cylinder containing a liquified gas, which expands with great force when subjected to an electric charge, is inserted into a prepared cavity in the fabric to be demolished. On being fired the expansion of the cylinder causes the fabric mass to be broken into fragments.

2. *Hydraulic burster* — consists of a steel cylinder with a number of pistons which are forced out radially under hydraulic pressure.

3. *Thermal reaction* — a structural steel member which is to be cut out and removed is surrounded by a mixture of a metal oxide and a reducing agent. This covering is ignited, usually by an electric current, which results in a liberation of a large quantity of heat causing the steel to become plastic. A small force such as a wire rope attached to a winch will be sufficient to cause collapse of the member.

4. *Thermic lance* — a steel tube, sometimes packed with steel rods, through which oxygen is passed. The tip of the lance is preheated by conventional means to melting point (approximately $1\,000°C$) when the supply of oxygen is introduced. This sets up a thermo-chemical reaction giving a temperature of around $3\,500°C$ at the reaction end

which will melt all the materials normally encountered causing very little damage to surrounding materials.

The dangers and risks encountered with any demolition works cannot be over-emphasised and all builders should seek the advice of and employ specialist contractors to carry out all but the simple demolition tasks.

Part II
Excavations

8
Excavations and timbering

Before a foundation can be laid it is necessary to excavate a trench of the required depth and width. On small contracts this is still carried out by hand but on large works it may be economic to use some form of mechanical trench digger. The general procedure for the excavation of foundation trenches is illustrated in **Fig. II.1**.

Timbering

This is a term used to cover temporary supports to the sides of excavations and is sometimes called planking and strutting. The sides of some excavations will need support to:

1. Protect the operatives while working in the excavation.
2. Keep the excavation open by acting as a retaining wall to the sides of the trench.

The type and amount of timbering required will depend upon the depth and nature of the subsoil. Over a short period many soils may not require any timbering but weather conditions, depth, type of soil and duration of the operations must all be taken into account and each excavation must be assessed separately.

Suitable timbers for this work are:

Scots pine
Baltic redwood
Baltic whitewood
Douglas fir

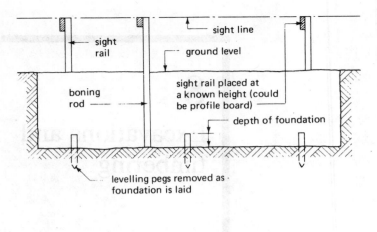

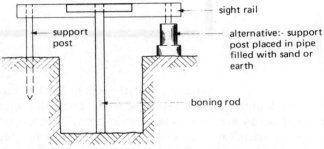

Fig. II.1 Trench excavations

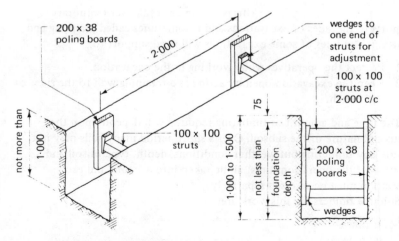

Fig. II.2 Typical timbering in hard soils

70

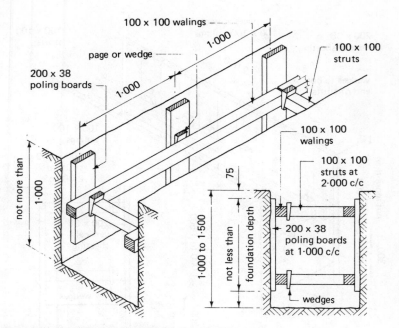

Fig. II.3 Typical timbering in firm soils

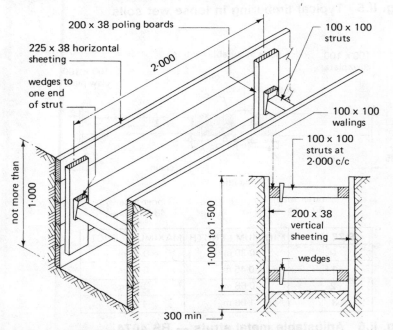

Fig. II.4 Typical timbering in dry loose soils

71

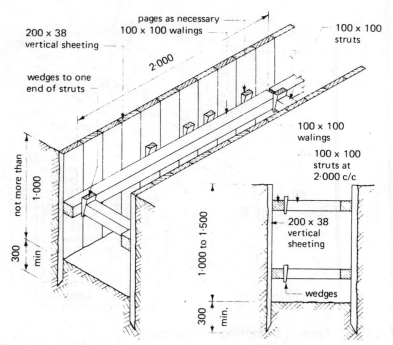

Fig. II.5 Typical timbering in loose wet soils

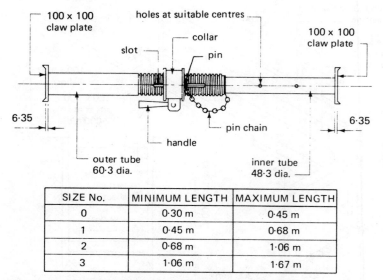

SIZE No.	MINIMUM LENGTH	MAXIMUM LENGTH
0	0·30 m	0·45 m
1	0·45 m	0·68 m
2	0·68 m	1·06 m
3	1·06 m	1·67 m

Fig. II.6 Adjustable metal struts — BS 4074

Larch
Hemlock.

Typical details of timbering to trenches are shown in Figs. II.2—II.6.

THE CONSTRUCTION (GENERAL PROVISIONS) REGULATIONS 1961

This document sets out the following requirements for the timbering of trenches:

Part II—Supervision of safe conduct of work
Every firm employing more than a total of 20 persons must appoint at least one experienced person to be responsible for the general supervision of the safety requirements of the regulations. He need not be fully employed on these duties providing that he can discharge his safety supervisor's duties with reasonable efficiency. He can be employed jointly for a group of sites or jointly by a group of employers.

Part IV—Excavations, shafts and tunnels:
Timber or other suitable material must be provided and used to prevent danger from a fall or dislodgement of materials forming the sides of the excavation.

Timbering must only be erected by a competent person or under his direction.

Before operatives are allowed to work in a trench, an inspection of the excavations must be made by the safety supervisor:

1. At least once a day if persons are employed therein.
2. After an unexpected fall of rock, earth or material.
3. Within the preceding seven days.

The material to be used for timbering the excavation must be inspected on each occasion before used.

All reports of inspections must be recorded on the prescribed form.

Every excavation which is over 1·98 m (6 ft 6 in) deep must have a fence or barrier placed as near to the edge as is practicable or be securely covered.

BUILDING REGULATIONS 1985

Notice of commencement and completion of certain stages of work
Building Regulation 14 requires the local authority to be notified by a person carrying out building work prior to commencement and at

certain stages during the building operations. The notice should be given in writing or by such other means as may be agreed with the local authority.

Notices are required under this regulation as follows:

48 hours prior to commencement of work.

24 hours before excavations are covered up.

24 hours before any concrete or material laid over a site is covered up.

24 hours before any drains or sewers are covered up.

7 days after completion of laying drains or sewers including bedding and backfilling.

7 days after completion of building work and/or 7 days before occupation.

In the calculation of a period of twenty-four hours or forty-eight hours no account shall be taken of a Saturday, Sunday, Christmas Day, Good Friday, Bank Holiday or a day appointed for public thanksgiving or mourning.

9

Trench and basement excavations

Excavations may be classified as shallow, medium or deep in the following manner:

1. Shallow — up to 1.500 m deep.
2. Medium — 1.500 to 3.000 m deep.
3. Deep — over 3.000 m deep.

A second year course of study is mainly concerned with the medium depth excavations.

The method of excavation and timbering to be used in any particular case will depend upon a number of factors:

1. Nature of the subsoil can determine the type of plant or hand tools required and the amount of timbering necessary.
2. Purpose of the excavation can determine minimum widths, minimum depths and the placing of support members to give a reasonable working space within the excavation.
3. Presence of ground water may necessitate the need for interlocking timbering, sump pits and pumps; large quantities of ground water may prompt the use of dewatering techniques.
4. Position of the excavation may impose certain restrictions such as the need for a licence or wayleave, Highway Authority or police requirements when excavating in a public road.
5. Non-availability of the right type of plant for bulk excavation may mean a different method must be used.
6. Presence of a large number of services may restrict the use of machinery to such an extent that it becomes uneconomic.
7. The disposal of the excavated spoil may restrict the choice of plant

due to the load and unload cycle not keeping pace with the machine output.

SAFETY

The Construction (General Provisions) Regulations 1961 is a Statutory Instrument which sets out the minimum requirements for the safe conduct of work in excavations for building operations and works of engineering construction.

This document states that an adequate supply of timber or other suitable material must be supplied and used to prevent danger to any person employed in an excavation over 1.200 m deep from a fall or dislodgement of materials forming the sides of an excavation.

The timbering should be carried out as the work proceeds and must be executed under the direction of a competent person who must ensure that all the material used is of adequate strength and suitable for its intended function. All excavations over 1.200 m deep in which persons are employed must be inspected by a competent person at least once a day and excavations over 2.000 m must be inspected before each shift commences. Unworked excavations must have been inspected within the preceding seven days before persons can recommence working within the excavation. Inspection of excavations must be carried out if there has been substantial damage of supports or if there has been an unexpected fall of earth or other material.

A suitable fence or barrier must be provided to the sides of excavations over 2.000 m deep or alternatively they must be securely covered; methods of providing a suitable barrier are shown in Fig. II.7. Materials must not be placed near the edge of any excavation, nor must plant be placed or moved near excavations so that persons working in the excavation are endangered.

TRENCH EXCAVATIONS

Long narrow trenches in firm soil may be excavated to the full depth by mechanical excavators enabling the support timbering to be placed in one continuous operation. Weak and waterlogged ground must be supported before excavation commences by driving timber runners or steel trench sheeting to a position below the formation level or by a drive and dig procedure. In the latter method the runners can be driven to a reasonable depth of approximately 1.500 m followed by an

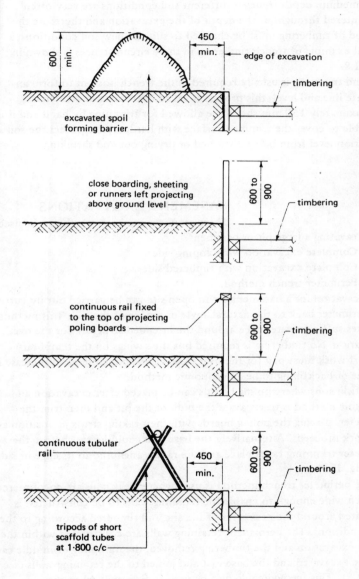

Fig. II.7 Barriers to excavations

excavation cut of 1.200 m and then the operation repeated until the required level has been reached; this will make the driving of the runners easier and enable a smaller driving appliance to be used.

In medium depth trenches different soil conditions are very often encountered throughout the depth of the excavation and therefore the method of timbering must be changed to suit the new soil conditions; a typical example of trench timbering in these circumstances is shown in Fig. II.8.

Hand trimming is usually required in the trench bottom to form an accurate line and level; this process is called bottoming of trenches. Approximately 150 mm should be allowed for trimming by hand and it is advisable to cover the trimmed surface with hardcore to protect the soil at formation level from being disturbed or drying out and shrinking.

BASEMENT EXCAVATIONS

There are three methods which can be used for excavating a large pit or basement:

1. Complete excavation with sloping sides.
2. Complete excavation with timbered sides.
3. Perimeter trench method.

Excavation for a basement on an open site can be carried out by cutting the perimeter back to the natural angle of repose of the soil. This method requires sufficient site space around the intended structure for the over excavation. No timbering is required but the savings on the temporary support work must pay for the over excavation and consequent increase in volume of backfilling to be an economic method.

In firm soils where poling boards can be placed after excavation an economic method is to excavate the bulk of the pit and then trim the perimeter, placing the poling boards with their raking struts in position as the work proceeds. Alternatively the base slab could be cast before the perimeter trimming takes place and the rakers anchored to its edge or side (see Fig. II.9).

The perimeter trench method is used where weak soils are encountered; a trench wide enough to enable the retaining walls to be constructed is excavated around the perimeter of the site and timbered according to the soil conditions. The permanent retaining walls are constructed within the trench excavation and the timbering removed, the dumpling or middle can then be excavated and the base cast and joined to the retaining walls (see Fig. II.9). This method could also be used in firm soils when the mechanical excavators required for bulk excavation are not available.

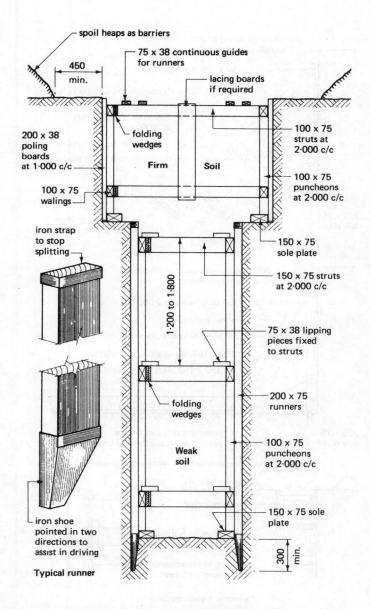

Fig. II.8   Trench timbering in different soils

Labels within the figure:

- spoil heaps as barriers
- 75 x 38 continuous guides for runners
- lacing boards if required
- 450 min.
- 200 x 38 poling boards at 1·000 c/c
- folding wedges
- Firm   Soil
- 100 x 75 struts at 2·000 c/c
- 100 x 75 walings
- 100 x 75 puncheons at 2·000 c/c
- iron strap to stop splitting
- 150 x 75 sole plate
- 1·200 to 1·800
- 150 x 75 struts at 2·000 c/c
- 75 x 38 lipping pieces fixed to struts
- 200 x 75 runners
- folding wedges
- Weak soil
- 100 x 75 puncheons at 2·000 c/c
- iron shoe pointed in two directions to assist in driving
- 150 x 75 sole plate
- 300 min.
- Typical runner

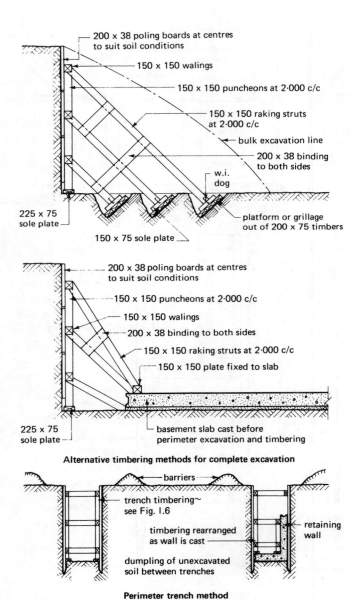

200 x 38 poling boards at centres to suit soil conditions

150 x 150 walings

150 x 150 puncheons at 2·000 c/c

150 x 150 raking struts at 2·000 c/c

bulk excavation line

200 x 38 binding to both sides

w.i. dog

225 x 75 sole plate

platform or grillage out of 200 x 75 timbers

150 x 75 sole plate

200 x 38 poling boards at centres to suit soil conditions

150 x 150 puncheons at 2·000 c/c

150 x 150 walings

200 x 38 binding to both sides

150 x 150 raking struts at 2·000 c/c

150 x 150 plate fixed to slab

225 x 75 sole plate

basement slab cast before perimeter excavation and timbering

Alternative timbering methods for complete excavation

barriers

trench timbering~ see Fig. I.6

timbering rearranged as wall is cast

retaining wall

dumpling of unexcavated soil between trenches

Perimeter trench method

Fig. II.9   Basement excavations and timbering

10
Deep trench excavations

Any form of excavation on a building site is a potential hazard, and although statistics show that of the 46 000 or so reportable accidents occurring each year on building sites excavations do not constitute the major hazard, but they can often prove to be serious; indeed, approximately 1 in 10 accidents occurring in excavations are fatal.

THE CONSTRUCTION (GENERAL PROVISIONS) REGULATIONS 1961

This is a statutory instrument made under the powers of the Factories Acts of 1937 and 1948. They were introduced to provide a minimum degree of safety to operatives when working in or near excavations, shafts, tunnels, demolitions, work involving the use of explosives and work on or adjacent to water. These regulations apply to building operations and works of engineering construction since the risks encountered in the two industries are similar and therefore a common code of safety is desirable.

In general the regulations set out the requirements for the supply and use of adequate timbering to excavations, the appointment of safety supervisors for firms employing a total of more than 20 persons engaged on constructional works and the frequency of inspections to ascertain the safe condition of the working areas.

Every contractor is responsible for the safety of his own employees and every person employed must co-operate in observing the various requirements of the regulations. If an employee discovers any defect or unsafe condition in a working area it is his duty to report the facts to his

81

employer, foreman or to a person appointed by the employer as safety supervisor. The requirements embodied in the Health and Safety at Work, etc., Act 1974 must also be observed.

DEEP TRENCH EXCAVATIONS

Deep trenches may be considered as those over 3.000 m deep and are usually required for the installation of services since deep foundations are not very often encountered due to the more economic alternatives such as piling and raft techniques. Trench excavations should not be opened too far in advance of the proposed work and any backfilling should be undertaken as soon as practicable after the completion of the work. These two precautions will lessen the risk of falls, flooding and damage to completed work as well as releasing the timbering for re-use at the earliest possible date. Great care must be taken in areas where underground services are present; these should be uncovered with care, protected and supported as necessary. The presence of services, in an excavation area, may restrict the use of mechanical plant to the point where its use becomes uneconomic. Hand trimming should be used for bottoming the trench, side trimming, end trimming and for forming the gradient just prior to the pipe, cable or drain laying.

In general all deep excavations should be close boarded or sheeted as a precautionary measure, the main exception being hard and stable rock subsoils. Any excavation in a rock strata should be carefully examined to ascertain its stability. Fissures or splits in the rock layers which slope towards the cut face may lead to crumbling or rock falls particularly when exposed to the atmosphere for long periods. In this situation it would be prudent to timber the faces of the excavation according to the extent and disposition of the fissures.

In firm subsoils it might be possible to complete the excavation dig before placing the timbering in position. The general method of support for the excavation sides follows that used in shallow and medium depth trench excavations studied in the first 2 years of a construction technology course, except that larger sections are used to resist the increased pressures encountered as the depth of excavation increases – see Fig. II.10.

If the subsoil is weak, waterlogged or running sand it will be necessary to drive timber runners, trench sheeting or interlocking sheet piles of steel, timber or precast concrete ahead of the excavation dig. This can be accomplished by driving to a depth exceeding the final excavation depth or by the drive and dig system ensuring that timbering is always in advance of the excavating operation. Long runners or sheet piles will require a driving frame to hold and guide the members whilst being driven. To avoid the use of large piling frames and heavy driving equipment the

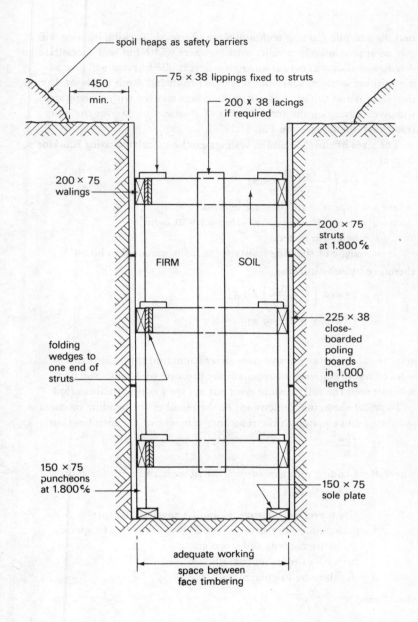

Spoil heaps as safety barriers

450 min.

75 × 38 lippings fixed to struts

200 × 38 lacings if required

200 × 75 walings

FIRM   SOIL

200 × 75 struts at 1.800 %

225 × 38 close-boarded poling boards in 1.000 lengths

folding wedges to one end of struts

150 × 75 puncheons at 1.800 %

150 × 75 sole plate

adequate working space between face timbering

Fig. II.10 Traditional deep trench timbering

tucking and pile framing techniques may be used. Tucking framing will give an approximately parallel working space width but will necessitate driving the short runners at an angle whereas pile framing will give a diminishing working space but it is easier to install. Both methods, having the bottom and top of consecutive members secured with a single strut, will give a saving on the total number of struts required over the more traditional methods — see Fig. II.11.

The sizes of suitable timber walings can be calculated using Rankine's formula:

$$p = wh \left(\frac{1 - \sin\theta}{1 + \sin\theta} \right) \times 9.81$$

where p = approximate pressure in N/m^2

w = mass of soil (typical value = 1 980 kg/m^3)

h = height in metres

e = angle of shearing resistance (usually assumed to be 30°)

therefore by substitution:

$$p = 1\ 980h \left(\frac{1 - 0.5}{1 + 0.5} \right) \times 9.81$$

$$= 1\ 980h \times 0.33 \times 9.81$$

$$\backsimeq 6\ 400h$$

in most cases where cohesive soils are encountered this value can be reduced by 50%, giving an approximate pressure of 3 200h, since in cohesive soils the full pressure does not act for a considerable period.

To select the actual dimensions of the member the bending moment is calculated and equated to the resistance moment of the member thus:

$$M = \frac{fbd^2}{6}$$

where M = bending moment of $\frac{wl^2}{10}$ for runners and $\frac{wl^2}{8}$ for short poling boards.

(w = average pressure 'p' and l = spacing of struts)

f = permissible fibre stress of the timber according to species, moisture content and stress grade

b = breadth of member (usually assumed)

d = depth to be calculated

therefore $d = \sqrt{\dfrac{6M}{fb}}$

It must be remembered that timbering is a general term used to cover all forms of temporary support to the sides of an excavation to:

1. Prevent collapse of the excavation sides and so endanger the operatives working in the immediate vicinity.

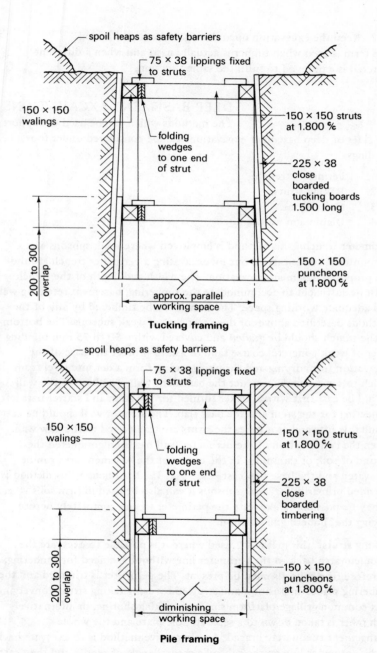

Fig. II.11   Timbering — tucking and pile framing

2. Keep the excavation open during the required period.
The term is used when timber is actually used and when a different
material is employed to fulfil the same function.

DEEP BASEMENT EXCAVATIONS

The methods which can be used to support
the sides of deep basement excavations can be considered under four
headings:

1. Perimeter trench.
2. Raking struts.
3. Cofferdams.
4. Diaphragm walls.

Perimeter trench: this method is employed where weak subsoils are
encountered and is carried out by excavating a perimeter trench around
the proposed basement excavation. The width and depth of the trench
must be sufficient to accommodate the timbering, basement retaining wall
and adequate working space. The trench can be timbered by any of the
methods described above for deep trenches in weak subsoils. The bottom
of the trench should be graded and covered with a 50 to 75 mm blinding
layer of weak concrete, coarse sand or ash to protect the base of the
excavation from drying and shrinking and to form a definite level from
which to set out and construct the basement wall. The base of the wall
should be cast first with a kicker formed for the stem and starter bars left
projecting for the stem and the base slab. The stem or wall should be cast
in suitable lifts and as it cures the struts are transferred to the new wall.
When the construction of the perimeter wall has been completed the
mound of soil, or dumpling, in the centre of the basement area can be
excavated and the base slab cast — see Fig. II.12. Although this method is
intended primarily for weak subsoils it can also be used in firm soils where
it may be possible to excavate the perimeter trench completely before
placing the timbering in position.

Raking struts: this method is used where it is possible to excavate the
basement area back to the perimeter line without the need for timbering,
therefore firm subsoils must be present. The perimeter is trimmed and the
timbering placed in position and strutted by using raking struts converging
on a common grillage platform similar to raking shoring, or alternatively
each raker is taken down to a separate sole plate and the whole
arrangement adequately braced. An alternative method is to excavate back
to the perimeter line on the subsoil's natural angle of repose and then cast
the base slab to protect the excavation bottom from undue drying out and

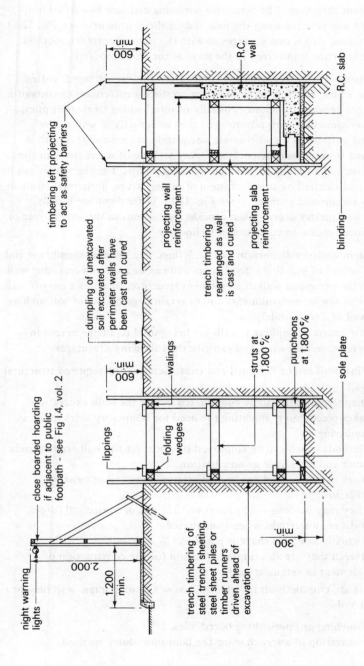

Fig. II.12 Basement timbering — perimeter trench method

R.C. wall

R.C. slab

timbering left projecting to act as safety barriers

projecting wall reinforcement

projecting slab reinforcement

blinding

600 min.

dumpling of unexcavated soil excavated after perimeter walls have been cast and cured

trench timbering rearranged as wall is cast and cured

walings

600 min.

struts at 1.800%

puncheons at 1.800%

sole plate

lippings

folding wedges

300 min.

night warning lights

close boarded hoarding if adjacent to public footpath - see Fig I.4, vol. 2

2.000

1.200 min.

trench timbering of steel trench sheeting, steel sheet piles or timber runners driven ahead of excavation

subsequent shrinkage. The perimeter trimming can now be carried out, timbered and strutted using the base slab as the abutment — see Fig. II.13. The retaining wall is cast in stages as with the perimeter trench method and the strutting transferred to the stem as the work proceeds.

Cofferdams: the term cofferdam comes from the French word 'coffre' meaning a box, which is an apt description since a cofferdam consists of a watertight perimeter enclosure, usually of interlocking steel sheet piles, used in conjunction with waterlogged sites or actually in water. The enclosing cofferdam is constructed, adequately braced and the earth is excavated from within the enclosure. Any seepage of water through the cofferdam can normally be handled by small pumps. The sheet piles can be braced and strutted by using a system of raking struts, horizontal struts or tie rods and ground anchors — see Fig. II.14. Cofferdams are usually studied to a greater degree when considering caissons in the second year of an advanced course in construction technology.

Diaphragm walls: a diaphragm can be defined as a dividing membrane and in the context of building a diaphragm wall can be used as a retaining wall to form the perimeter wall of a basement structure, to act as a cut-off wall for river or similar embankments and to retain large masses of soil such as a side wall of a road underpass.

In situ concrete diaphragm walls are being used to a large extent in modern construction work and can give the following advantages:

1. Final wall can be designed and constructed as the required structural wall.
2. Diaphragm walls can be constructed before the bulk excavation takes place thus eliminating the need for temporary works such as timbering.
3. Methods which can be employed to construct the wall are relatively quiet and have little or no vibration.
4. Work can be carried out immediately adjacent to an existing structure.
5. They may be designed to resist vertical and/or horizontal forces.
6. Walls are watertight when constructed.
7. Virtually any plan shape is possible.
8. Overall they are an economic method for the construction of basement or retaining walls.

There are two methods by which a cast *in situ* diaphragm wall may be constructed:

1. Touching or interlocking bored piles.
2. Excavation of a trench using the bentonite slurry method.

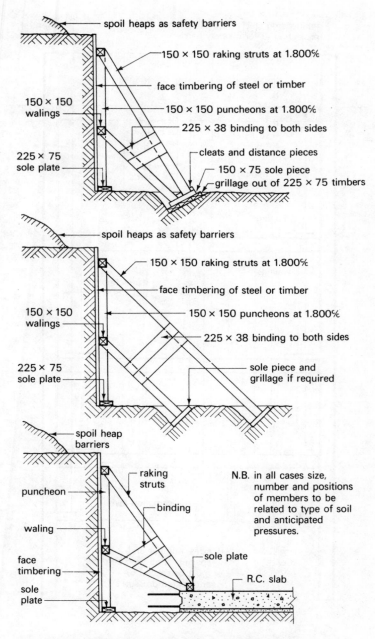

spoil heaps as safety barriers

150 × 150 raking struts at 1.800%

face timbering of steel or timber

150 × 150 puncheons at 1.800%

225 × 38 binding to both sides

cleats and distance pieces

150 × 75 sole piece

grillage out of 225 × 75 timbers

150 × 150 walings

225 × 75 sole plate

spoil heaps as safety barriers

150 × 150 raking struts at 1.800%

face timbering of steel or timber

150 × 150 puncheons at 1.800%

225 × 38 binding to both sides

sole piece and grillage if required

150 × 150 walings

225 × 75 sole plate

spoil heap barriers

puncheon

raking struts

binding

waling

face timbering

sole plate

sole plate

R.C. slab

N.B. in all cases size, number and positions of members to be related to type of soil and anticipated pressures.

Fig. II.13   Basement timbering — raking struts

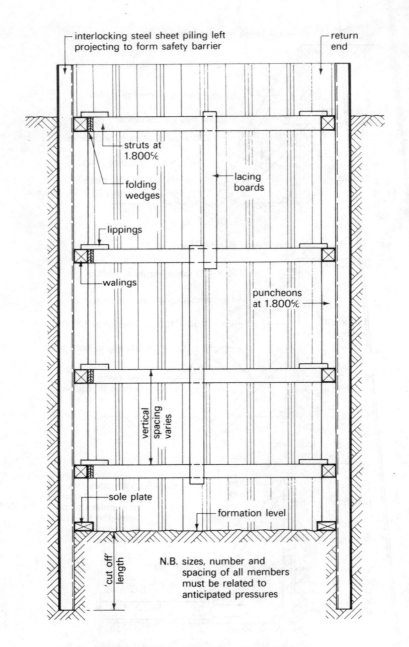

interlocking steel sheet piling left projecting to form safety barrier

return end

struts at 1.800%

folding wedges

lacing boards

lippings

walings

puncheons at 1.800%

vertical spacing varies

sole plate

formation level

'cut off' length

N.B. sizes, number and spacing of all members must be related to anticipated pressures

Fig. II.14   Cofferdams — basic principles

The formation of bored piles is fully described later in the chapter on piling. The piles can be bored so that their interfaces are just touching; or by boring for piles in alternate positions and using a special auger the intermediate pile positions can be bored so that the interfaces interlock. The main advantage of using this method is that the wall can be formed within a restricted headroom of not less than 2.000 m. The disadvantages are the general need for a reinforced tie beam over the heads of the piles and the necessity for a facing to take out the irregularities of the surface. This facing usually takes the form of a cement rendering lightly reinforced with a steel welded fabric mesh.

The general method used to construct diaphragm walls is the bentonite slurry system. Bentonite is manufactured from a montmorillonite clay which is commonly called fullers' earth because of its use by fullers in the textile industry to absorb grease from newly woven cloth. When mixed with the correct amount of water bentonite produces thixotropic properties giving a liquid behaviour when agitated and a gel structure when undisturbed.

The basic procedure is to replace the excavated spoil with the bentonite slurry as the work proceeds. The slurry forms a soft gel or 'filter cake' at the interface of the excavation sides with slight penetration into the subsoil. Hydrostatic pressure caused by the bentonite slurry thrusting on the 'filter cake' cushion is sufficient to hold back the subsoil and any ground water which may be present. This alleviates the need for timbering and/or pumping and can be successfully employed up to 36.000 m deep.

Diaphragm walls constructed by this method are executed in alternate panels from 4.500 m to 7.000 m long with widths ranging from 500 to 900 mm using a specially designed hydraulic grab attached to a standard crane or by using a continuous cutting and recirculating machine. Before the general excavation commences a guide trench, about 1.000 m deep is excavated and lined with lightly reinforced walls. These walls act as a guide line for the excavating machinery, provide a reservoir for the slurry, enables pavings and underground services to be broken out ahead of the excavation.

To form an interlocking and watertight joint at each end of the panel, circular stop end pipes are placed in the bentonite-filled excavation before the concrete is placed. The continuous operation of concreting the panel is carried out using a tremie pipe and a concrete mix designed to have good flow properties without the tendency to segregate. This will require a concrete with a high slump of about 200 mm but with high strength properties ranging from 20 to 40 N/mm^2. Generally the rate of pour is in the region of 15 to 20 m^3 per hour and as the concrete is introduced into the excavated panel it will displace the bentonite slurry, which is less dense

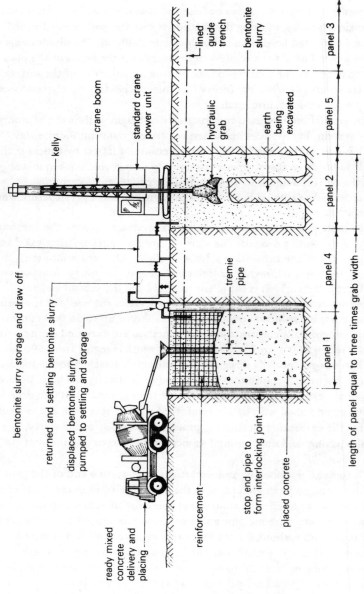

Fig. II.15 Diaphragm wall construction — bentonite slurry method

kelly

crane boom

standard crane power unit

hydraulic grab

bentonite slurry

earth being excavated

lined guide trench

bentonite slurry storage and draw off

returned and settling bentonite slurry

displaced bentonite slurry pumped to settling and storage

ready mixed concrete delivery and placing

reinforcement

tremie pipe

stop end pipe to form interlocking joint

placed concrete

panel 1

panel 4

panel 2

panel 5

panel 3

length of panel equal to three times grab width

than the concrete, which can be stored for re-use or transferred to the next panel being excavated. The ideal situation is to have the two operations acting simultaneously and in complete unison — see Fig. II.15.

Before the concrete is placed reinforcement cages of high yield or mild steel bars are fabricated on site in one or two lengths. Single length cages of up to 20.000 m are possible; where cages in excess of this are required they are usually spot welded together when the first cage is projecting about 1.000 m above the slurry level. The usual recommended minimum cover is 100 mm which is maintained by having spacing blocks or rings attached to the outer bars of the cage. Upon completion of the concreting the bentonite slurry must be removed from the site either by tanker or by diluting so that it can be discharged into the surface water sewers by agreement with the local authority.

11
Tunnelling

A tunnel may be defined as an artificial underground passage and has been used by man as a means of communication or for transportation for several thousand years. Prehistoric man is known to have connected his natural cave habitats by tunnels hewn in the rock. A Babylonian king *circa* 2180-2160 B.C. connected his royal palace to the Temple of Jupiter on the opposite bank of the Euphrates by a brick arched tunnel under the river. Other examples of early tunnels are those hewn in the rock in the tomb of Mineptah at Thebes in Egypt and the early Greek tunnel, constructed about 687 B.C., used for conveying water on the Island of Samos.

The majority of these early tunnels were constructed in rock subsoils and therefore required no permanent or temporary support. Today, tunnelling in almost any subsoil is possible. Permanent tunnels for underground railways and roads can be lined with metal and/or concrete but such undertakings are the province of the civil engineer. The general building contractor would normally only be involved with temporary tunnelling for the purposes of gaining access to existing services or installing new services, constructing small permanent tunnels for pedestrian subways under road or railway embankments and forming permanent tunnels for services.

When the depth of a projected excavation is about 6.000 m the alternative of working in a heading or tunnel should be considered taking into account the following factors:

1. *Nature of subsoils* — the amount of timbering that will be required in the tunnel as opposed to that required in deep trench excavations.

2. *Depth of excavation* — over 9.000 m deep it is usually cheaper to tunnel or use one of the alternative methods such as thrust boring. The cover of ground over a tunnel to avoid disturbance of underground services, roads, pavings and tree roots is generally recommended to be 3.000 m minimum.
3. *Existing services* — in urban areas buried services can be a problem with open deep-trench excavations; this can generally be avoided by tunnelling techniques.
4. *Carriageways* — it may be deemed necessary to tunnel under busy roads to avoid disturbance of the flow of traffic.
5. *Means of access* — the proposed tunnel may be entered by means of an open trench if the tunnel excavation is into an embankment or access may be gained by way of a shaft.
6. *Construction Regulations* — Part IV of the Construction (General Provisions) Regulations 1961 sets out the minimum requirements for the protection of operatives working in excavations, shafts and tunnels covering such aspects as temporary timbering, supervision of works and means of egress in case of flooding. Part VII deals with the ventilation of excavations and Regulation 47 in Part XI covers the provision of adequate lighting.

SHAFTS

These are by definition vertical passages but in the context of building operations they can also be used to form the excavation for a deep isolated base foundation. In common with all excavations, the extent and nature of the temporary support or timbering required will depend upon:
1. Subsoil conditions encountered.
2. Anticipated ground and hydrostatic pressures.
3. Materials used to provide temporary support.
4. Plan size and depth of excavation.

In loose subsoils a system of sheet piling could be used by driving the piles ahead of the excavation operation. This form of temporary support is called a cofferdam and is fully covered in the second year of advanced study — see Fig. II.14.

Alternatives to the cofferdam techniques for shaft timbering are tucking framing and pile framing. These methods consist of driving short timber runners, 1.000 to 2.000 m long, ahead of the excavation operation and then excavating and strutting within the perimeter of the runners. The process is repeated until the required depth has been reached. It is essential with all drive and dig methods that at all times the depth to which the runner has been driven is in excess of the excavation depth. The installation of tucking framing and pile framing in shafts is as described for deep trench timbering — see Fig. II.11. Both tucking framing and pile framing have the advantages over sheet piling of not requiring large guide trestles and heavy driving equipment.

In firm subsoils the shaft excavation would be carried out in stages of 1.000 to 2.000 m deep according to the ability of the subsoil to remain stable for short periods. Each excavated stage is timbered before proceeding with the next digging operation. The sides of the excavated shaft can be supported by a system of adequately braced and strutted poling boards — see Figs II.16 and II.17. Sometimes a series of cross beams are used at the head of shaft timbering to reduce the risk of the whole arrangement sliding down the shaft as excavation work is proceeding at the lower levels.

Shafts are usually excavated square in plan with side dimensions of 1.200 to 3.000 m depending on:
1. Total depth required.
2. Method of timbering.
3. Sizes of support lining to save unnecessary cutting to width.
4. Number of operatives using or working within the shaft.
5. Size of skip or container to be used for removing spoil.
6. Type of machinery used for bulk excavation.

If the shaft is for the construction of an isolated base then an access or ladder bay should be constructed. This bay would be immediately adjacent to the shaft and of similar dimensions, making in plan a rectangular shaft. The most vulnerable point in any shaft timbering is the corners, where high pressures are encountered, and these positions should be specially strengthened by using corner posts or runners of larger cross section — see Fig. II.16.

TUNNELS

The operational sequence of excavating and timbering a tunnel or heading by traditional methods can be enumerated thus:
1. In firm soils excavate first 1.000 m long stage or bay; if weak subsoil is encountered it may be necessary to drive head boards and lining boards as the first operation.
2. Head boards 1.000 m long are placed against the upper surface.
3. Sole plate and stretcher are positioned; these are partly bedded into the ground to prevent lateral movement and are levelled through from stretcher to stretcher.
4. Cut and position head tree.

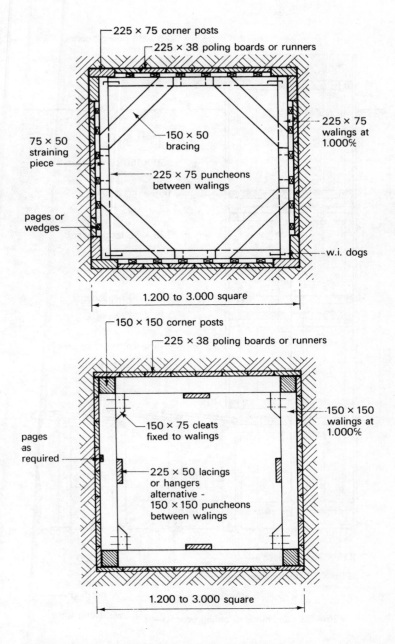

Fig. II.16 Shaft timbering — typical plans

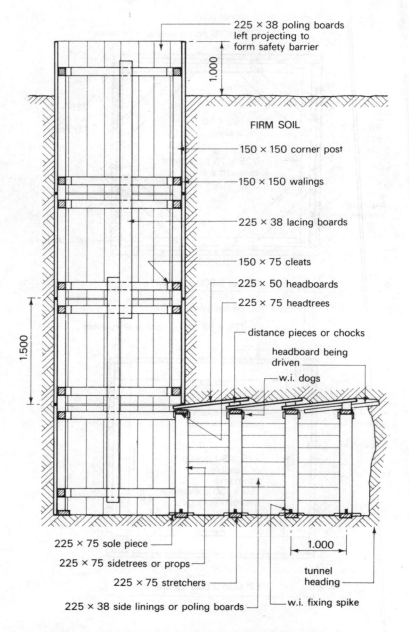

225 × 38 poling boards
left projecting to
form safety barrier

1.000

FIRM SOIL

150 × 150 corner post

150 × 150 walings

225 × 38 lacing boards

150 × 75 cleats

225 × 50 headboards

225 × 75 headtrees

distance pieces or chocks

headboard being
driven

w.i. dogs

1.500

1.000

tunnel
heading

225 × 75 sole piece

225 × 75 sidetrees or props

225 × 75 stretchers

225 × 38 side linings or poling boards

w.i. fixing spike

Fig. II.17 Typical shaft and tunnel timbering

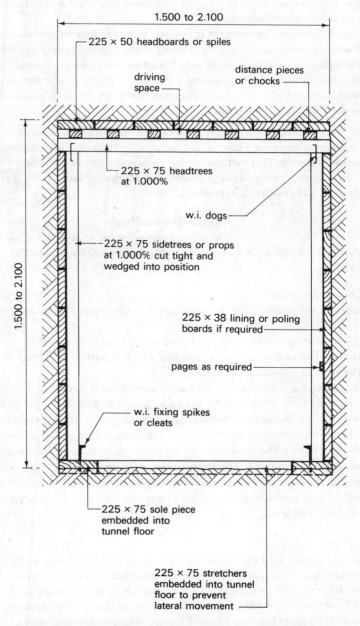

1.500 to 2.100

225 × 50 headboards or spiles

driving space

distance pieces or chocks

225 × 75 headtrees at 1.000%

w.i. dogs

1.500 to 2.100

225 × 75 sidetrees or props at 1.000% cut tight and wedged into position

225 × 38 lining or poling boards if required

pages as required

w.i. fixing spikes or cleats

225 × 75 sole piece embedded into tunnel floor

225 × 75 stretchers embedded into tunnel floor to prevent lateral movement

Fig. II.18 Typical section through tunnel timbering

5. Cut side trees or struts to fit tightly between sole plate and head tree and wedge into position.
6. Secure frames using wrought iron dogs, spikes and cleats as required.
7. Excavate next stage or bay by starting at the top and taking out just enough soil to allow the next set of head boards to be positioned.
8. If loose subsoils are encountered it will be necessary to line the sides with driven or placed horizontal poling boards as the work proceeds — see Figs. II.17 and II.18.

After the construction work has been carried out within the tunnel it can be backfilled with hand-compacted material, extracting the timbering as the work proceeds. This method is time consuming and costly; the general procedure is to backfill the tunnel with pumped concrete and leave the temporary support work in position.

Alternative methods
Where the purpose of the excavation is for the installation of pipework alternative methods to tunnelling should be considered.

Small diameter pipes
Two methods are available for the installation of small pipes up to 200 mm diameter.
1. *Thrust boring* — a bullet-shaped solid metal head is fixed to the leading end of the pipe to be installed which is pushed or jacked into the ground displacing the earth.
2. *Auger boring* — carried out with a horizontal auger boring tool operating from a working pit having at least 2.400 m long × 1.500 m wide clear dimensions between any temporary supporting members. The boring operation can be carried out without casings but where the objective is the installation of services, concrete or steel casings are usually employed. The auger removes the spoil by working within the bore of the casing which is being continuously rammed or jacked into position. It is possible to use this method for diameters of up to 1.000 m.

Pipe jacking
This method can be used for the installation of pipes from 150 to 3 600 mm diameter but it is mainly employed on the larger diameters of over 1.000 m. Basically the procedure is to force the pipes into the subsoil by means of a series of hydraulic jacks and excavate, as the driving proceeds, from within the pipes by hand or machine according to site conditions. The leading pipe is usually fitted with a steel shield or hood to aid the

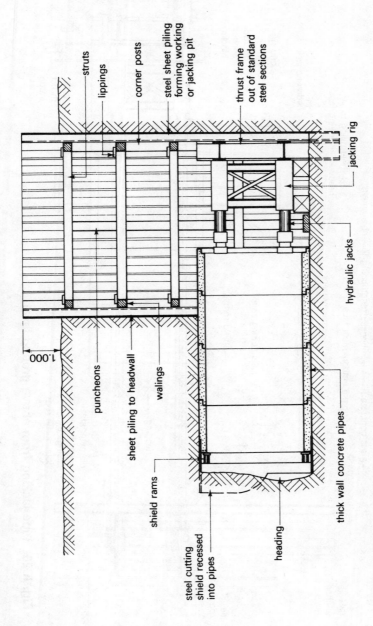

struts

lippings

corner posts

steel sheet piling forming working or jacking pit

thrust frame out of standard steel sections

jacking rig

1.000

puncheons

sheet piling to headwall

walings

shield rams

hydraulic jacks

thick wall concrete pipes

steel cutting shield recessed into pipes

heading

Fig. II.19 Pipe jacking from below ground level

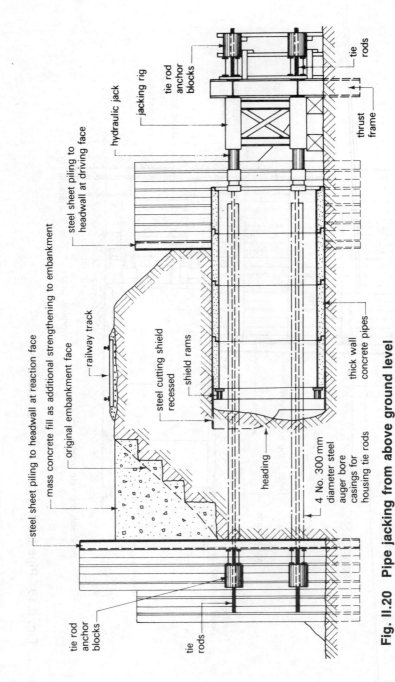

steel sheet piling to headwall at reaction face

mass concrete fill as additional strengthening to embankment

original embankment face

railway track

steel sheet piling to headwall at driving face

hydraulic jack

jacking rig

tie rod anchor blocks

tie rods

thrust frame

thick wall concrete pipes

steel cutting shield recessed

shield rams

heading

4 No. 300 mm diameter steel auger bore casings for housing tie rods

tie rod anchor blocks

tie rods

Fig. II.20 Pipe jacking from above ground level

driving process. This is a very safe method since the excavation work is carried out from within the casing or liner and the danger of collapsing excavations is eliminated; there is also no disruption of the surface or underground services and it is a practical method for most types of subsoil.

The most common method is to work from a jacking or working pit which is formed in a similar manner to traditional shafts except that a framed thrust pad is needed from which to operate the hydraulic jacks. The working pit must be large enough for the jacks to be extended and to allow for new pipe sections to be lowered into the working bay at the bottom — see Fig. II.19.

Pipe jacking can also be carried out from ground level and is particularly suitable for driving pipes through an embankment to form a pedestrian subway. A series of 300 mm diameter lined augered bore holes are driven through the embankment to accommodate tie bars which are anchored to a bulkhead frame on the opposite side of the embankment. The reactions from the ramming jacks are thus transferred through the tie bars to the bulkhead frame and the driving action becomes one of pushing and pulling — see Fig. II.20. In firm soils the rate of bore by this method is approximately 3.000 m per day.

Pipes can also be jacked, from ground level, into the earth at a gradient of up to 1:12 using a jacking block attached to a row of tension piles sited below the commencing level.

PIPES

The pipes used in the above techniques are usually classified in diameter ranges thus:

1. *Small pipes* — 150 to 900 mm diameter — thrust or auger bored.
2. *Medium pipes* — 900 to 1 800 mm diameter — pipe jacking techniques.
3. *Large pipes* — 1 800 to 3 600 mm diameter — pipe jacking techniques.

Two materials are in common use for the pipes, namely concrete and steel. Spun concrete pipes are specially designed with thick walls and have a rubber joint making them especially suitable for sewers without the need for extra strengthening. Larger diameter pipes for pedestrian subway constructions are usually made of cast concrete and can have special bolted connections making the joints watertight which also renders them suitable for use as sewer pipes. Steel pipes have a wall thickness relative to their diameter and usually have welded joints to give high tensile strength, the alternative being a flanged and bolted joint. They are obtainable with various coatings and linings to meet special requirements such as corrosive-bearing effluents.

12
Cofferdams and caissons

A cofferdam may be defined as a temporary box structure constructed in earth or water to exclude soil and/or water from a construction area. It is usually formed to enable the formation of foundations to be carried out in safe working conditions. It is common practice to use interlocking steel trench sheeting or steel sheet piling to form the cofferdam but any material which will fulfil the same function can be used, including timber piles, precast concrete piles, earth-filled crib walls and banks of soil and rock. It must be clearly understood that to be economic and effective cofferdams must be structurally designed and such calculations are usually covered in the structural design syllabus of a typical course of study and have therefore been omitted from this text.

SHEET PILE COFFERDAMS

Cofferdams constructed from steel sheet piles or steel trench sheeting can be considered under two headings:

1. Single-skin cofferdams.
2. Double-skin cofferdams.

Single-skin cofferdams: these consist of a suitably supported single enclosing row of trench sheeting or sheet piles forming an almost completely watertight box. Trench sheeting could be considered for light loadings up to an excavation depth of 3.000 below the existing soil or water level whereas sheet piles are usually suitable for excavation depths of up to 15.000. The small amount of seepage which will occur through the interlocking joints must not be in excess of that which can be comfortably handled by a pump, or alternatively the joints can be sealed by caulking with asbestos rope, suitable mastics or a bitumastic compound.

Single-skin cofferdams constructed to act as cantilevers are possible in all soils but the maximum amount of excavation height will be low relative to the required penetration of the toe of the pile and this is particularly true in cohesive soils. Most cofferdams are therefore either braced and strutted or anchored using tie rods or ground anchors. Standard structural steel sections or structural timber members can be used to form the support system but generally timber is only economically suitable for low loadings. The total amount of timber required to brace a cofferdam adequately would be in the region of 0.25 to 0.3 m^3 per tonne of steel sheet piling used whereas the total weight of steel bracing would be in the region of 30 to 60% of the total weight of sheet piling used to form the cofferdam. Typical cofferdam support arrangements are shown in Figs. II.21 and II.22. Single-skin cofferdams that are circular in plan can also be constructed using ring beams of concrete or steel to act as bracing without the need for strutting. Diameters up to 36.000 are economically possible using this method.

Cofferdams constructed in water, particularly those being erected in tidal waters, should be fitted with sluice gates to act as a precaution against unanticipated weaknesses in the arrangement and in the case of tidal waters to enable the water levels on both sides of the dam to be equalised during construction and before final closure. Special piles with an integral sluice gate forming a 200 mm wide x 400 mm deep opening are available. Alternatively a suitable gate can be formed by cutting a pair of piles and fitting them with a top-operated screw gear so that they can be raised to form an opening of any desired depth.

Double-skin cofferdams: these are self-supporting gravity structures constructed by using two parallel rows of piles with a filling material placed in the void created. Gravity-type cofferdams can also be formed by using straight-web sheet pile sections arranged as a cellular construction — see Figs. II.23 and II.24.

The stability of these forms of cofferdam depends upon the design and arrangement of the sheet piling and upon the nature of the filling material. The inner wall of a double-skin cofferdam is designed as a retaining wall which is suitably driven into the sub-strata whereas the outer wall acts primarily as an anchor wall. The two parallel rows of piles are tied together with one or two rows of tie rods acting against external steel walings. Inner walls should have a series of low level weep holes to relieve the filling material of high water pressures and thus increase its shear resistance. For this reason the filling material selected should be capable of being well

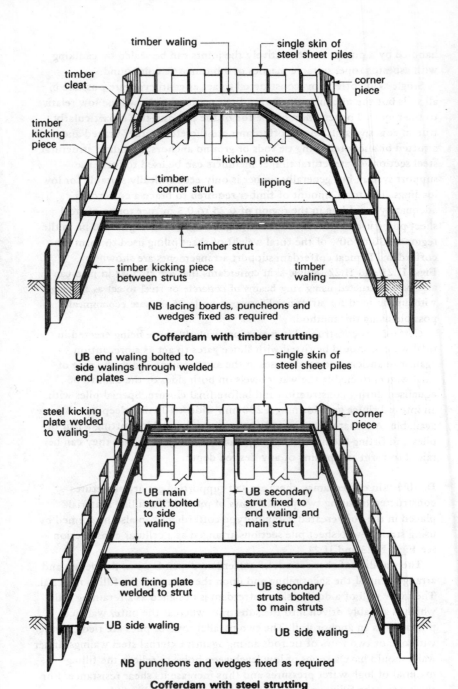

Fig. II.21 Typical cofferdam strutting arrangements

Cofferdam with timber strutting

- timber waling
- single skin of steel sheet piles
- timber cleat
- corner piece
- timber kicking piece
- kicking piece
- timber corner strut
- lipping
- timber strut
- timber kicking piece between struts
- timber waling

NB lacing boards, puncheons and wedges fixed as required

Cofferdam with steel strutting

- UB end waling bolted to side walings through welded end plates
- single skin of steel sheet piles
- steel kicking plate welded to waling
- corner piece
- UB main strut bolted to side waling
- UB secondary strut fixed to end waling and main strut
- end fixing plate welded to strut
- UB secondary struts bolted to main struts
- UB side waling
- UB side waling

NB puncheons and wedges fixed as required

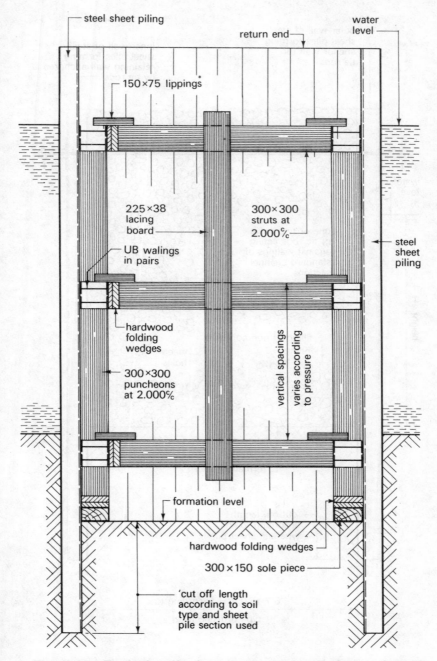

Fig. II.22 Typical cofferdam section using timber and steel strutting

The labels in the figure are:

- steel sheet piling
- return end
- water level
- 150×75 lippings
- 225×38 lacing board
- 300×300 struts at 2.000%
- steel sheet piling
- UB walings in pairs
- hardwood folding wedges
- 300×300 puncheons at 2.000%
- vertical spacings varies according to pressure
- formation level
- hardwood folding wedges
- 300×150 sole piece
- 'cut off' length according to soil type and sheet pile section used

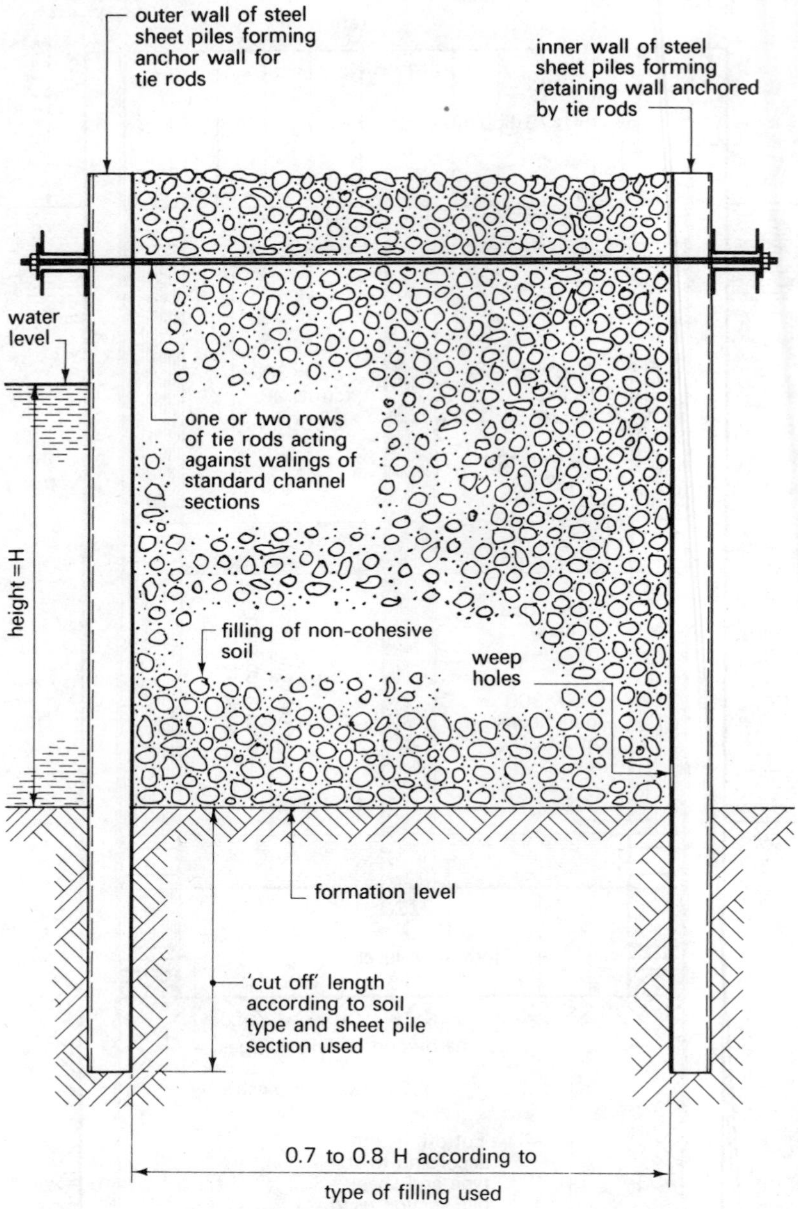
outer wall of steel sheet piles forming anchor wall for tie rods
inner wall of steel sheet piles forming retaining wall anchored by tie rods
water level
one or two rows of tie rods acting against walings of standard channel sections
height = H
filling of non-cohesive soil
weep holes
formation level
'cut off' length according to soil type and sheet pile section used
0.7 to 0.8 H according to type of filling used

Fig. II.23 Typical double skin cofferdam details

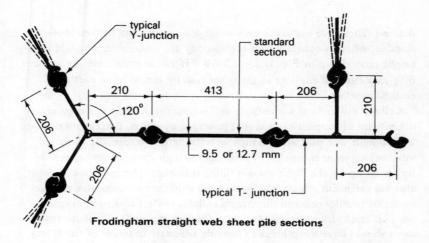

Frodingham straight web sheet pile sections

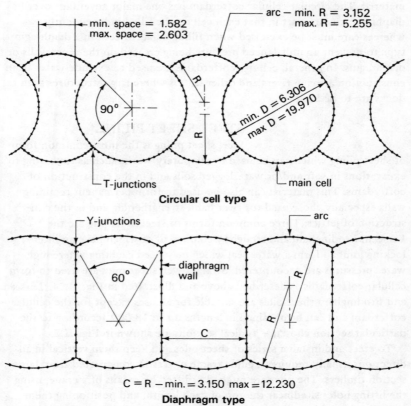

Circular cell type

Diaphragm type

Fig. II.24 Cellular cofferdam arrangements

drained. Therefore materials such as sand, hardcore and broken stone are suitable, whereas cohesive soils such as clay are unsuitable. The width-to-height ratio shown in Fig. II.23 of 0.7:0.8 H can in some cases be reduced by giving external support to the inner wall by means of an earth embankment or berm.

Cellular cofferdams are entirely self supporting and do not require any other form of support such as that provided by struts, braces and tie rods. The straight web pile with its high web strength and specially designed interlocking joint is capable of resisting the high circumferential tensile forces set up by the non-cohesive filling materials. The interlocking joint also has sufficient angular deviation to enable the two common arrangements of circular cell and diaphragm cellular cofferdams to be formed — see Fig. II.24. Like the double-skin cofferdam the walls of cellular cofferdams should have weep holes to provide adequate drainage of the filling material. The circular cellular cofferdam has one major advantage over its diaphragm counterpart in that each cell can be filled independently whereas care must be exercised when filling adjacent cells in a diaphragm type to prevent an unbalanced pressure being created on the cross-walls or diaphragms. In general, cellular cofferdams are used to exclude water from construction areas in rivers and other waters where large structures such as docks are to be built.

STEEL SHEET PILING

Steel sheet piling is the most common form of sheet piling which can be used in temporary works such as timbering to excavations in soft and/or waterlogged soils and in the construction of cofferdams. This material can also be used to form permanent retaining walls especially those used for river bank strengthening and in the construction of jetties. Three common forms of steel sheet pile are the Larseen, Frodingham and straight-web piles all of which have an interlocking joint to form a water seal which may need caulking where high water pressures are encountered. Straight-web sheet piles are used to form cellular cofferdams as described above and illustrated in Fig. II.24. Larseen and Frodingham sheet piles are suitable for all uses except for the cellular cofferdam and can be obtained in lengths up to 18.000 according to the particular section chosen — typical sections are shown in Fig. II.25.

To erect and install a series of sheet piles and keep them vertical in all directions usually requires a guide frame or trestle constructed from large section timbers. The piles are pitched or lifted by means of a crane, using the lifting holes sited near the top of each length, and positioning them between the guide walings of the trestle — see Figs. II.26 and II.27. When sheet piles are being driven there is a tendency for them to creep or lean in

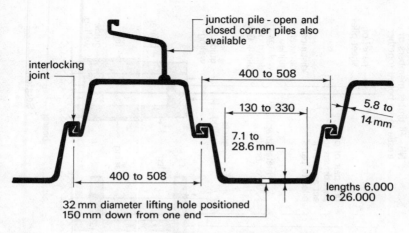

Larseen steel sheet piles

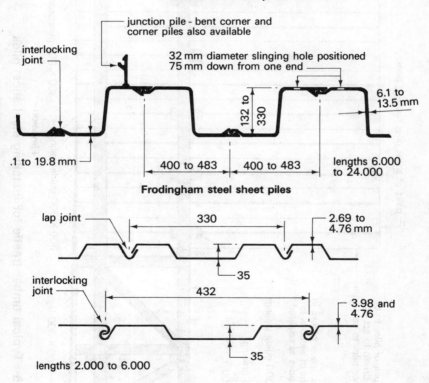

Frodingham steel sheet piles

Steel trench sheeting

Fig. II.25 Typical steel sheet pile and trench sheeting sections

111

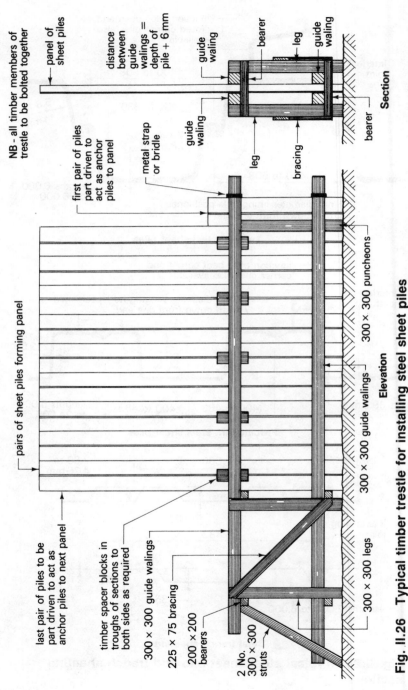

NB - all timber members of trestle to be bolted together

panel of sheet piles

distance between guide walings = depth of pile + 6 mm

guide waling

bearer

leg

guide waling

Section

first pair of piles part driven to act as anchor piles to panel

metal strap or bridle

guide waling

leg

bracing

pairs of sheet piles forming panel

300 × 300 puncheons

300 × 300 guide walings

300 × 300 legs

bearer

last pair of piles to be part driven to act as anchor piles to next panel

timber spacer blocks in troughs of sections to both sides as required

300 × 300 guide walings

225 × 75 bracing

200 × 200 bearers

2 No. 300 × 300 struts

Elevation

Fig. II.26 Typical timber trestle for installing steel sheet piles

112

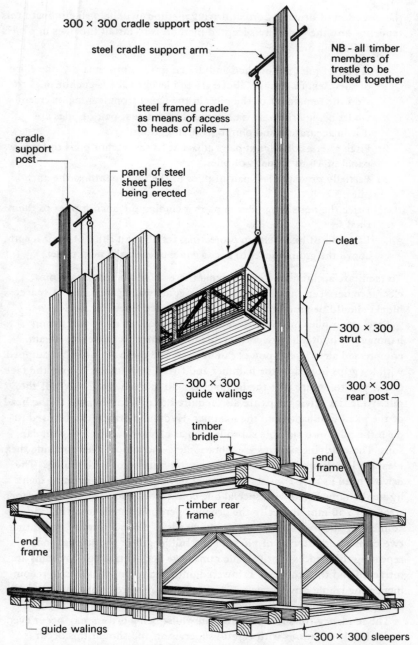

300 × 300 cradle support post

steel cradle support arm

NB - all timber members of trestle to be bolted together

steel framed cradle as means of access to heads of piles

cradle support post

panel of steel sheet piles being erected

cleat

300 × 300 strut

300 × 300 guide walings

timber bridle

300 × 300 rear post

end frame

timber rear frame

end frame

guide walings

300 × 300 sleepers

Fig. II.27 Typical timber trestle for large steel sheet piles

the direction of driving. Correct driving methods will help to eliminate this tendency and the generally accepted method is to install the piles in panels in the following manner:

1. A pair of piles are pitched and driven until approximately one-third of their length remains above ground level to act as anchor piles to stop the remainder of the piles in the panel from leaning or creeping whilst being driven. It is essential that this first pair of piles are driven accurately and plumb in all directions.
2. Pitch a series of piles in pairs adjacent to the anchor piles to form a panel of 10 to 12 pairs of piles.
3. Partially drive the last pair of piles to the same depth as the anchor piles.
4. Drive the remaining piles in pairs including the anchor piles to their final set.
5. Last pair of piles remain projecting, for about a third of their length, above the ground level to act as guide piles to the next panel.

To facilitate accurate and easy driving there should be about a 6 mm clearance between the pile faces and the guide walings and timber spacer blocks should be used in the troughs of the piles — see Fig. II.26.

Steel sheet piles may be driven to the required set using percussion hammers or hydraulic drivers. Percussion hammers activated by steam, compressed air or diesel power can be used and these are usually equipped with leg grips bolted to the hammer and fitted with inserts to grip the face of the pile to ensure that the hammer is held in line with the axis of the pile. Wide flat driving caps are also required to prevent damage to the head of the pile by impact from the hammer. Hydraulic drivers can be used to push the piles into suitable subsoils such as clays, silts and fine granular soils. These driving systems are vibrationless and almost silent making them ideal for installing sheet piling in close proximity to other buildings. The driving head usually consists of a power pack crosshead containing eight hydraulic rams fitted with special pile connectors, each ram having a short stroke of 750 mm. Basically the driving operation entails lowering and connecting the hydraulic driver to the heads of a panel of piles, activating two rams to drive a pair of piles for the full length of the stroke, and repeating this process until all the rams have been activated. The rams are retracted and the crosshead is lowered onto the top of the piles to recommence the whole driving cycle. This process is repeated until the required penetration of the piles has been reached.

The tendency for sheet piles to lean whilst being driven may occur even under ideal conditions with careful supervision and should this occur immediate steps must be taken to correct the fault or it may get out of control. The following correction methods can be considered:

1. Attach a winch rope to the pair of piles being driven and exert a corrective pulling force as driving continues.
2. Attach a winch rope to the previously driven adjacent pair of piles and exert a corrective pulling force as driving continues.
3. Reposition the hammer towards the previously driven pair of piles to give an eccentric blow.
4. Combinations of any of the above methods.

If the above correction techniques are not suitable or effective it is possible to form tapered piles by making use of the tolerances within the interlocking joint by welding steel straps across the face of the pair of piles to hold them in tapered form. This technique is only suitable if the total amount of taper required does not exceed 50 mm in the length of the pile. To insert a special tapered pile within a panel it will of course be necessary to extract a pair of piles from the panel. Typical examples of correction techniques are shown in Fig. II.28.

Water jetting
In soft and silty subsoils the installation of steel sheet piles can be assisted by using high-pressure water jetting to the sides and toes of the piles. The jets should be positioned in the troughs of the piles and to both sides of the section. In very soft subsoils this method can sometimes be so effective that the assistance of a driving hammer is not required. To ensure that the pile finally penetrates into an undisturbed layer of subsoil the last few metres or so of driving should be carried out without jetting.

Access
Access in the form of a working platform to the heads of sheet piles is often necessary during installation to locate adjacent piles, position and attach the driving hammer and to carry out inspections of the work in progress. Suitable means of access are:

1. Independent scaffolding
2. Suspended cradle — see Fig. II.27
3. Mobile platform mounted on a hydraulic arm
4. Working platform in the form of a cage suspended from a mobile crane and hooked onto the pile heads — see Fig. II.28.

Extraction of piles
Piles which are used in temporary works should have well-greased interlocking joints to enable them to be extracted with ease. Inverted double-acting hammers can be used to extract sheet piles but these have been

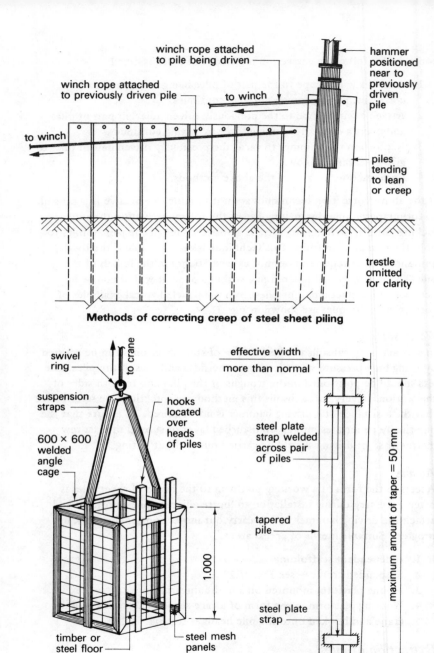

Methods of correcting creep of steel sheet piling

winch rope attached to pile being driven

hammer positioned near to previously driven pile

winch rope attached to previously driven pile

to winch

to winch

piles tending to lean or creep

trestle omitted for clarity

swivel ring

to crane

suspension straps

hooks located over heads of piles

600 × 600 welded angle cage

steel plate strap welded across pair of piles

effective width more than normal

tapered pile

1.000

maximum amount of taper = 50 mm

timber or steel floor

steel mesh panels

steel plate strap

effective width less than normal

Fig. II.28 Creep correction techniques and access cage

generally superseded by specially designed sheet pile extractors. These usually consist of a compressed air- or steam-activated ram giving between 120 and 200 upward blows per minute which causes the jaws at the lower end to grip the pile and force it out of the ground.

CAISSONS

These are box-like structures which can be sunk through ground or water to install foundations or similar structures below the water line or table. They differ from cofferdams in that they usually become part of the finished foundation or structure and should be considered as an alternative to the temporary cofferdam if the working depth below the water level exceeds 18.000. The design and installation of the various types of caissons is usually the task of a specialist organisation but building contractors should have a fundamental knowledge of the different types and their uses.

There are four basic types of caisson in general use, namely:

1. Box caissons.
2. Open caissons.
3. Monolithic caissons.
4. Pneumatic or compressed air caissons.

Box caissons: these are prefabricated precast concrete boxes which are open at the top and closed at the bottom. They are usually constructed on land and designed to be launched and floated to the desired position where they are sunk onto a previously prepared dredged or rock blanket foundation — see Fig. II.29. If the bed strata is unsuitable for the above preparations it may be necessary to lay a concrete raft by using traditional cofferdam techniques onto which the caisson can be sunk. During installation it is imperative that precautions are taken to overcome the problems of floatation by flooding the void with water or adding kentledge to the caisson walls. The sides of the caisson will extend above the water line after it has been finally positioned providing a suitable shell for such structures as bridge piers, breakwaters and jetties. The void is filled with *in situ* concrete placed by pump, tremie pipe or crane and skip. Box caissons are suitable for situations where the bed conditions are such that it is not necessary to sink the caisson below the prepared bed level.

Open caissons: sometimes referred to as cylinder caissons because of their usual plan shape. They are of precast concrete and open at both top and bottom ends with a cutting edge to the bottom rim. They are suitable for installation in soft subsoils where the excavation can be carried out by conventional grabs enabling the caisson to sink under its own weight as the

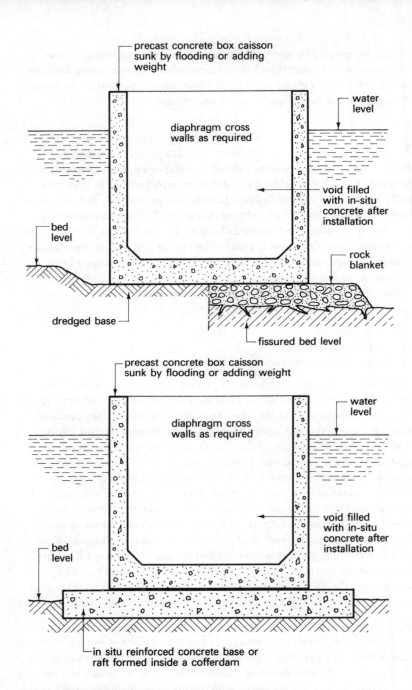

Fig. II.29 Typical box caisson details

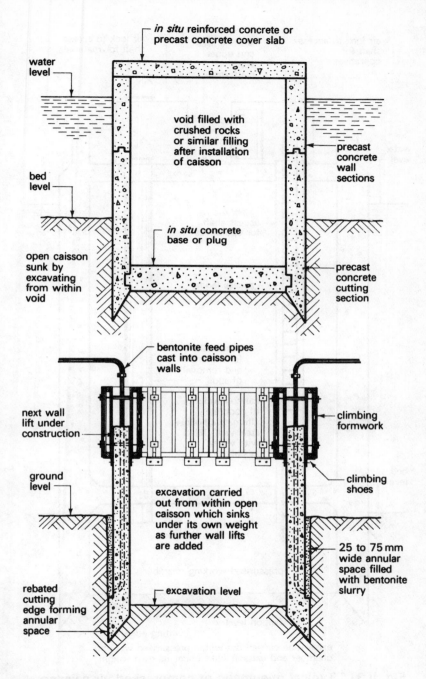

water level

in situ reinforced concrete or precast concrete cover slab

void filled with crushed rocks or similar filling after installation of caisson

precast concrete wall sections

bed level

in situ concrete base or plug

open caisson sunk by excavating from within void

precast concrete cutting section

bentonite feed pipes cast into caisson walls

next wall lift under construction

climbing formwork

climbing shoes

ground level

excavation carried out from within open caisson which sinks under its own weight as further wall lifts are added

25 to 75 mm wide annular space filled with bentonite slurry

rebated cutting edge forming annular space

excavation level

Fig. II.30 Typical open caisson details

119

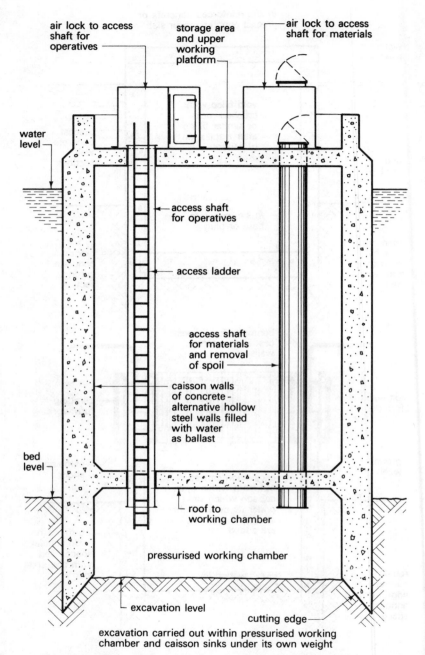

air lock to access shaft for operatives

storage area and upper working platform

air lock to access shaft for materials

water level

access shaft for operatives

access ladder

access shaft for materials and removal of spoil

caisson walls of concrete - alternative hollow steel walls filled with water as ballast

bed level

roof to working chamber

pressurised working chamber

excavation level

cutting edge

excavation carried out within pressurised working chamber and caisson sinks under its own weight

Fig. II.31 Typical pneumatic or compressed air caisson details

excavation proceeds. These caissons can be completely or partially pre-formed whereas in the case of the latter further sections can be added or cast on as the structure sinks to the required depth. When the desired depth has been reached a concrete plug in the form of a slab is placed in the bottom by tremie pipe to prevent further ingress of water. The cell void can now be pumped dry and filled with crushed rocks or similar material if necessary to overcome floatation during further construction works.

Open caissons can also be installed in land if the subsoil conditions are suitable. The shoe or cutting edge is formed so that it is wider than the wall above to create an annular space some 75 to 100 mm wide into which a bentonite slurry can be pumped to act as a lubricant and thus reduce the skin friction to a minimum. Excavation is carried out by traditional means within the caisson void, the caisson sinking under its own weight. The excavation operation is usually carried out simultaneously with the construction of the caisson walls above ground level — see Fig. II.30.

Monolithic caissons: these are usually rectangular in plan and are divided into a number of voids or wells through which the excavation is carried out. They are similar to open caissons but have greater self weight and wall thickness, making them suitable for structures such as quays which may have to resist considerable impact forces in their final condition.

Pneumatic or compressed-air caissons: these are similar to open caissons except that there is an air-tight working chamber some 3.000 high at the cutting edge. They are used where difficult subsoils exist and where hand excavation in dry working conditions is necessary. The working chamber must be pressurised sufficiently to control the inflow of water and/or soil and at the same time provide safe working conditions for the operatives. The maximum safe working pressure is usually specified as 310 kN/m^2 which will limit the working depth of this type of caisson to about 28.000. When the required depth has been reached the floor of the working chamber can be sealed over with a 600 mm thick layer of well vibrated concrete. This is followed by further well-vibrated layers of concrete until only a small space remains which is pressure grouted to finally seal the working chamber. The access shafts are finally sealed with concrete some three to four days after sealing off the working chamber — for typical details see Fig. II.31.

13

Subsoil drainage

Building Regulation C3

Wherever the dampness or position of the site of a building renders it necessary, the subsoil of the site shall be effectively drained or such other steps shall be taken as will effectively protect the building against damage from moisture.

The ideal site (see Fig. II.32) will not require any treatment but sites with a high water table will require some form of subsoil drainage. The water table is the level at which water occurs naturally below the ground and this level will vary with the seasonal changes.

The object of subsoil drainage is to lower the water table to a level such that it will comply with the above building regulation. It also has the advantage of improving the stability of the ground, lowering the humidity of the site and improving its horticultural properties.

MATERIALS

The pipes used in subsoil drainage are usually dry jointed and are either porous or perforated pipes. The porous pipes absorb the water through their walls and thus keep out the fine particles of soil or silt, whereas perforated pipes, which are laid with the perforations at the base, allow the water to rise into the pipe leaving any silt behind.

Suitable pipes
Perforated glazed-ware pipes—BS 65.

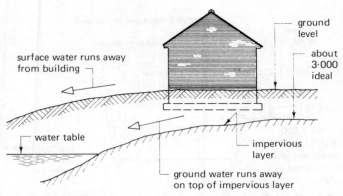

surface water runs away from building ⌐

ground level

about 3·000 ideal

water table ⌐

impervious layer

ground water runs away on top of impervious layer

Fig. II.32   The ideal site

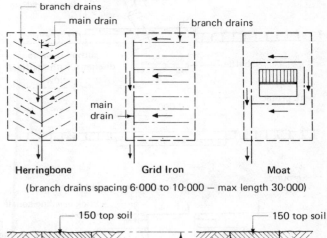

⌐ branch drains
⌐ main drain

⌐ branch drains

main drain

Herringbone   **Grid Iron**   **Moat**

(branch drains spacing 6·000 to 10·000 – max length 30·000)

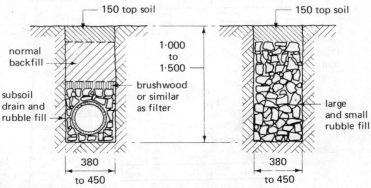

⌐ 150 top soil

⌐ 150 top soil

normal backfill

1·000 to 1·500

subsoil drain and rubble fill

brushwood or similar as filter

large and small rubble fill

380 to 450

380 to 450

Fig. II.33   Subsoil drainage systems and drains

123

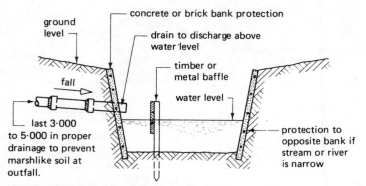

concrete or brick bank protection

drain to discharge above water level

timber or metal baffle

water level

fall

last 3·000 to 5·000 in proper drainage to prevent marshlike soil at outfall.

protection to opposite bank if stream or river is narrow

Fig. II.34   Outfall to stream or river

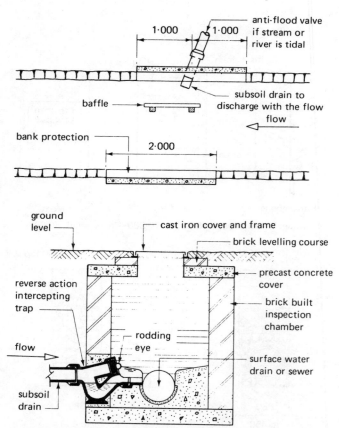

anti-flood valve if stream or river is tidal

1·000   1·000

baffle

subsoil drain to discharge with the flow

flow

bank protection

2·000

ground level

cast iron cover and frame

brick levelling course

precast concrete cover

brick built inspection chamber

reverse action intercepting trap

rodding eye

flow

surface water drain or sewer

subsoil drain

Fig. II.35   Outfall to surface water sewer or drain

Concrete porous pipes—BS 1194.
Clayware field pipes—BS 1196.
Perforated pitchfibre pipes—BS 2760.

DRAINAGE LAYOUTS

The pipes are arranged in a pattern to cover as much of the site as is
necessary. Typical arrangements are shown on the plans in Fig. II.33.
Water will naturally flow towards the easy passage provided by the
drainage runs. The system is terminated at a suitable outfall such as a
river, stream or surface water sewer. In all cases permission must be
obtained before discharging a subsoil system. The banks of streams and
rivers will need protection against the turbulence set up by the discharge
and if the stream is narrow the opposite bank may also need protection
(see Fig. II.34). If discharge is into a tidal river or stream precautions
should be taken to ensure the system will not work in reverse by providing
an outlet for the rising tide. On large schemes sediment chambers or
catch pits are sometimes included to trap some of the silt which is the
chief cause of blockages in subsoil drainage work. The construction of a
catch pit is similar to the manhole shown in Fig. II.35 except that in a
catch pit the inlet and outlet are at a high level, this interrupts the flow of
subsoil water in the drains and enables some of the silt to settle on the
base of the catch pit. The collected silt in the catch pit must be removed
at regular intervals.

14
Ground water control

Ground water can be defined as water which is held temporarily in the soil above the level of the water table. Below the water table level is the subsoil water which is the result of the natural absorption by subsoils of the ground water. Both types of water can be effectively controlled by a variety of methods which have been designed either to exclude the water from a particular area or merely to lower the water table to give reasonably dry working conditions especially for excavation activities.

The extent to which water affects the stability and bearing capacity of a subsoil will depend upon the physical characteristics of the soil and in particular upon the particle size which ranges from the very fine particles of clay soils to the larger particles or boulders of some granular soils. The effect of the water on these particles is that of a lubricant enabling them to move when subjected to a force such as a foundation loading or simply causing them to flow by movement of the ground water. The number and disposition of the particles together with the amount of water present will determine the amount of movement which could take place. The finer particles will be displaced more easily than the larger particles which could create voids thus encouraging settlement of the larger particles.

The voids caused by excavation works encourage water to flow since the opposition to the ground water movement provided by the soil has been removed. In cases where the flow of water is likely an artificial opposition must be installed or the likelihood of water movement must be restricted by geotechnical processes. These processes can be broadly classified into one of two groups:

1. Permanent exclusion of ground water.
2. Temporary exclusion of ground water by lowering the water table.

PERMANENT EXCLUSION OF GROUND WATER

Sheet piling: suitable for all types of soils except boulder beds and is used to form a barrier or cut-off wall to the flow of ground water. The sheet piling can be of a permanent nature, being designed to act as a retaining wall or it can be a temporary enclosure to excavation works in the form of a cofferdam (for details see Chapter 12). Vibration and noise due to the driving process may render this method as unacceptable and the capital costs can be high unless they can be apportioned over several contracts on a use and re-use basis.

Diaphragm walls: suitable for all types of soils and are usually of *in situ* reinforced concrete installed using the bentonite slurry method (see Chapter 10, Fig. II.15 for details). This form of diaphragm wall has the advantages of low installation noise and vibration, can be used in restricted spaces and can be installed close to existing foundations. Generally, unless the diaphragm wall forms part of the permanent structure, this method is uneconomic.

Slurry trench cut-off: these are non-structural thin cast *in situ* unreinforced diaphragm walls suitable for subsoils of silts, sands and gravels. They can be used on sites where there is sufficient space to enclose the excavation area with a cut-off wall of this nature sited so that there is sufficient earth remaining between the wall and the excavation to give the screen or diaphragm wall support. Provided adequate support is given these walls are rapidly installed and are cheaper than the structural version.

Thin-grouted membrane: alternative method to the slurry trench cut-off wall when used in silt and sand subsoils, they are also suitable for installation in very permeable soils and made up ground where bentonite methods are unsuitable. Like the previous example ample earth support is required for this non-structural cut-off wall. The common method of formation is to drive into the ground a series of touching universal beam or column sections, sheet pile sections or alternatively small steel box sections to the required depth. A grout injection pipe is fixed to the web or face of the section and this is connected, by means of a flexible pipe, to a grout pump at ground level. As the sections are withdrawn the void created is filled with cement grout to form the thin membrane — see Fig. II.36.

Contiguous piling: an alternative method to the reinforced concrete

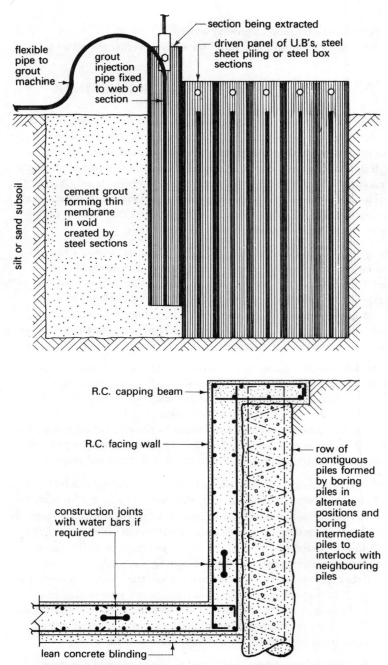

Fig. II.36 Thin grouted membrane and contiguous piling

128

diaphragm wall consisting of a series of interlocking reinforced concrete-bored piles. The formation of the bored piles can be carried out as described in Chapter 22, ensuring that the piles interlock for their entire length. This will require special cutting tools to form the key in the alternate piles for the interlocking intermediate piles. The pile diameter selected will be determined by the strength required after completion of the excavations to one side of the wall. The usual range of diameters used is between 300 and 600 mm. Contiguous piling can be faced with a reinforced rendering or covered with a mesh reinforcement sprayed with concrete to give a smooth finish. This latter process is called Shotcrete or Gunite. An alternative method is to cast in front of the contiguous piling a reinforced wall terminating in a capping beam to the piles — see Fig. II.36.

Cement grouts: in common with all grouting methods cement grouts are used to form a 'curtain' in soils which have high permeability making temporary exclusion pumping methods uneconomic. Cement grouts are used in fissured and jointed rock stratas and are injected into the ground through a series of grouting holes bored into the ground in lines with secondary intermediate borehole lines if necessary. The grout can be a mixture of neat cement and water, cement and sand up to a ratio of 1 : 4 or PFA (pulverised fuel ash) and cement in the ratio of 1 : 1 with 2 parts of water by weight. The usual practice is to start with a thin grout and gradually reduce the water : cement ratio as the process proceeds to increase the viscosity of the mixture. To be effective this form of treatment needs to be extensive.

Clay/cement grouting: suitable for sands and gravels where the soil particles are too small for cement grout treatment. The grout is introduced by means of a sleeve grout pipe which limits its spread and like the cement grouting the equipment is simple and can be used in a confined space. The clay/cement grout is basically bentonite with additives such as Portland cement or soluble silicates to form the permanent barrier. One disadvantage of this method is that at least 4.000 of natural cover is required to provide support for the non-structural barrier.

Chemical grouting: suitable for use in medium-to-coarse sands and gravels to stabilise the soil and can also be used for underpinning works below the water table level. The chemicals are usually mixed prior to their injection into the ground through injection pipes inserted at 600 mm centres. The chemicals form a permanent gel or sol in the earth which increases the strength of the soil and also reduces its permeability. This method in which a liquid base diluted with water is mixed with a catalyst to control the gel setting time before being injected into the ground is called the one-shot method. An alternative two-shot method can be used and is carried out by injecting the first chemical (usually sodium silicate) into the ground and immediately afterwards injecting the second chemical (calcium chloride) to form a 'silica-gel'. The reaction of the two chemicals is immediate, whereas in the one-shot method the reaction of the chemicals can be delayed to allow for full penetration of the subsoil which will in turn allow a wider spacing of the boreholes. One main disadvantage of chemical grouting is the need for at least 2.000 of natural cover.

Resin grouts: suitable for silty fine sands or for use in conjunction with clay/cement grouts for treating fine strata but like the chemical grouts described above they can be costly unless used on large works. Resin grouts are similar in application to the chemical grouts but having a low viscosity this enables them to penetrate the fine sands unsuitable for chemical grouting applications.

Bituminous grouts: suitable for injection into fine sands to decrease the permeability of the soil but they will not increase the strength of the soil and are therefore unsuitable for underpinning work.

Grout injection: grouts of all kinds are usually injected into the subsoil by pumping in the mixture at high pressure through tubes placed at the appropriate centres according to the solution being used and/or the soil type. Soil investigation techniques will reveal the information required to enable the engineer to decide upon the pattern and spacing of the grout holes which can be drilled with pneumatic tools or tipped drills. The pressure needed to ensure a satisfactory penetration of the subsoil will depend upon the soil conditions and results required but is usually within the range of 1 N/mm^2 for fine soils to 7 N/mm^2 for cement grouting in fissured and jointed rock stratas.

Freezing: suitable method for all types of subsoils with a moisture content in excess of 8% of the voids. The basic principle is to insert freezing tubes into the ground and circulate a freezing solution around the tubes to form ice in the voids, thus creating a wall of ice to act as the impermeable barrier. This method will give the soil temporary extra mechanical strength but there is a slight risk of ground heave particularly when operating in clays and silts. The circulating solution can be a brine of magnesium chloride or calcium chloride at a temperature of between $-15°$ and $-25°$C which would take between 10 to 17 days to produce an ice wall 1.000 thick according to the type of subsoil. For works of short duration where quick freezing is required the more expensive liquid nitrogen can be used as the circulating medium. A typical freezing arrangement is shown in

130

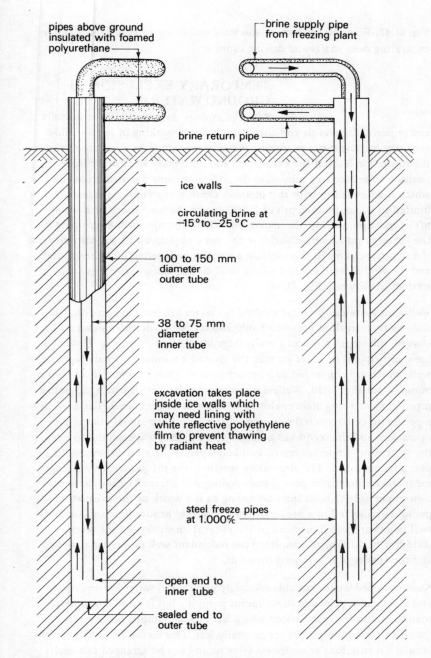

pipes above ground insulated with foamed polyurethane

brine supply pipe from freezing plant

brine return pipe

ice walls

circulating brine at −15° to −25 °C

100 to 150 mm diameter outer tube

38 to 75 mm diameter inner tube

excavation takes place inside ice walls which may need lining with white reflective polyethylene film to prevent thawing by radiant heat

steel freeze pipes at 1.000%

open end to inner tube

sealed end to outer tube

Fig. II.37   Exclusion of ground water by freezing

Fig. II.37. Freezing methods of soil stabilisation are especially suitable for excavating deep shafts and driving tunnels.

TEMPORARY EXCLUSION OF GROUND WATER

Sump pumping: suitable for most subsoils and in particular gravels and coarse sands when working in open shallow excavations. The sump or water collection pit should be excavated below the formation level of the excavation and preferably sited in a corner position to reduce to a minimum the soil movement due to settlement which is a possibility with this method. Open sump pumping is usually limited to a maximum depth of 7.500 due to the limitations of suction lift of most pumps. An alternative method to the open sump pumping is the jetted sump which will achieve the same objective and will also prevent the soil movement. In this method a metal tube is jetted into the ground and the void created is filled with a sand media, a disposable hose and strainer as shown in Fig. II.38.

Wellpoint systems: popular method for water lowering in non-cohesive soils up to a depth of between 5.000 and 6.000. To dewater an area beyond this depth requires a multi-stage installation — see Fig. II.40. The basic principle is to water jet into the ground a number of small diameter wells which are connected to a header pipe which is attached to a vacuum pump — see Fig. II.39. Wellpoint systems can be installed with the header pipe acting as a ring main enclosing the area to be excavated. The header pipe should be connected to two pumps, the first for actual pumping operations and the second as a standby pump since it is essential to keep the system fully operational to avoid collapse of the excavation should a pump failure occur. The alternative system is the progressive line arrangement where the header pipe is placed alongside a trench or similar excavation to one side or both sides according to the width of the excavation. A pump is connected to a predetermined length of header pipe and further well points are jetted in ahead of the excavation works. As the work including backfilling is completed the redundant well points are removed and the header pipe is moved forwards.

Shallow-bored wells: suitable for sandy gravels and water-bearing rocks and is similar in principle to wellpoint pumping but is more appropriate than the latter for installations which have to be pumped for several months since running costs are generally less. This method is subject to the same lift restrictions as wellpoint systems and can be arranged as a multi-stage system if the depth of lowering exceeds 5.000.

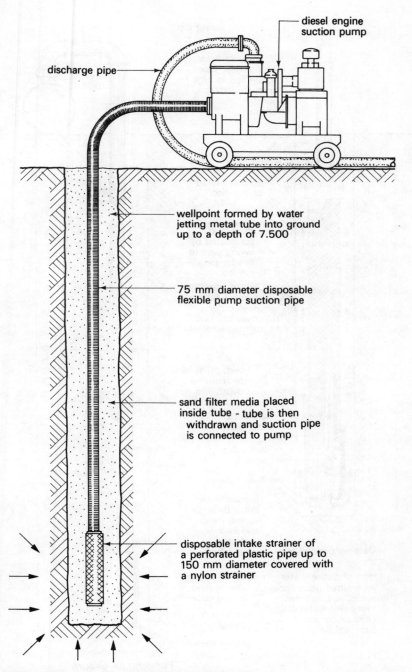

diesel engine
suction pump

discharge pipe

wellpoint formed by water
jetting metal tube into ground
up to a depth of 7.500

75 mm diameter disposable
flexible pump suction pipe

sand filter media placed
inside tube - tube is then
withdrawn and suction pipe
is connected to pump

disposable intake strainer of
a perforated plastic pipe up to
150 mm diameter covered with
a nylon strainer

Fig. II.38   Typical jetted sump detail

133

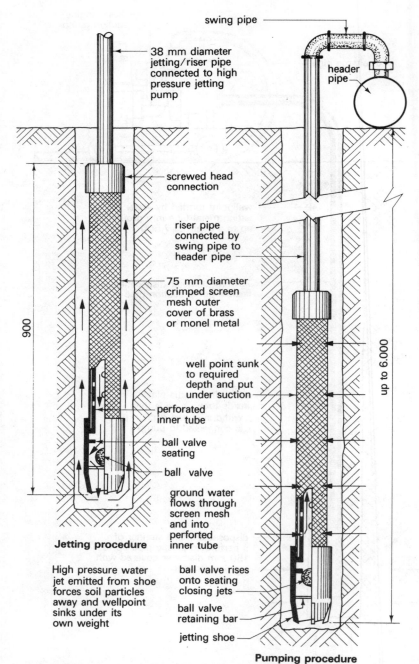

swing pipe

38 mm diameter
jetting/riser pipe
connected to high
pressure jetting
pump

header
pipe

screwed head
connection

riser pipe
connected by
swing pipe to
header pipe

75 mm diameter
crimped screen
mesh outer
cover of brass
or monel metal

well point sunk
to required
depth and put
under suction

perforated
inner tube

ball valve
seating

ball valve

ground water
flows through
screen mesh
and into
perforated
inner tube

900

up to 6.000

Jetting procedure

High pressure water
jet emitted from shoe
forces soil particles
away and wellpoint
sinks under its
own weight

ball valve rises
onto seating
closing jets

ball valve
retaining bar

jetting shoe

Pumping procedure

Fig. II.39   Typical wellpoint installation details

134

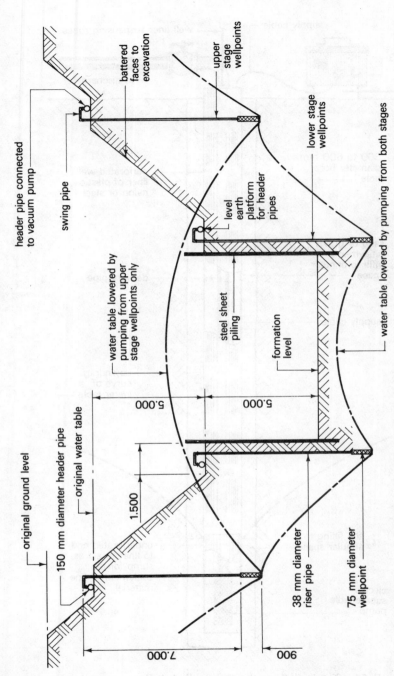

Fig. II.40 Typical example of a multi-stage wellpoint dewatering installation

header pipe connected to vacuum pump

swing pipe

battered faces to excavation

upper stage wellpoints

lower stage wellpoints

level earth platform for header pipes

steel sheet piling

formation level

water table lowered by pumping from both stages

water table lowered by pumping from upper stage wellpoints only

original ground level

150 mm diameter header pipe

original water table

38 mm diameter riser pipe

75 mm diameter wellpoint

5.000

5.000

1.500

7.000

900

135

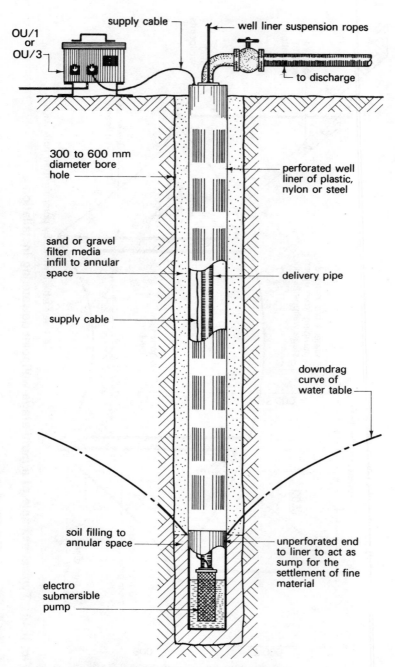

Fig. II.41 Typical deep-bored well details

136

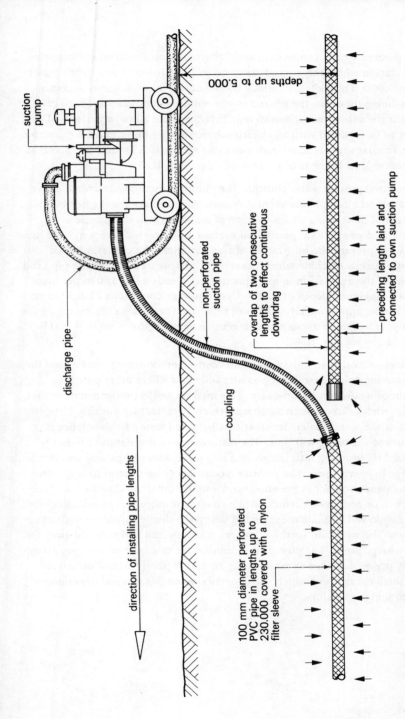

suction pump

discharge pipe

non-perforated suction pipe

overlap of two consecutive continuous lengths to effect downdrag

preceding length laid and connected to own suction pump

depths up to 5.000

direction of installing pipe lengths

coupling

100 mm diameter perforated PVC pipe in lengths up to 230.000 covered with a nylon filter sleeve

Fig. II.42 Horizontal system of dewatering

137

Deep-bored wells: can be used as an alternative to a multi-stage wellpoint installation where the ground water needs to be lowered to a depth greater than 9.000. The wells are formed by sinking a 300 to 600 mm diameter steel lining tube into the ground to the required depth and at spacings to suit the subsoil being dewatered. This bore hole allows a perforated well liner to be installed with an electro submersible pump to extract the water. The annular space is filled with a suitable media such as sand and gravel as the outer steel lining tube is removed — see Fig. II.41.

Horizontal ground water control: the pumping methods described above all work on a completely vertical system. An alternative is the horizontal system of dewatering which consists of installing into the ground a 100 mm diameter PVC perforated suction pipe covered with a nylon filter sleeve to prevent the infiltration of fine particles. The pipe is installed using a special machine which excavates a narrow trench, lays the pipe and backfills the excavation in one operation at speeds up to 180 m per hour with a maximum depth of 5.000. Under average conditions a single pump can handle approximately 230 m of pipe run; for distances in excess of the pumping length an overlap of consecutive pipe lengths of up to 4.000 is required — see Fig. II.42.

Electro-osmosis: an uncommon and costly method which can be used for dewatering cohesive soils such as silts and clays where other pumping methods would not be adequate. This method works on the principle that soil particles carry a negative charge which attracts the positively charged ends of the water molecules creating a balanced state; if this balance is disturbed the water will flow. The disturbance of this natural balance is created by inserting into the ground two electrodes and passing an electric charge between them. The positive electrode can be of steel rods or sheet piling which will act as the anode and a wellpoint is installed to act as the cathode or negative electrode. When an electric current is passed between the anode and cathode it causes the positively charged water molecules to flow to the wellpoint (cathode) where it is collected and pumped away to a discharge point. The power consumption for this method can vary from 1 kW per m^3 for large excavations up to 12 kW per m^3 of soil dewatered for small excavations which will generally make this method uneconomic on running costs alone.

Part III
Foundations

Part III

Foundations

15
Foundations I

A foundation is the base on which a building rests and its purpose is to safely transfer the load of a building to a suitable subsoil.

Building Regulation 4 requires that all foundations of buildings shall:

1. Safely sustain and transmit to the ground the combined dead and imposed loads so as not to cause any settlement or other movement in any part of the building or of any adjoining building or works.

TABLE 3.1 *Typical subsoil bearing capacities*

Type	Bearing capacity (kN/m^2)
Rocks, granites and chalks	10 000-600
Non-cohesive soils Compact sands Loose uniform sands	600-100
Cohesive soils Hard clays Soft clays and silts	600-0
Peats and made ground	To be determined by investigation

2. Be of such a depth, or be so constructed, as to avoid damage by swelling, shrinkage or freezing of the subsoil.
3. Approved Document 7 recommends foundations to be capable of resisting attack by deleterious material, such as sulphates, in the sub-soil.

Subsoils are the soils below the top-soil; the topsoil being about 300 mm deep. Typical bearing capacities of subsoils are given in Table 3.1.

Terminology

Backfill: materials excavated from site and if suitable used to fill in around the walls and foundations.

Bearing capacity: safe load per unit area which the ground can carry.

Bearing pressure: the pressure produced on the ground by the loads.

Made ground: refuse, excavated rock or soil deposited for the purpose of filling in a depression or for raising the site above its natural level.

Settlement: ground movement which may be caused by:

(a) Deformation of the soil due to imposed loads.
(b) Volume changes of the soil as a result of seasonal conditions.
(c) Mass movement of the ground in unstable areas.

Choice of foundation type

The choice and design of foundations for domestic and small types of buildings depends mainly on two factors:

1. The total loads of the building.
2. The nature and bearing capacity of the subsoil.

The total loads of a building are taken per metre run and calculated for the worst case. The data required is:

(a) Roof load on the wall—1 m wide strip from ridge to eaves.
(b) Floor load on the wall—1 m wide strip from centre of the floor to the wall.
(c) Wall load on the foundations—1 m wide strip of wall from top to foundation.
(d) Total load on the foundations—summation of (a), (b) and (c).

The average loading for a two-storey domestic dwelling of traditional construction is 30–50 kN/m.

The nature and bearing capacity of the subsoil can be determined by:

1. Trial holes and subsequent investigation.

142

2. Bore holes and core analysis.
3. Local knowledge.

Approved Document A gives a table of subsoil types, field tests and suitable minimum widths for strip foundations.

Clay is the most difficult of all subsoils with which to deal. Down to a depth of about 1 m clays are subject to seasonal movement which occurs when the clay dries and shrinks in the summer and conversely swells in the winter with heavier rainfall. This movement occurs whenever a clay soil is exposed to the atmosphere and special foundations may be necessary.

Subsoils which readily absorb and hold water are subject, in cold weather, to frost heave. This is a swelling of the subsoil due to the expansion of freezing water held in the soil and like the movement of clay soils it is unlikely to be even and special foundations may be needed to overcome the problem.

TYPES OF FOUNDATIONS

Having ascertained the nature and bearing capacity of the subsoil the width of the foundation can be determined by either:

1. The minimum as given in the table to Approved Document A.
2. $\dfrac{\text{Total load of building per metre}}{\text{bearing capacity of subsoil}} = \text{minimum width.}$

Foundations are usually made of either mass or reinforced concrete and can be considered under two headings:

Shallow foundations: those which transfer the loads to subsoil at a point near to the ground floor of the building such as strips and rafts.

Deep foundations. Those which transfer the loads to a subsoil some distance below the ground floor of the building such as a pile.

Raft foundations are often used on poor soils for lightly loaded buildings and are considered capable of accommodating small settlements of the soil. In poor soils the upper crust of soil (450-600 mm) is often stiffer than the lower subsoil and to build a light raft on this crust is usually better than penetrating it with a strip foundation.

Typical details of the types of foundations suitable for domestic and similar buildings are shown in Figs. III.1—III.3.

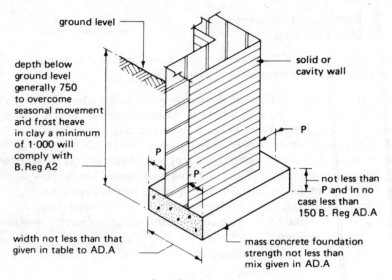

ground level

depth below
ground level
generally 750
to overcome
seasonal movement
and frost heave
in clay a minimum
of 1·000 will
comply with
B. Reg A2

solid or
cavity wall

P

P

P

not less than
P and in no
case less than
150 B. Reg AD.A

width not less than that
given in table to AD.A

mass concrete foundation
strength not less than
mix given in AD.A

Strip Foundations

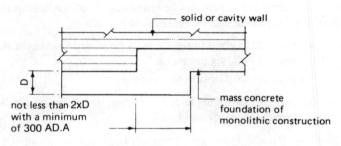

solid or cavity wall

D

not less than 2xD
with a minimum
of 300 AD.A

mass concrete
foundation of
monolithic construction

Change in Level

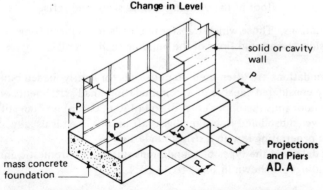

solid or cavity
wall

P

P

P

P

Q

Q

Projections
and Piers
AD. A

mass concrete
foundation

Fig. III.1 Strip foundations and Building Regulations

144

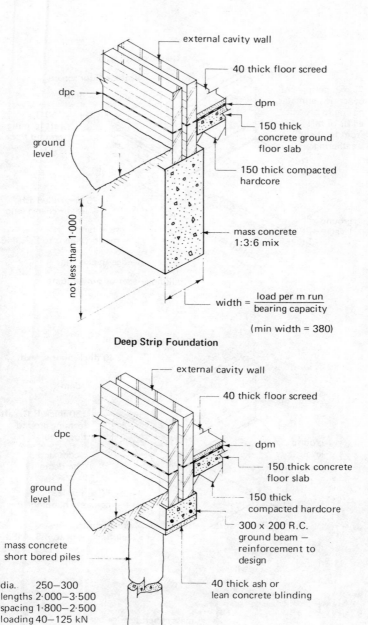

external cavity wall

40 thick floor screed

dpc

dpm

ground level

150 thick concrete ground floor slab

150 thick compacted hardcore

not less than 1·000

mass concrete 1:3:6 mix

$$\text{width} = \frac{\text{load per m run}}{\text{bearing capacity}}$$

(min width = 380)

Deep Strip Foundation

external cavity wall

40 thick floor screed

dpc

dpm

ground level

150 thick concrete floor slab

150 thick compacted hardcore

mass concrete short bored piles

300 x 200 R.C. ground beam — reinforcement to design

dia. 250—300
lengths 2·000—3·500
spacing 1·800—2·500
loading 40—125 kN per pile

40 thick ash or lean concrete blinding

Fig. III.2 Alternative foundations for clay soils

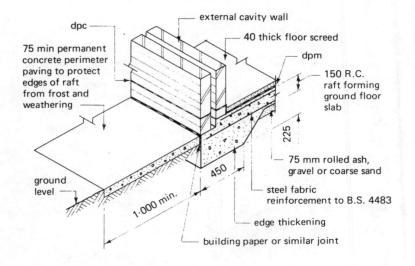

external cavity wall

40 thick floor screed

dpc

75 min permanent concrete perimeter paving to protect edges of raft from frost and weathering

dpm

150 R.C. raft forming ground floor slab

225

75 mm rolled ash, gravel or coarse sand

steel fabric reinforcement to B.S. 4483

edge thickening

building paper or similar joint

ground level

1·000 min.

450

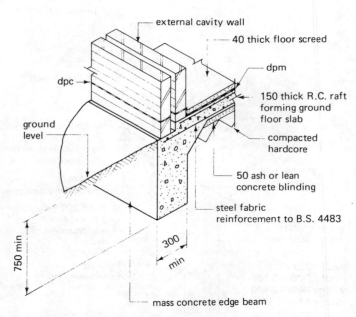

external cavity wall

40 thick floor screed

dpc

dpm

150 thick R.C. raft forming ground floor slab

compacted hardcore

50 ash or lean concrete blinding

steel fabric reinforcement to B.S. 4483

mass concrete edge beam

ground level

750 min

300 min

Fig. III.3 Typical raft foundations

16
Concrete

Concrete is a mixture of cement, fine aggregate, coarse aggregate and water. The proportions of each material control the strength and quality of the resultant concrete.

Portland cement

Cement is the setting agent of concrete and the bulk of cement used in this country is Portland cement. This is made from chalk or limestone and clay and is generally produced by the wet process.

In this process the two raw materials are washed, broken up and mixed with water to form a slurry. This slurry is then pumped into a steel rotary kiln which is from 3-4 m in diameter and up to 150 m long and lined with refractory bricks. While the slurry is fed into the top end of the kiln a pulverised coal is blown in at the bottom end and fired. This raises the temperature at the lower end of the kiln to about $1\,400°C$. The slurry passing down the kiln first gives up its moisture, then the chalk or limestone is broken down into carbon dioxide and lime, and finally forms a white hot clinker which is transferred to a cooler before being ground. The grinding is carried out in a ball mill which is a cylinder some 15 m long and up to 4·5 m in diameter containing a large number of steel balls of various sizes, which grind the clinker into a fine powder. As the clinker is being fed into the ball mill gypsum (about 5%) is added to prevent a flash setting off the cement.

The alternative method for the preparation of Portland cement is the dry process. The main difference between this and the wet process is the reduction in the amount of water that has to be driven off in the kiln. A mixture of limestone and shale is used which is proportioned, ground and blended to form a raw meal of low moisture content. The meal is granulated in rotating pans with a small amount of water before being passed to a grate for preheating prior to entering the kiln. The kiln is smaller than that used in the wet process but its function is the same, that is, to form a clinker, which is then cooled, ground and mixed with a little gypsum as described for the previous process.

Rapid-hardening Portland cement is more finely ground than ordinary Portland cement. Its main advantage is that it gains its working strength earlier than ordinary cement. The requirements for both ordinary Portland and rapid-hardening Portland cement are given in BS 12.

High alumina cement

This is made by firing limestone and bauxite (aluminium ore) to a molten state, casting it into pigs and finally grinding it into a fine powder. Its rate of hardening is very rapid and produces a concrete which is resistant to the natural sulphates found in some subsoils. It can, however, cost up to two and a half times as much as ordinary Portland cement. The requirements of this type of cement are covered in BS 915.

Other forms of cement available are as follows:

Portland blast-furnace—BS 146.
Sulphate-resisting—BS 4027.
Low heat blast-furnace—BS 4246.
Supersulphated—BS 4248.

Cement should be stored on a damp-proof floor in the dry and kept for short periods only because eventually cement will harden as a result of the action of moisture in the air. This is known as air hardening and any hardened cement should be discarded.

Aggregates

These are the materials which are mixed with the cement to form concrete and are classed as a fine or coarse aggregate. Fine aggregates are those which will pass a standard 5 mm sieve and coarse aggregates are those which are retained on a standard 5 mm sieve. All-in aggregate is a material composed of both fine and coarse aggregates.

A wide variety of materials (for example, gravel, crushed stone, brick, furnace slag and lightweight substances, such as foamed slag, expanded clay and vermiculite) are available as aggregates for the making of concrete.

In making concrete aggregates must be graded so that the smaller particles of the fine aggregate fill the voids created by the coarse aggregate. The cement paste fills the voids in the fine aggregate thus forming a dense mix.

Aggregates from natural sources are covered in BS 882.

Water

The water used in the making of concrete must be clean and free from impurities which could affect the concrete. It is usually specified as being of a quality fit for drinking. A proportion of the water will set up a chemical reaction which will harden the cement. The remainder is required to give the mix workability and will evaporate from the mix while it is curing, leaving minute voids. An excess of water will give a porous concrete of reduced durability and strength.

The quantity of water to be used in the mix is usually expressed in terms of the water/cement ratio which is:

$$\frac{\text{the total weight of water in the concrete}}{\text{weight of cement}}$$

for most mixes the ratio is between 0·4 and 0·7.

Concrete mixes can be expressed as volume ratios thus:

1 : 2 : 4 = 1 part cement, 2 parts fine aggregate and 4 parts coarse aggregate.

1 : 5 = 1 part cement and 5 parts all-in aggregate.

SOME COMMON MIXES

1 : 10—not a strong mix but it is suitable for filling weak pockets in excavations and for blinding layers.

1 : 8—slightly better than the last, suitable for paths and pavings.

1 : 6—a strong mix suitable for mass concrete foundations, paths and pavings.

1 : 3 : 6—the weakest mix equivalent to that quoted in Approved Document A as deemed to satisfy the requirements of Building Regulation A1.

1 : 2 : 4—strong mix which is practically impervious to water, in common use especially for reinforced concrete.

MIXING CONCRETE

Concrete can be mixed or batched by two methods:

1. By volume.
2. By mass.

One bag of cement has a volume of approximately 0·04 m^3 and a mass of 50 kg.

Batching by volume

This method is usually carried out using an open bottom box (of such dimensions as to make manual handling possible) called a 'gauge box'. For a 1 : 2 : 4 mix a gauge box is filled once with cement, twice with fine aggregate and four times with coarse aggregate, the top of the gauge box being struck off level each time.

If the fine aggregate is damp or wet its volume will increase by up to 25% and therefore the amount of fine aggregate should be increased by this amount. This increase in volume is called bulking.

Batching by mass

This method involves the use of a balance which is linked to a dial giving the exact mass of the materials as they are placed in the scales. This is the best method since it has a greater accuracy and the balance can be attached to the mixing machine.

Hand mixing

This should be carried out on a clean hard surface. The materials should be thoroughly mixed in the dry state before the water is added. The water should be added slowly, preferably using a rose head until a uniform colour is obtained.

Machine mixing

The mix should be turned over in the mixer for at least two minutes after adding the water. The first batch from the mixer tends to be harsh since some of the mix will adhere to the sides of the drum. This batch should be used for some less important work such as filling in weak pockets in the bottom of the excavation.

Handling

If concrete is to be transported for some distance over rough ground the runs should be kept as short as possible since vibrations of this nature can cause segregation of the materials in the mix. For the same reason
150

concrete should not be dropped from a height of more than 1 m. If this is unavoidable a chute should be used.

Placing

If the concrete is to be placed in a foundation trench it will be levelled from peg to peg (see Fig. III.1) or if it is to be used as an oversite bed the external walls could act as a levelling guide. The levelling is carried out by tamping with a straight edge board; this tamping serves the dual purpose of compacting and bringing the excess water to the surface so that it can evaporate. Concrete must not be over tamped as this will not only bring the water to the surface but also the cement paste which is required to act as the matrix. Concrete should be placed as soon as possible after mixing to ensure that the setting action has not commenced. Concrete which dries out too quickly will not develop its full strength, therefore new concrete should be protected from the drying winds and sun by being covered with canvas, straw, polythene sheeting or damp sawdust. This protection should be continued for at least three days since concrete takes about twenty-eight days to obtain its working strength.

17
Reinforced concrete foundations

The function of any foundation is to transmit to the subsoil the loads of the structure. Where a structure has only light loadings such as a domestic dwelling house it is sufficient to use a mass concrete strip foundation or a simple raft. Where buildings are either heavy or transmit the loadings at a series of points such as in a framed building it is uneconomic to use a mass concrete. The plan size of a foundation is a constant feature being derived from:

$$\frac{\text{load}}{\text{bearing capacity of subsoil}}$$

but the thickness of a mass concrete foundation for a heavy load would result in a foundation which is costly and adds unnecessary load to the subsoil. Reinforced concrete foundations are generally cheaper and easier to construct than equivalent mass concrete foundations but will generally require the services of a structural engineer to formulate an economic design. The engineer must define the areas in which tension occurs and specify the reinforcement required, since concrete is a material which is weak in tension.

TYPES OF FOUNDATIONS

The principal types of reinforced concrete foundations for buildings are:

1. Strip foundations.

2. Isolated or pad foundations.
3. Raft foundations.
4. Combinations of 1, 2 and 3.
5. Piled foundations.

The foundations listed in 4 and 5 above are generally studied during advance courses in construction technology and are therefore not considered in this volume.

Strip foundations

Reinforced concrete strip foundations are used to support and transmit the loads from heavy walls. The effect of the wall on the relatively thin foundation is to act as a point load and the resultant ground pressure will induce tension on the underside across the width of the strip. Tensile reinforcement is therefore required in the lower face of the strip with distribution bars in the second layer running longitudinally (see Fig. III.4). The reinforcement will also assist the strip in spanning any weak pockets of soil encountered in the excavations.

Isolated or pad foundations

This type of foundation is used to support and transmit the loads from piers and columns. The most economic plan shape is a square but if the columns are close to the site boundary it may be necessary to use a rectangular plan shape of equivalent area. The reaction of the foundation to the load and ground pressures is to cup, similar to a saucer, and therefore main steel is required in both directions. The depth of the base will be governed by the anticipated moments and shear forces, the calculations involved being beyond the scope of this volume. Incorporated in the base will also be the starter bars for a reinforced concrete column or the holding down bolts for a structural steel column (see Fig. III.4).

Raft foundations

The principle of any raft foundation is to spread the load over the entire area of the site. This method is particularly useful where the column loads are heavy and thus requiring large bases or where the bearing capacity is low, again resulting in the need for large bases. Raft foundations can be considered under three headings:

153

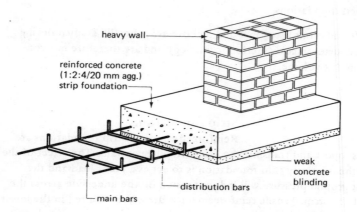

R.C. strip foundation

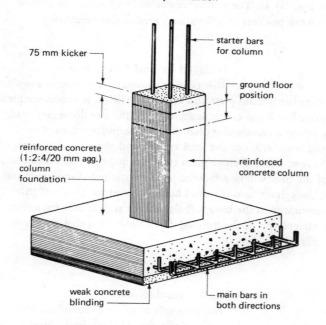

R.C. isolated or pad foundation

Fig. III.4 R.C. strip and pad foundations

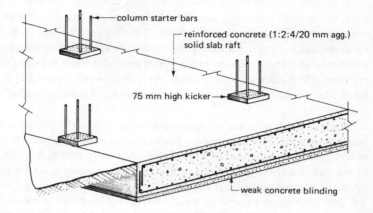

column starter bars

reinforced concrete (1:2:4/20 mm agg.) solid slab raft

75 mm high kicker

weak concrete blinding

R.C. solid slab raft foundation

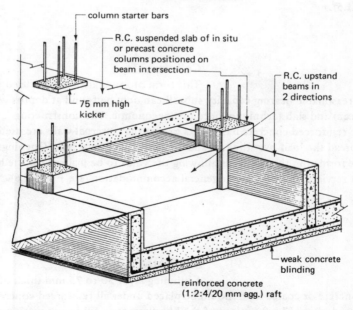

column starter bars

R.C. suspended slab of in situ or precast concrete columns positioned on beam intersection

R.C. upstand beams in 2 directions

75 mm high kicker

weak concrete blinding

reinforced concrete (1:2:4/20 mm agg.) raft

R.C. beam and slab raft foundation

Fig. III.5   R.C. raft foundations

1. Solid slab rafts.
2. Beam and slab rafts.
3. Cellular rafts.

Solid slab rafts are constructed of uniform thickness over the whole raft area, which can be wasteful since the design must be based on the situation existing where the heaviest load occurs. The effect of the load from columns and the ground pressure is to create areas of tension under the columns and areas of tension in the upper part of the raft between the columns. Very often a nominal mesh of reinforcement is provided in the faces where tension does not occur to control shrinkage cracking of the concrete (see Fig. III.5).

Beam and slab rafts are an alternative to the solid slab raft and are used where poor soils are encountered. The beams are used to distribute the column loads over the area of the raft, which usually results in a reduction of the slab thickness. The beams can be upstand or downstand depending upon the bearing capacity of the soil near the surface. Downstand beams will give a saving on excavation costs whereas upstand beams create a usable void below the ground floor if a suspended slab is used (see Fig. III.5).

Cellular rafts

This form of foundation can be used where a reasonable bearing capacity subsoil can only be found at depths where beam and slab techniques become uneconomic. The construction is similar to reinforced concrete basements except that internal walls are used to spread the load over the raft and divide the void into cells. Openings can be formed in the cell walls allowing the voids to be utilised for the housing of services, store rooms or general accommodation (see Fig. III.6).

BLINDING

A blinding layer 50 to 75 mm thick of weak concrete or coarse sand should be placed under all reinforced concrete foundations. The functions of the blinding are to fill in any weak pockets encountered during excavations and to provide a true level surface from which the reinforcement can be positioned. If formwork is required for the foundation some contractors prefer to lay the blinding before

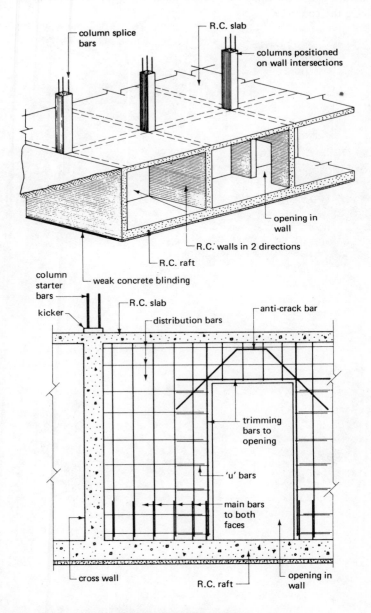

Fig. III.6 Typical cellular raft details

157

assembling the formwork; the alternative is to place the blinding within the formwork and allow this to set before positioning the reinforcement and placing the concrete.

18
Foundations II

Loadings in buildings consist of the combined dead and imposed loads which exert a downward pressure upon the soil on which the structure is founded and this in turn promotes a reactive force in the form of an upward pressure from the soil. The structure is in effect sandwiched between these opposite pressures and the design of the building must be able to resist the resultant stresses set up within the structural members and the general building fabric. The supporting subsoil must be able to develop sufficient reactive force to give stability to the structure to prevent failure due to unequal settlement and to prevent failure of the subsoil due to shear. To enable a designer to select, design and detail a suitable foundation he must have adequate data regarding the nature of the soil on which the structure will be founded and this is normally obtained from a planned soil investigation programme.

SOIL INVESTIGATION

Soil investigation is specific in its requirements whereas site investigation is all embracing, taking into account such factors as topography, location of existing services, means of access and any local restrictions. Soil investigation is a means of obtaining data regarding the properties and characteristics of subsoils by providing samples for testing or providing a means of access for visual inspection. The actual data required and the amount of capital which can be reasonably expended on any soil investigation programme will depend upon the type of structure proposed and how much previous knowledge the designer has of a particular region or site.

The main methods of soil investigation can be enumerated as follows:

1. Trial pits — small contracts where foundation depths are not likely to exceed 3.000.
2. Boreholes — medium to large contracts with foundations up to 30.000 deep.

Trial pits: relatively cheap and easy method of obtaining soil data by enabling easy visual inspection of the soil strata in its natural condition. The pits can be hand or machine excavated to a plan size of 1.200 x 1.200 and spaced at centres to suit the scope of the investigation. A series of pits set out on a 20.000 grid would give a reasonable coverage of most sites. The pits need to be positioned so that the data obtained is truly representative of the actual conditions but not in such a position where their presence could have a detrimental effect on the proposed foundations. In very loose soils or soils having a high water table trial pits can prove to be uneconomical due to the need for pumps and/or timbering to keep the pits dry and accessible. The spoil removed will provide disturbed samples for testing purposes whereas undisturbed samples can be cut and extracted from the walls of the pit.

Boreholes: these enable disturbed or undisturbed samples to be removed for analysis and testing but undisturbed samples are sometimes difficult to obtain from soils other than rock or cohesive soils. The core diameter of the samples obtained vary from 100 to 200 mm according to the method employed in extracting the sample. Disturbed samples can be obtained by using a rotary flight auger or by percussion boring in a similar manner to the formation of small diameter bored piles using a tripod or shear leg rig. Undisturbed samples can be obtained from cohesive soils using 450 mm long x 100 mm diameter sampling tubes which are driven into the soil to collect the sample within itself; upon removal the tube is capped, labelled and sent off to a laboratory for testing. Undisturbed rock samples can be obtained by core drilling with diamond tipped drills where necessary.

CLASSIFICATION OF SOILS

Soils may be classified by any of the following methods:

1. Physical properties.
2. Geological origin.
3. Chemical composition.
4. Particle size.

It has been established that the physical properties of soils can be closely associated with their particle size both of which are of importance to the foundation engineer, architect or designer. All soils can be defined as being coarse-grained or fine-grained each resulting in different properties.

Coarse-grained soils: these would include sands and gravels having a low proportion of voids, negligible cohesion when dry, high permeability and slight compressibility, which takes place almost immediately upon the application of load.

Fine-grained soils: these include the cohesive silts and clays having a high proportion of voids, high cohesion, very low permeability and high compressibility which takes place slowly over a long period of time.

There are of course soils which can be classified in between the two extremes described above. BS 1377 deals with the methods of testing soils and divides particle sizes as follows:

Clay particles	less than 0.002 mm
Silt particles	between 0.002 and 0.06 mm
Sand particles	between 0.06 and 2 mm
Gravel particles	between 2 and 60 mm
Cobbles	between 60 and 200 mm

The silt, sand and gravel particles are also further subdivided into fine, medium and coarse with particle sizes lying between the extremes quoted above.

Fine-grained soils such as clays are difficult to classify positively by their particle size distribution alone and therefore use is made of the reaction of these soils to a change in their moisture content. If the moisture content is high the volume is consequently large and the soil is basically a suspension of clay particles in water. As the moisture content decreases the soil passes the liquid limit and becomes plastic. The liquid limit of a soil is defined as 'the moisture content at which a soil passes from the plastic state to the liquid state' and this limit can be determined by the test set out in BS 1377.

Further lowering of the moisture content will enable the soil to pass the plastic limit and begin to become a solid. The plastic limit of a soil is reached when a 20 g sample just fails to roll into a 3 mm diameter thread when rolled between the palm of the hand and a glass plate. When soils of this nature reach the solid state the volume tends to remain constant and any further decrease in moisture content will only alter the appearance and colour of the sample. It must be clearly understood that the change from one definable state to another is a gradual process and not a sudden change.

161

Shear strength of soils

The resistance which can be offered by a soil to the sliding of one portion over another or its shear strength is of importance to the designer since it can be used to calculate the bearing capacity of a soil and the pressure it can exert on such members as timbering in excavations. Resistance to shear in a soil under load depends mainly upon its particle composition. If a soil is granular in form the frictional resistance between the particles increases with the load applied and consequently its shear strength also increases with the magnitude of the applied load. Conversely clay particles being small develop no frictional resistance and therefore its shear strength will remain constant whatever the magnitude of the applied load. Intermediate soils such as sandy clays normally give only a slight increase in shear strength as the load is applied.

To ascertain the shear strength of a particular soil sample the triaxial compression test as described in BS 1377 is usually employed for cohesive soils. Non-cohesive soils can be tested in a shear box which consists of a split box into which the sample is placed and subjected to a standard vertical load whilst a horizontal load is applied to the lower half of the box until the sample shears.

Compressibility

Another important property of soils which must be ascertained before a final choice of foundation type and design can be made is compressibility and two factors must be taken into account:

1. Rate at which compression takes place.
2. Total amount of compression when full load is applied.

When dealing with non-cohesive soils such as sands and gravels the rate of compression will keep pace with the construction of the building and therefore when the structure is complete there should be no further settlement if the soil remains in the same state. A soil is compressed when loaded by the expulsion of air and/or water from the voids and by the natural rearrangement of the particles. In cohesive soils the voids are very often completely saturated with water which in itself is nearly incompressible and therefore compression of the soil can only take place by the water moving out of the voids thus allowing settlement of the particles. Expulsion of water from the voids within cohesive soils can occur but only at a very slow rate due mainly to the resistance offered by the plate-like particles of the soil through which it must flow. This gradual compressive movement of a soil is called consolidation. Uniform settlement will not normally cause undue damage to a structure but uneven settlement can cause progressive structural damage.

Stresses and pressures

The above comments on shear strength and compressibility clearly indicate that cohesive soils present the most serious problems when giving consideration to foundation choice and design. The two major conditions to be considered are:

1. Shearing stresses.
2. Vertical pressures.

Shearing stress: the maximum stress under a typical foundation carrying a uniformly distributed load will occur on a semi-circle whose radius is equal to half the width of the foundation and the isoshear line value will be equal to about one-third the applied pressure — see Fig. III.7. The magnitude of this maximum pressure should not exceed the shearing resistance value of the soil.

Vertical pressure: this acts within the mass of the soil upon which the structure is founded and should not be of such a magnitude as to cause unacceptable settlement of the structure. Vertical pressures can be represented on a drawing by connecting together points which have the same value forming what are termed pressure bulbs. Most pressure bulbs are plotted up to a value of 0.2 of the pressure per unit area which is considered to be the limit of pressure which could influence settlement of the structure. Typical pressure bulbs are shown in Figs. III.7 and III.8. A comparison of these typical pressure bulbs will show that generally vertical pressure decreases with depth, the 0.2 value will occur at a lower level under strip foundations than under rafts, isolated bases and bases in close proximity to one another which form combined pressure bulbs. The pressure bulbs illustrated in Figs. III.7 and III.8 are based on the soil being homogeneous throughout the depth under consideration. As in reality this is not always the case it is important that soil investigation is carried out at least to the depth of the theoretical pressure bulb. Great care must be taken where an underlying strata of highly compressible soil is encountered to ensure that these are not over stressed if cut by the anticipated pressure bulb.

Contact pressure

It is very often incorrectly assumed that a foundation which is uniformly loaded will result in a uniform contact pressure under the foundation. This would only be true if the foundation was completely flexible such as the bases to a pin jointed frame. The actual contact pressure under a founda-

163

tion will be governed by the nature of the soil and the rigidity of the foundation, and since in practice most large structures have a rigid foundation the contact pressure distribution is not uniform. In cohesive soils there is a tendency for high stresses to occur at the edges which is usually reduced slightly by the yielding of the clay soil. Non-cohesive soils give rise to a parabolic contact pressure distribution with increasing edge pressures as the depth below ground level of the foundation increases. When selecting the basic foundation format consideration must be given to the concentration of the major loads over the position where the theoretical contact pressures are at a minimum to obtain a balanced distribution of contact pressure — see Fig. III.9.

Plastic failure

This is a form of failure which can occur in cohesive soils if the ultimate bearing capacity of the soil is reached or exceeded. As the load on a foundation is increased the stresses within the soil also increases until all resistance to settlement has been overcome. Plastic failure, which can be related to the shear strength of the soil, occurs when the lateral pressure being exerted by the wedge of relatively undisturbed soil immediately below the foundation causes a plastic shear failure to develop resulting in a heaving of the soil at the sides of the foundation moving along a slip circle or plane. In practice this movement tends to occur on one side of the building, causing it to tilt and settle — see Fig. III.10. Plastic failure is likely to happen when the pressure applied by the foundation is approximately six times the shear strength of the soil.

FOUNDATION TYPES

There are many ways in which foundations can be classified but one of the most common methods is by form resulting in five basic types thus:

1. *Strip foundations* — light loadings particularly in domestic buildings — see Chapter 3, Volume 1. Heavier loadings can sometimes be founded on a reinforced concrete strip foundation as described and illustrated in Chapter 7, Volume 2.
2. *Raft foundations* — light loadings, average loadings on soils with low bearing capacities and structures having a basement storey — see Chapter 7, Volume 2.
3. *Pad or isolated foundations* — common method of providing the foundation for columns of framed structures and for the supporting members of portal frames — see Chapter 7, Volume 2 and Chapter 7, Volume 3.

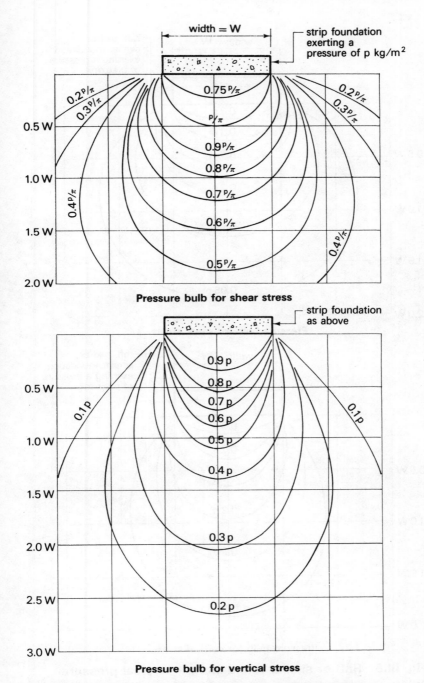

Fig. III.7   Strip foundations — typical pressure bulbs

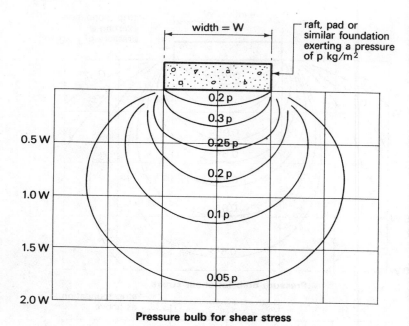

Pressure bulb for shear stress

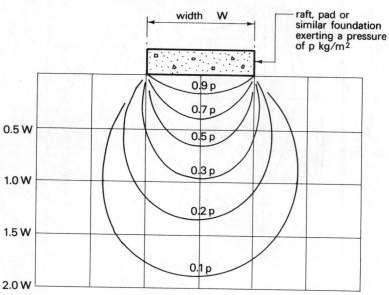

Pressure bulb for vertical stress

Fig. III.8   Raft or similar foundations — typical pressure bulbs

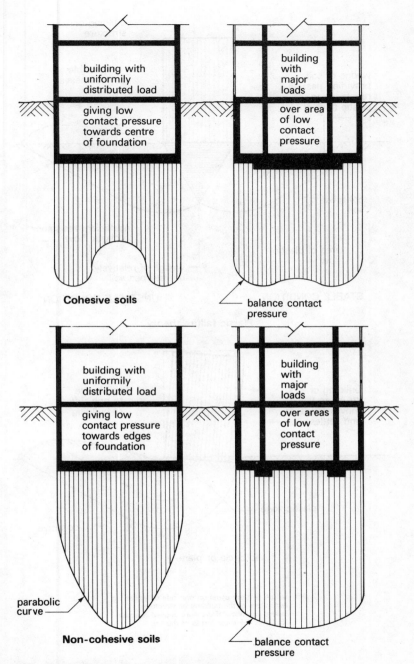

Fig. III.9 Typical contact pressures

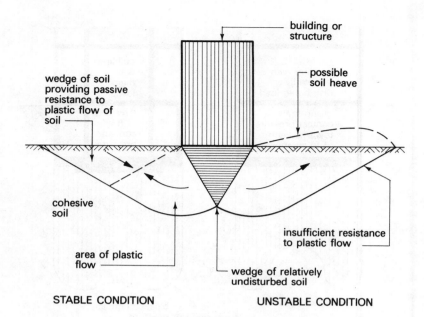

building or
structure

wedge of soil
providing passive
resistance to
plastic flow of
soil

possible
soil heave

cohesive
soil

insufficient resistance
to plastic flow

area of plastic
flow

wedge of relatively
undisturbed soil

STABLE CONDITION

UNSTABLE CONDITION

Plastic failure theory

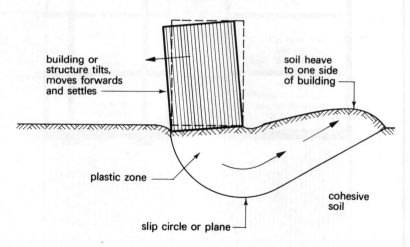

building or
structure tilts,
moves forwards
and settles

soil heave
to one side
of building

plastic zone

cohesive
soil

slip circle or plane

NB - failure is more usual on one side only than on
both sides of the building or structure
failure can occur if pressure applied is about
six times the shear stress of the soil

Fig. III.10   Plastic failure of foundations

4. *Pile foundations* — method for structures where the loads have to be transmitted to a point at some distance below the general ground level — see Chapter 22.

Combined foundations

When designing a foundation the area of the base must be large enough to ensure that the load per unit area does not exceed the bearing capacity of the soil upon which it rests. The ideal situation when considering column foundations is to have a square base of the appropriate area with the column positioned centrally. Unfortunately this ideal condition is not always possible. When developing sites in urban areas the proposed structure is very often required to abut an existing perimeter wall with the proposed perimeter columns in close proximity to the existing wall. Such a situation would result in an eccentric column loading if conventional isolated bases were employed. One method of overcoming this problem is to place the perimeter columns on a reinforced concrete continuous column foundation in the form of a strip. The strip is designed as a beam with the columns acting as point loads which will result in a negative bending moment occurring between the columns requiring top tensile reinforcement in the strip.

If sufficient plan area cannot be achieved by using a continuous column foundation a combined column foundation could be considered. This form of foundation consists of a reinforced concrete slab placed at right angles to the line of columns linking together an outer or perimeter column to an inner column. The base slab must have sufficient area to ensure that the load per unit area will not cause overstressing of the soil leading to unacceptable settlement. To alleviate the possibility of eccentric loading the centres of gravity of the columns and slab should be designed to coincide — see Fig. III.11. Combined foundations of this type are suitable for a pair of equally loaded columns or where the outer column carries the lightest load. The effect of the column loadings on the slab foundation is similar to that described above for continuous column foundations where a negative bending moment will occur between the columns.

In situations where the length of the slab foundation is restricted or where the outer column carries the heavier load the slab plan shape can be in the form of a trapezium with the widest end located nearest to the heavier loaded column — see Fig. III.11. As with the rectangular base the trapezoidal base will have negative bending moments between the columns and to eliminate eccentric loading the centres of gravity of columns and slab should coincide.

Alternative column foundations to the combined and trapezoidal forms

169

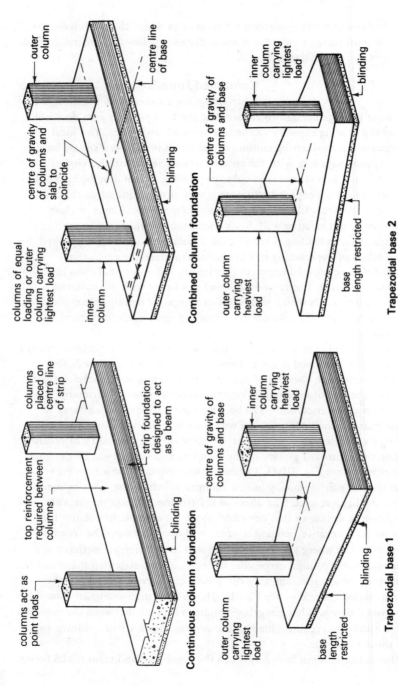

Fig. III.11 Typical combined foundations

Continuous column foundation

columns placed on centre line of strip

top reinforcement required between columns

strip foundation designed to act as a beam

columns act as point loads

blinding

Combined column foundation

outer column

inner column

columns of equal loading or outer column carrying lightest load

centre of gravity of columns and slab to coincide

centre line of base

blinding

Trapezoidal base 1

outer column carrying lightest load

inner column carrying heaviest load

centre of gravity of columns and base

base length restricted

blinding

Trapezoidal base 2

inner column carrying lightest load

outer column carrying heaviest load

centre of gravity of columns and base

base length restricted

blinding

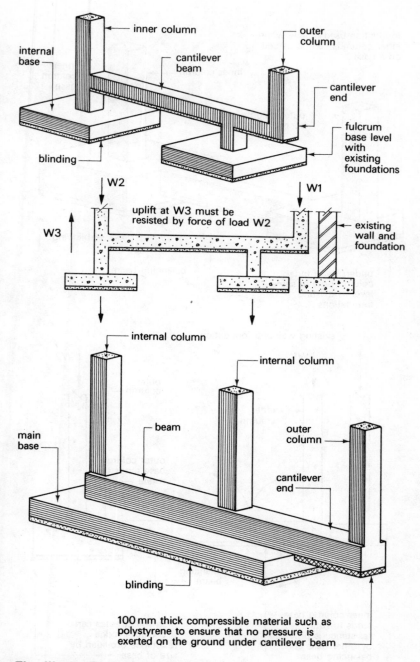

Fig. III.12 Typical cantilever bases

Labels in figure:
- inner column
- internal base
- cantilever beam
- outer column
- cantilever end
- fulcrum base level with existing foundations
- blinding
- W2
- W1
- W3
- uplift at W3 must be resisted by force of load W2
- existing wall and foundation
- internal column
- internal column
- outer column
- main base
- beam
- cantilever end
- blinding
- 100 mm thick compressible material such as polystyrene to ensure that no pressure is exerted on the ground under cantilever beam

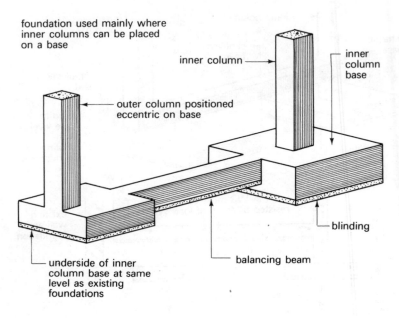

foundation used mainly where inner columns can be placed on a base

inner column

inner column base

outer column positioned eccentric on base

blinding

underside of inner column base at same level as existing foundations

balancing beam

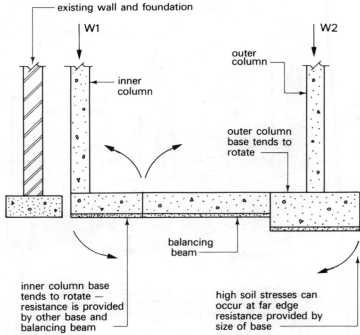

existing wall and foundation

W1

inner column

W2

outer column

outer column base tends to rotate

inner column base tends to rotate — resistance is provided by other base and balancing beam

balancing beam

high soil stresses can occur at far edge resistance provided by size of base

Fig. III.13 Typical balanced base foundation

172

described above are the balanced base foundations which can be designed in one of two basic forms namely:

1. Cantilever foundations.
2. Balanced base foundations.

These foundations are usually specified where it is necessary to ensure that no pressure is imposed on an existing substructure or adjacent service such as a drain or sewer. A cantilever foundation can take two forms both of which use a cantilever beam which in one case acts about a short fulcrum column positioned near to the existing structure, while in the alternative version the beam cantilevers beyond a slab base — see Fig. III.12.

A balanced base foundation can be considered where it is possible to place the inner columns directly onto a base foundation. These columns are usually eccentric on the inner base causing within the base a tendency to rotate. This movement must be resisted or balanced by the inner column base and the connecting beam — see Fig. III.13.

19
Retaining walls

The basic function of a retaining wall is to retain soil at a slope which is greater than it would naturally assume, usually at a vertical or near vertical position. The natural slope taken up by any soil is called its angle of repose and is measured in relationship to the horizontal. Angles of repose for different soils range from 45° to near 0° for wet clays but for most soils an average angle of 30° is usually taken. It is the wedge of soil resting on this upper plane of the angle of repose which a retaining wall has to support. The walls are designed to offer the necessary resistance by using their own mass to resist the thrust or relying upon the principles of leverage. The terminology used in retaining wall construction is shown in Fig. III.14.

DESIGN PRINCIPLES

The design of any retaining wall is basically concerned with the lateral pressures of the retained soil and any subsoil water. It must be designed to ensure that:

1. Overturning does not occur.
2. Sliding does not occur.
3. The soil on which the wall rests is not overloaded.
4. The materials used in construction are not overstressed.

It is difficult to accurately define the properties of any soil since they are variable materials and the calculation of pressure exerted at any point on the wall is a task for the expert who must take into account the following factors:

1. Nature and type of soil.

174

2. Height of water table.
3. Subsoil water movements.
4. Type of wall.
5. Materials used in the construction of the wall.

The actual design and calculations for the various types of retaining walls are beyond the scope of this book, but it is essential that a student of construction technology has an appreciation of the factors and considerations involved in retaining wall design.

EARTH PRESSURES

The designer is mainly concerned with the effect of two forms of earth pressure:
1. Active earth pressure.
2. Passive earth pressure.

Active earth pressures are those which at all times are tending to move or overturn the retaining wall and is composed of the earth wedge being retained together with any hydrostatic pressure caused by the presence of ground water. The latter can be reduced by the use of subsoil drainage behind the wall or by inserting drainage openings called weep holes through the thickness of the stem enabling the water to drain away.

Passive earth pressures are reactionary pressures which will react in the form of a resistance to movement of the wall. If the wall tends to move forward the earth in front of the toe will be compressed and a reaction in the form of passive pressure will build up in front of the toe to counteract the forward movement. This pressure can be increased by enlarging the depth of the toe or by forming a rib on the underside of the base. Typical examples of these pressures are shown in Fig. III.14.

STABILITY

The overall stability of a retaining wall is governed by the result of the action and reaction of a number of loads:

Applied loads: such as soil and water pressure on the back of the wall; the mass of the wall and in the case of certain forms of cantilever walls the mass of the soil acting with the mass of the wall.

Induced loads: such as the ground pressure under the base, the passive pressure at the toe and the friction between the underside of the base and the soil.

Effects of water

Ground water behind a retaining wall whether static or percolating through a subsoil can have adverse effects

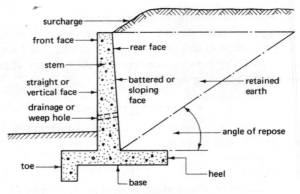

Retaining wall terminology

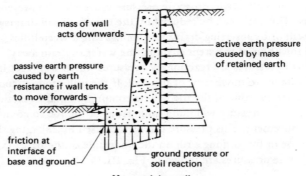

Mass retaining walls

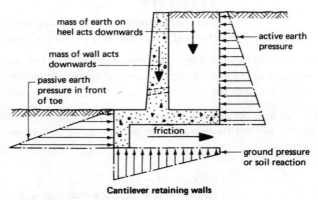

Cantilever retaining walls

Fig. III.14   Retaining wall terminology and pressures

upon the design and stability. It will increase the pressure on the back of the wall and by reducing the soil shear strength it can reduce the bearing capacity of the soil; it can reduce the frictional resistance between the base and the soil and reduce the possible passive pressure in front of the wall. It follows therefore that the question of drainage of the water behind the retaining wall is of the utmost importance in the design.

Slip circle failure

This is a form of failure sometimes encountered with retaining walls in clay soils particularly if there is a heavy surcharge. It takes the form of a rotational movement of the soil and wall along a circular arc which starts behind the wall and passes under the base, resulting in a tilting and forward movement of the wall. If the movement is not unacceptable further movement can be prevented by driving sheet piles into the ground in front of the toe to a depth that will cut the slip circle arc.

TYPES OF WALLS

Mass retaining walls

Sometimes called gravity walls and relying upon their own mass together with the friction on the underside of the base to overcome the tendency to slide or overturn. They are generally only economic up to a height of 1.800 m. Mass walls can be constructed of semi-engineering quality bricks bedded in a 1 : 3 cement mortar or of mass concrete. The latter could have some light fabric reinforcement to control surface cracking. Natural stone is suitable for small walls up to 1.000 m high but generally it is used as a facing material for walls over 1.000 m. Typical examples of this are shown in Fig. III.15.

Cantilever walls

Usually of reinforced concrete and work on the principles of leverage. Two basic forms can be considered, a base with a large heel so that the mass of earth above can be added to the mass of the wall for design purposes, or if this form is not practicable a cantilever wall with a large toe must be used (see Fig. III.16). The drawings show typical sections and patterns of reinforcement encountered with these basic forms of cantilever retaining walls. The main steel occurs on the tension face of the wall and nominal steel (0.15% of the cross sectional area of the wall) is very often included in the opposite face to control the shrinkage cracking which occurs in *in situ* concrete work. Reinforcement

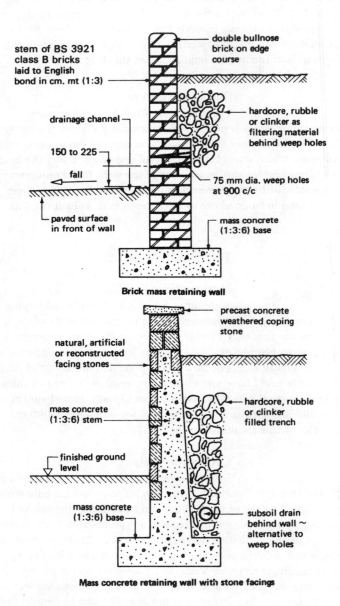

Fig. III.15   Typical mass retaining walls

178

requirements, bending, fabricating and placing are dealt with in detail in the section on reinforced concrete.

Reinforced cantilever walls have an economic height range of 1.200 to 6.000 m; walls in excess of this height have been economically constructed using prestressing techniques. Any durable facing material may be applied to the surface to improve the appearance of the wall but it must be remembered that such finishes are decorative and add nothing to the structural strength of the wall.

Counterfort retaining walls

These walls can be constructed of reinforced or prestressed concrete and are considered suitable if the height is over 4.500 m. The counterforts are triangular beams placed at suitable centres behind the stem and above the base to enable the stem and base to act as slabs spanning horizontally over or under the counterforts. Fig. III.17 shows a typical section and pattern of reinforcement for a counterfort retaining wall.

If the counterforts are placed on the face of the stem they are termed buttresses and the whole arrangement is called a buttress retaining wall. In both formats the design and construction principles are similar.

Precast concrete retaining walls

Manufactured from high grade precast concrete on the cantilever principle usually to a 600 mm wide module (see Fig. III.18). They can be erected on a foundation as a permanent retaining wall or be free standing to act as a dividing wall between heaped materials such as aggregates for concrete. In the latter situation they can increase by approximately three times the storage volume for any given area. Other advantages are a reduction in time by eliminating the curing period which is required for *in situ* walls and eliminating the need for costly formwork together with the time required to erect and dismantle the temporary forms. The units are reinforced on both faces to meet all forms of stem loading. Lifting holes are provided which can be utilised as strap fixing holes if required. Special units to form internal angles, external angles, junctions and curved walls are also available to provide flexible layout arrangements.

Precast concrete crib retaining walls

Crib walls are designed on the principle of a mass retaining wall. They consist of a framework or crib of precast

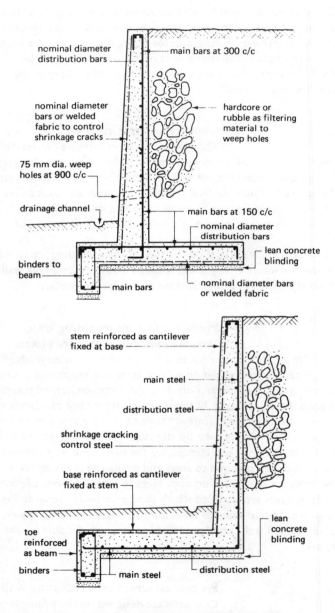

Fig. III.16   Typical R.C. cantilever retaining walls

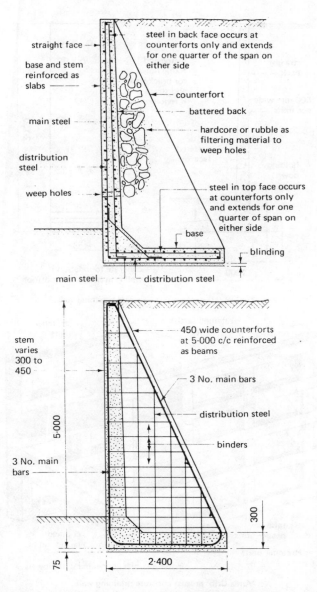

straight face

base and stem reinforced as slabs

main steel

distribution steel

weep holes

steel in back face occurs at counterforts only and extends for one quarter of the span on either side

counterfort

battered back

hardcore or rubble as filtering material to weep holes

steel in top face occurs at counterforts only and extends for one quarter of span on either side

base

blinding

main steel

distribution steel

stem varies 300 to 450

5·000

3 No. main bars

450 wide counterforts at 5·000 c/c reinforced as beams

3 No. main bars

distribution steel

binders

300

75

2·400

Fig. III.17 Typical R.C. counterfort retaining wall

181

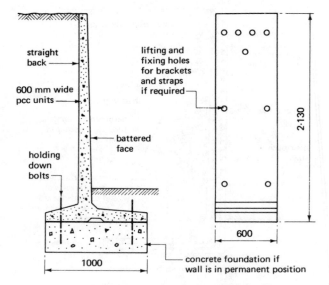

straight
back

600 mm wide
pcc units

holding
down
bolts

battered
face

lifting and
fixing holes
for brackets
and straps
if required

2·130

600

1000

concrete foundation if
wall is in permanent position

Typical 'Marley' precast concrete retaining wall

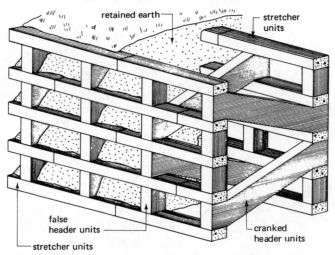

retained earth

stretcher
units

false
header units

stretcher units

cranked
header units

Note: all units connected with dowels

'Anda-Crib' precast concrete retaining wall

Fig. III.18 Precast concrete retaining walls

concrete or timber units within which the soil is retained. They are constructed with a face batter of between 1 : 6 and 1 : 8 unless the height is less than the width of the crib ties when the face can be constructed vertical. Subsoil drainage is not required since the open face provides for adequate drainage (see Fig. III.18).

20
Basements

Appendix L in Approved Document B of the Building Regulations 1985 defines a basement storey as a storey with a floor which at some point is more than 1.200 m below the highest level of ground adjacent to the outside walls. This definition is given in the context of inhibiting the spread of fire within a building and generally the fire resistance requirements for basements are more onerous than the ground or upper storeys in the same building. This section on basements is only concerned with basement storeys which are below ground level.

The structural walls of a basement below ground level are in fact retaining walls which have to offer resistance to the soil and ground water pressures as well as assisting to transmit the superstructure loads to the foundations. It is possible to construct a basement free of superstructural loadings but these techniques are beyond the scope of this book.

WATERPROOFING

Apart from the structural design of the basement walls and floor, waterproofing presents the greatest problem in basement construction. Building Regulation C4 requires such walls to be constructed so that they will not transmit moisture from the ground to the inside of the building or to any material used in the construction that would adversely be affected by moisture. Building Regulation C4 also imposes similar conditions on the construction of floors. Basement structures can be waterproofed by one of three basic methods:

1. Monolithic structures.

2. Drained cavities.
3. Membranes.

Monolithic structures

These are basements of dense reinforced concrete using impervious aggregates for the walls and floor to form the barrier to water penetration. Great care must be taken with the design of the mix, the actual mixing and placing together with careful selection and construction of the formwork if a satisfactory water barrier is to be achieved. Shrinkage cracking can largely be controlled by forming construction joints ar regular intervals. These joints should provide continuity of reinforcement and by the incorporation of a PVC or rubber water bar a barrier to the passage of water; typical examples are shown in Fig. III.19. Monolithic structures, whilst providing an adequate barrier to the passage of water, are not always vapourproof.

Drained cavities

This method provides an excellent barrier to moisture penetration of basements by allowing any moisture which has passed through the structural wall to drain down within a cavity formed between the inner face of the structural wall and an inner non-load bearing wall. This internal wall is built of a floor covering of special triangular precast concrete tiles which allows the moisture, from the cavity, to flow away under the tiles to a sump where it is discharged into a drainage system either by gravity or pumping. This method of waterproofing is usually studied in detail during advance courses in construction technology.

Membranes

A membrane is a relatively thin material placed either on the external or internal face of a basement wall or floor to provide the resistance to the passage of moisture to the inside of the basement. If the membrane is applied externally protection is also given to the structural elements and the hydrostatic pressure will keep it firmly in place, but a reasonable working space must be allowed around the perimeter of the basement. This working space will entail extra excavation and subsequent backfilling after the membrane has been applied. If adequate protection is not given to the membrane it can easily be damaged during the backfilling operation. An internally applied membrane gives no protection to the structural elements and there is the danger that the membrane may be forced away from the surfaces, by water pressure, unless it is adequately loaded. These loading coats will reduce the usable volume within the basement (see Figs. III.20 and III.21).

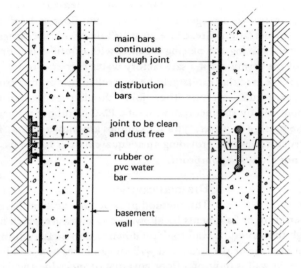

main bars
continuous
through joint

distribution
bars

joint to be clean
and dust free

rubber or
pvc water
bar

basement
wall

Note: horizontal joints positioned at 12 to 15 times
wall thickness

Construction joints

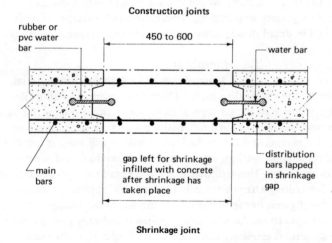

rubber or
pvc water
bar

450 to 600

water bar

main
bars

gap left for shrinkage
infilled with concrete
after shrinkage has
taken place

distribution
bars lapped
in shrinkage
gap

Shrinkage joint

Fig. III.19 Joints and water bars

186

Suitable materials which can be used for forming membranes are bituminous felt; polythene sheeting; polyisobutylene plastic; epoxy resin compounds; bituminous compounds and mastic asphalt. Asphalt in the form of tanking is the method which is considered in detail in a second year course of study.

Asphalt tanking

Asphalt is a natural or manufactured mixture of bitumen with a substantial proportion of inert mineral matter. When heated, asphalt becomes plastic and can be moulded by hand pressure into any shape. Bitumen is a complex mixture of hydrocarbons and has both waterproofing and adhesive properties. In its natural state asphalt occurs as a limestone rock impregnated with bitumen and is mined notably in France, Switzerland and Sicily. Another source of asphalt is the asphalt lake in Trinidad in the West Indies which was discovered by Sir Walter Raleigh in 1595 and today still yields about 100 000 tonnes annually. In the centre of this lake the asphalt is a liquid but nearer the edges it is a semi-fluid, and although large quantities are removed during the day the lake refills during the night. The lake asphalt is refined or purified in Trinidad and shipped in barrels for use in building construction all over the world. Natural rock asphalt is crushed and processed to remove unwanted mineral matter before being compounded into mastic asphalt. Bitumen for use with mastic asphalt is also made on a large scale as a residue in the distillation of petroleum.

Mastic asphalt is a type of asphalt composed of suitably graded mineral matter and asphaltic cement to form a coherent, voidless and impermeable mass. The asphalt cement consists of bitumen, lake asphalt, asphaltite or blends of these, sometimes with the addition of flux oil, which is used for softening bitumen or rendering it less viscous. The fine aggregates used in mastic asphalt are natural rock asphalt and limestone aggregate which are covered by BS 1162 and 988 respectively. Coarse aggregates of angular stones of igneous and calcareous origin together with naturally occurring graded siliceous material can be added to the compound if required.

The basic principle of asphalt tanking is to provide a continuous waterproof membrane to the base and walls of the basement. Continuity between the vertical and horizontal membranes is of the utmost importance, and since asphalt will set rapidly once removed from the heat source used to melt the blocks, it is applied in layers over small areas; again continuity is the key factor to a successful operation. Joints in successive coats should be staggered by at least 150 mm in horizontal work and at least 75 mm in vertical work.

187

On horizontal and surfaces up to 30° from the horizontal three coats of asphalt should be applied to give a minimum total thickness of 30 mm. Vertical work should also be a three-coat application to give a total thickness of 20 mm. The junction between horizontal and vertical work should be strengthened by a two-coat angle fillet forming a 50 x 50 mm chamfer. To prevent curling and consequent infiltration of moisture behind the vertical tanking the top edge should be turned into a splayed chase or groove 25 mm wide x 25 mm deep.

It is essential that vertical asphalt is suitably keyed to its background. Concrete formed by using sawn boards for the formwork will usually provide an acceptable surface but smooth concrete will need treatment such as bush hammering the surface and washing to remove all loose particles. Alternatively a primer of sand/cement plastic emulsion or pitch/polymer rubber emulsion can be used. Brick walls can be constructed of keyed bricks or the joints can be raked out to a depth of 20 mm as the work proceeds to provide the necessary keyed surface.

During the construction period the asphalt tanking must be protected against damage from impact, following trades and the adverse effects of petrol and oil. Horizontal asphalt tanking coats should be covered with a fine concrete screed at least 50 mm thick as soon as practicable after laying. Vertical asphalt tanking coats should be protected by building a half brick or block wall 30 mm clear of the asphalt; the cavity so formed should be filled with a mortar grout as the work proceeds to ensure perfect interface contact. In the case of internal tanking this protective wall will also act as the loading coat.

Any openings for the passages of pipes or ducts may allow moisture to penetrate unless adequate precautions are taken. The pipe or duct should be primed and coated with three coats of asphalt so that the sleeve formed extends at least 75 mm on either side of the tanking membrane before being placed in the wall or floor. The pipe or duct is connected to the tanking by a two-coat angle fillet (see Fig. III.20).

The main advantages of mastic asphalt as a waterproof membrane are:
1. It is a thermoplastic material and can therefore be heated and reheated if necessary to make it pliable for moulding with a hand float to any desired shape or contour.
2. Durability: bituminous materials have been used in the construction of buildings for over 5 000 years and have remained intact to this day as shown by excavations in Babylonia.
3. Impervious to both water and water vapour.
4. Non-toxic, vermin and rot proof and it is odourless after laying.
5. It is unaffected by sulphates in the soil, which if placed externally will greatly improve the durability of a concrete structure.

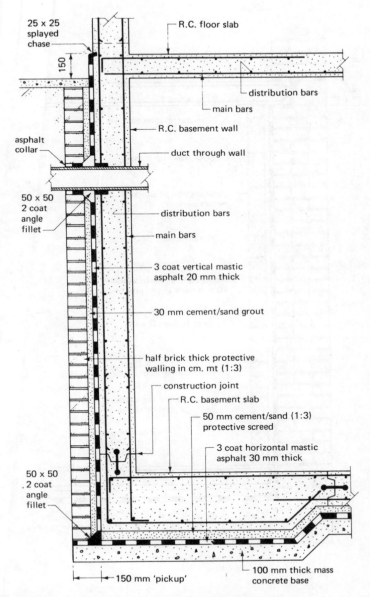

25 x 25 splayed chase

150

R.C. floor slab

distribution bars

main bars

R.C. basement wall

asphalt collar

duct through wall

50 x 50 2 coat angle fillet

distribution bars

main bars

3 coat vertical mastic asphalt 20 mm thick

30 mm cement/sand grout

half brick thick protective walling in cm. mt (1:3)

construction joint

R.C. basement slab

50 mm cement/sand (1:3) protective screed

3 coat horizontal mastic asphalt 30 mm thick

50 x 50 2 coat angle fillet

150 mm 'pickup'

100 mm thick mass concrete base

Fig. III.20 External tanking in mastic asphalt

189

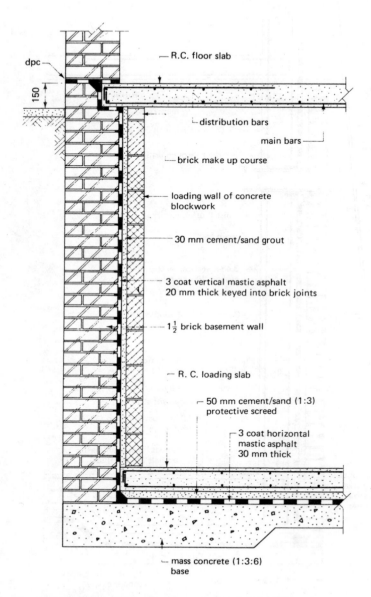

dpc

150

- R.C. floor slab

- distribution bars

main bars

- brick make up course

- loading wall of concrete blockwork

- 30 mm cement/sand grout

- 3 coat vertical mastic asphalt 20 mm thick keyed into brick joints

- $1\frac{1}{2}$ brick basement wall

- R. C. loading slab

- 50 mm cement/sand (1:3) protective screed

- 3 coat horizontal mastic asphalt 30 mm thick

- mass concrete (1:3:6) base

Fig. III.21   Internal tanking in mastic asphalt

The application of mastic asphalt is recognised as a specialist trade in the building industry and therefore most asphalt work is placed in the hands of specialist sub-contractors, most of which are members of the Mastic Asphalt Council and Employers Federation Limited. The Federation is a non-profit making organisation whose objectives are to provide technical information and promote the use of mastic asphalt as a high quality building material.

21
Deep basements

The construction of shallow single-storey basements and methods of waterproofing should have been covered in the previous three years of study and at this stage it is a useful exercise for students to recapitulate these basic concepts in terms of excavation, types, methods of construction, jointing techniques and waterproofing methods. These aspects are covered in the relevant chapters in Volumes 2 and 3.

One of the main concerns of the contractor and designer when constructing deep and/or multi-storey basements is the elimination as far as practicable of the need for temporary works such as timbering which in this context would be extensive, elaborate and costly. The solution is to be found in the use of diaphragm walling as the structural perimeter wall by constructing this ahead of the main excavation activity or alternatively by using a reinforced concrete land sunk open caisson if the subsoil conditions are favourable — see Fig. II.30.

Diaphragm walls can be designed to act as pure cantilevers in the first instance, but this is an expensive and usually unnecessary method. Therefore the major decision is one of providing temporary support until the floors which offer lateral restraint can be constructed or, alternatively, providing permanent support if the deep basement is to be constructed free of intermediate floors. Diaphragm walls can take the form of *in situ* reinforced concrete walling installed using the bentonite slurry trench system (see Fig. II.15, Chapter 10), contiguous piling techniques as described in Chapter 14 or by using one of the precast concrete diaphragm walls.

PRECAST CONCRETE DIAPHRAGM WALLS

The main concept of precast concrete diaphragm walls is based on the *in situ* reinforced concrete walling installed using a bentonite slurry filled trench but has the advantages obtained by using factory produced components. The wall is constructed by forming a bentonite slurry filled trench of suitable width and depth and inserting into this the precast concrete panel or posts and panels according to the system being employed. As a normal bentonite slurry mix would not effectively seal the joints between the precast concrete components, a special mixture of bentonite and cement with a special retarder additive to control setting time is used. The precast units are placed into position within this mixture which will set sufficiently within a few days to enable excavation to take place within the basement area right up to the face of the diaphragm wall. To ensure that a clean wall face is exposed upon excavation it is usual practice to coat the proposed exposed wall faces with a special compound to reduce adhesion between the faces of the precast concrete units and the slurry mix.

The usual formats for precast concrete diaphragm walls are either simple tongue and groove jointed panels or a series of vertical posts with precast concrete infill panels as shown in Fig. III.22. If the subsoil is suitable it is possible to use a combination of precast concrete and *in situ* reinforced concrete to form a diaphragm wall by installing precast concrete vertical posts or beams at suitable centres and linking these together with an *in situ* reinforced concrete wall constructed in 2.000 deep stages as shown in Fig. III.23. The main advantage of this composite walling is the greater flexibility in design.

CONSTRUCTION METHODS

Four basic methods can be used in the construction of deep basements without the need for timbering or excessive timbering and these can be briefly described thus:

1. A series of lattice beams are installed so that they span between the tops of opposite diaphragm walls enabling the walls to act initially as propped cantilevers receiving their final lateral restraint when the internal floors have been constructed — see Fig. III.24.
2. The diaphragm walls are exposed by carrying out the excavation in stages and ground anchors are used to stabilise the walls as the work proceeds. This is a very popular method where no lateral restraint in the form of floors is to be provided — see Fig. III.24. The technique and details of ground anchor installations are given in conjunction with prestressing systems in Chapter 21 — *Building Superstructure*.

193

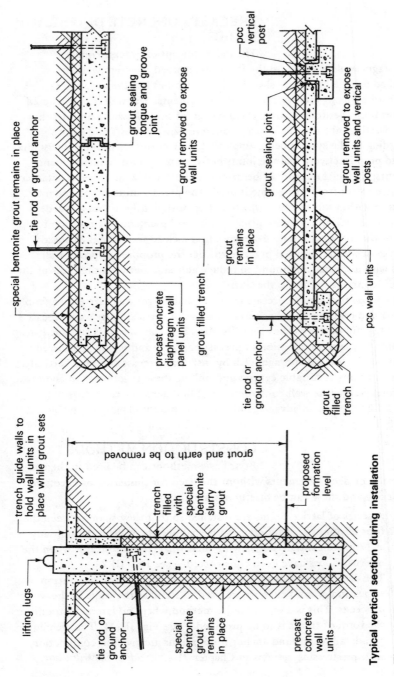

Typical vertical section during installation

Fig. III.22 Typical precast concrete panel diaphragm wall details

194

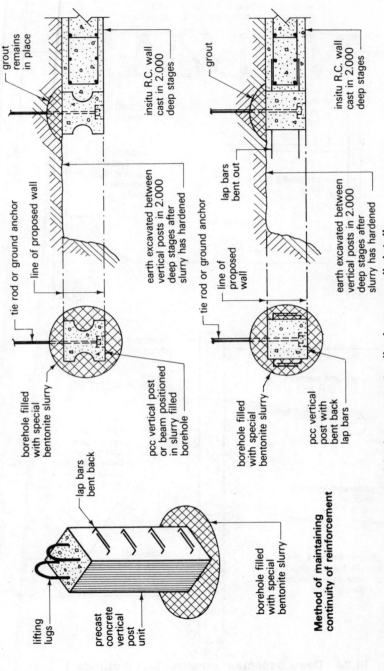

grout remains in place

insitu R.C. wall cast in 2.000 deep stages

tie rod or ground anchor

line of proposed wall

earth excavated between vertical posts in 2.000 deep stages after slurry has hardened

borehole filled with special bentonite slurry

pcc vertical post or beam positioned in slurry filled borehole

grout

lap bars bent out

insitu R.C. wall cast in 2.000 deep stages

tie rod or ground anchor

line of proposed wall

earth excavated between vertical posts in 2.000 deep stages after slurry has hardened

borehole filled with special bentonite slurry

pcc vertical post with bent back lap bars

lap bars bent back

lifting lugs

precast concrete vertical post unit

borehole filled with special bentonite slurry

Method of maintaining continuity of reinforcement

Fig. III.23 Typical precast and insitu concrete diaphragm wall details

195

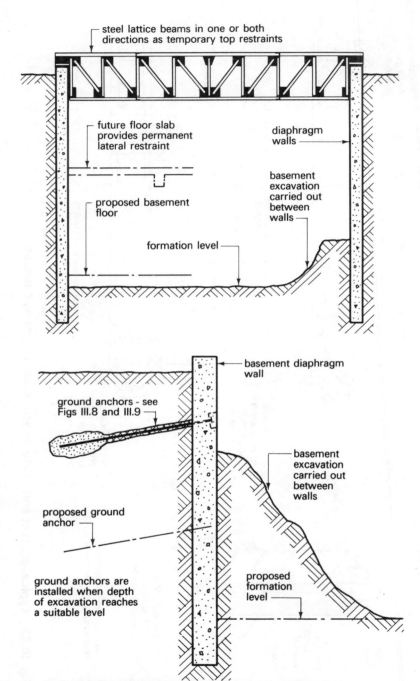

steel lattice beams in one or both directions as temporary top restraints

future floor slab provides permanent lateral restraint

diaphragm walls

proposed basement floor

basement excavation carried out between walls

formation level

basement diaphragm wall

ground anchors - see Figs III.8 and III.9

basement excavation carried out between walls

proposed ground anchor

ground anchors are installed when depth of excavation reaches a suitable level

proposed formation level

Fig. III.24 Deep basement construction methods 1

196

3. After the perimeter diaphragm walls have been constructed the ground floor slab and beams are cast providing top edge lateral restraint to the walls. An opening is left in this initial floor slab through which men, materials and plant can pass to excavate the next stage and cast the floor slab and beams. This method can be repeated until the required depth has been reached — see Fig. III.25.

4. The centre area between the diaphragm walls can be excavated leaving an earth mound or berm around the perimeter to support the walls whilst the lowest basement floor is constructed. Slots to accommodate raking struts acting between the wall face and the floor slab are cut into the berm; final excavation and construction of the remainder of the basement can take place working around the raking struts — see Fig. III.25.

Waterproofing basements

The common methods of waterproofing basements such as the application of membranes, using dense monolithic concrete structural walls and tanking techniques using mastic asphalt, are covered in the context of single-storey basements — see Chapter 20. Another method which can be used for waterproofing basements is the drained or cavity tanking system using special floor tiles produced by the Atlas Stone Company Ltd.

Drained cavity system

This system of waterproofing is suitable for basements of any depth where there are no intermediate floors or where such floors are so constructed that they would not bridge the cavity. The basic concept of this system is very simple in that it accepts that it is possible to have a small amount of water seepage or moisture penetration through a dense concrete structural perimeter wall and therefore the best method of dealing with any such penetration is to allow it to be collected and drained away without it reaching the interior of the building. This is achieved by constructing an inner non-loadbearing wall to create a cavity and laying a floor consisting of precast concrete Dryangle tiles over the structural floor of the basement. This will allow any water trickling down the inside face of the outer wall to flow beneath the floor tiles where it can be discharged into the surface water drains or alternatively pumped into the drains if these are at a higher level than the invert of the sump. Typical details are shown in Fig. III.26.

The concrete used to form the structural basement wall should be designed as if it were specified for waterproof concrete which, it must be remembered, is not necessarily vapourproof. All joints should be carefully

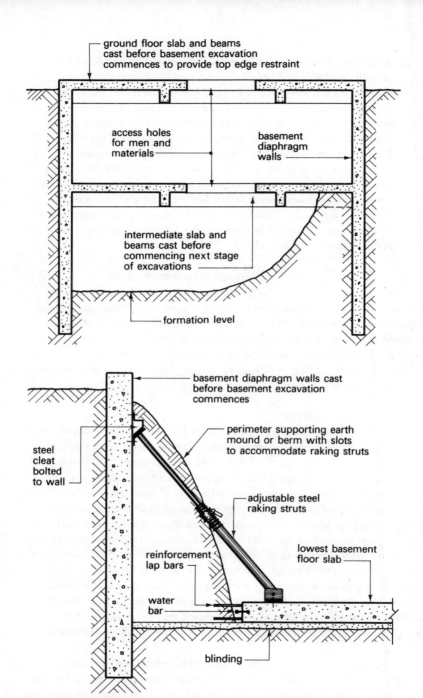

ground floor slab and beams
cast before basement excavation
commences to provide top edge restraint

access holes
for men and
materials

basement
diaphragm
walls

intermediate slab and
beams cast before
commencing next stage
of excavations

formation level

basement diaphragm walls cast
before basement excavation
commences

perimeter supporting earth
mound or berm with slots
to accommodate raking struts

steel
cleat
bolted
to wall

adjustable steel
raking struts

lowest basement
floor slab

reinforcement
lap bars

water
bar

blinding

Fig. III.25   Deep basement construction methods 2

198

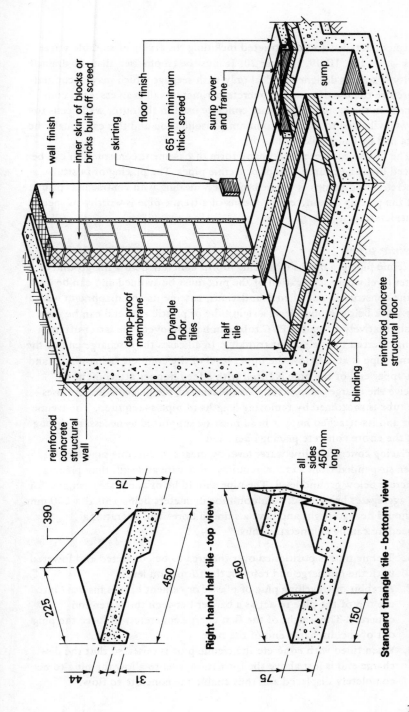

Fig. III.26 Drained cavity system of waterproofing basements

wall finish

inner skin of blocks or bricks built off screed

skirting

floor finish

65 mm minimum thick screed

sump cover and frame

sump

reinforced concrete structural floor

blinding

half tile

Dryangle floor tiles

damp-proof membrane

reinforced concrete structural wall

Right hand half tile - top view

390

225

75

450

44

31

Standard triangle tile - bottom view

all sides 450 mm long

450

150

75

199

designed, detailed and constructed including the fixing of suitable water bars — see Fig. III.19, Chapter 20. It must be emphasised that the drained cavity system is designed to deal only with seepage which may occur and therefore the use of a dense concrete perimeter wall is an essential component in the system. The dense concrete used in the outer wall needs to be well vibrated to obtain maximum consolidation and this can usually be obtained by using poker vibrators.

The *in situ* concrete used in any form of basement construction can be placed by using chutes, pumps or tremie pipes. The placing of *in situ* concrete using pumps is covered in Part V dealing with contractors' plant but the placing of concrete by means of a tremie pipe is worthy of special consideration.

Tremie pipes

A tremie pipe is a means of placing *in situ* concrete below the ground or water level where segregation of the mix must be avoided and can be used in the construction of piled foundations, basements and diaphragm walls. For work below ground level a rigid tube of plastic or metal can be used or alternatively a flexible PVC tube can be employed, the latter often being referred to as elephant trunking. In all cases the discharge end of the tremie pipe is kept below the upper level of the concrete being placed and the upper end of the pipe is fitted with a feed hopper attachment to receive the charges of concrete. As the level of the placed concrete rises the tube is shortened by removing lengths of pipe as required. The tremie pipe and its attached hopper head must be supported as necessary throughout the entire concrete placing operation.

Placing concrete below water level by means of a tremie pipe, very often suspended from a crane, requires more care and skill than placing concrete below ground level. The pipe should be of adequate diameter for the aggregates being used, common tube diameters being 150 and 200 mm. It should be watertight and have a smooth bore. The operational procedure can be enumerated thus:

1. Tremie pipe is positioned over the area to be concreted and lowered until the discharge end rests on the formation level.
2. A rabbit or travelling plug of plastic or cement bags is inserted into the top of the pipe to act as a barrier between the water and concrete. The weight of the first charge concrete will force the plug out of the discharge end of the tube.
3. When filled with concrete the tremie pipe is raised so that the discharge end is just above the formation level to allow the plug to be completely displaced and thus enable the concrete to flow.

4. Further concrete charges are introduced into the pipe and allowed to discharge within the concrete mass already placed, the rate of flow being controlled by raising and lowering the tremie pipe.
5. As the depth of the placed concrete increases the pipe is shortened by removing tube sections as necessary.

When placing concrete below the water level by the tremie pipe method great care must be taken to ensure that the discharge end of the pipe is not withdrawn clear of the concrete being placed as this could lead to a weak concrete mix by water mixing with the concrete. One tremie pipe will cover an area of approximately 30 m^2 and if more than one tremie pipe is being used simultaneous placing is usually recommended.

Sulphate-bearing soils

A problem which can occur when using concrete below ground level is the deterioration of the set cement due to sulphate attack by naturally occurring sulphates such as calcium, magnesium and sodium sulphates which are found particularly in clay soils. The main factors which influence the degree of attack are:

1. Amount and nature of sulphate in the soil.
2. Level of water table and amount of ground water movement.
3. Form of construction.
4. Type and quality of concrete.

The permanent removal of the ground water in the vicinity of the concrete structure is one method of limiting sulphate attack but this is very often impracticable and/or uneconomic. The only real alternative is to use a fully compacted concrete of low permeability. Once the chemical reaction between the sulphates and the set cement has taken place further deterioration can only come about when fresh sulphates are brought into contact with the concrete by ground water movement. Therefore concrete which is situated above the water table is not likely to suffer to a great extent.

Generally, precast concrete components suffer less than their *in situ* counterparts owing to the better control possible during casting under factory conditions. Basement walls and similar structural members usually have to resist lateral water pressure on one side only which increases the risk of water penetration and if evaporation can occur from the inner face sulphate attack can take place throughout the wall thickness.

Ordinary Portland cement manufactured to the recommendations of BS 12 usually contains a significant amount of tricalcium aluminate which is reacted upon by sulphates in the soil resulting in an expansion of the set

201

cement causing a breakdown of the concrete. Sulphate-resisting Portland cement manufactured to the recommendations of BS 4027 has the proportion of tricalcium aluminate present limited to a maximum of 3.5% which will give the set cement a considerable resistance to sulphate attack. The minimum cement content and maximum free water : cement ratio of a concrete to be placed in a sulphate-bearing soil is related to the concentration of sulphate present in the soil and students seeking further information are advised to consult the table given in the Building Research Establishment Digest No. 250.

22
Piled foundations

A pile can be loosely defined as a column inserted in the ground to transmit the structural loads to a lower level of subsoil. Piles have been used in this context for hundreds of years and until the twentieth century were invariably of driven timber. Today a wide variety of materials and methods are available to solve most of the problems encountered when confronted with the need for deep foundations. It must be remembered that piled foundations are not necessarily the answer to all awkward foundation problems but should be considered as an alternative to other techniques when suitable bearing capacity soil is not found near the lowest floor of the structure.

The unsuitability of the upper regions of a subsoil may be caused by:

1. Low bearing capacity of the subsoil.
2. Heavy point loads of the structure exceeding the soil bearing capacity.
3. Presence of highly compressible soils near the surface such as filled ground and underlying peat strata.
4. Subsoils such as clay which may be capable of moisture movement or plastic failure.
5. High water table.

CLASSIFICATION OF PILES

Piles may be classified by the way in which they transmit their loads to the subsoils or by the way they are formed. Piles may transmit their loads to a lower level by:

1. *End bearing* — the shafts of the piles act as columns carrying the loads through the overlaying weak subsoils to firm strata into which the pile toe has penetrated. This can be a rock strata or a layer of firm sand or gravel which has been compacted by the displacement and vibration encountered during the driving.
2. *Friction* — any foundation imposes on the ground a pressure which spreads out to form a bulb of pressure. If a suitable load bearing strata cannot be found at an acceptable level, particularly in stiff clay soils, it is possible to use a pile to carry this bulb of pressure to a lower level where a higher bearing capacity is found. The friction or floating pile is mainly supported by the adhesion or friction action of the soil around the perimeter of the pile shaft.

In most situations piles work on a combination of the two principles outlined above but the major design consideration identifies the pile class.

Piles may be preformed and driven thus displacing the soil through which they pass and are therefore classified as displacement piles. Alternatively the soil can be bored out and subsequently replaced by a pile shaft and such piles are classified as replacement piles.

DOWNDRAG

When piles are driven through weak soils such as alluvial or silty clay, peat layers and reclaimed land the long term settlement and consolidation of the ground can cause downdrag of the piles. This is in simple terms a transference of the downdrag load of consolidating soil on to a pile shaft and is called negative skin friction since the resistance to this transfer of load is the positive skin friction of the pile shaft. Downdrag loads have been known to equal the design bearing capacity of the pile. The anticipated negative skin friction can be calculated but such evaluations are beyond the scope of this text.

Three methods to counteract the effects of downdrag are possible:

1. Increase the number of piles being used to carry the structural loads to accommodate the anticipated downdrag loads. This method may necessitate the use of twice the number of piles required to carry only the structural loadings.
2. Increase the size of the piles designed for structural loads only; this can be expensive, since the cost of forming piles does not increase pro rata with its size.
3. To design for the structural loads only and prevent the transference of downdrag loads by coating the external face of the shaft with a slip layer, thus reducing the negative skin friction. A special bituminous compound has been developed to fulfil this task and is

applied in a 10 mm thick coat to that part of the shaft where negative skin friction can be expected. The toe of the pile is never coated so that the end bearing capacity is not reduced. Care must be taken to ensure that the coating is not damaged during transportation, storage and driving particularly in hot weather when a reflective coating of lime wash may be necessary.

DISPLACEMENT PILES

General term applied to piles which are driven, thus displacing the soil, and includes those piles which are preformed, partially preformed or are driven *in situ* piles.

Timber piles: usually square sawn hardwood or softwood in lengths up to 12.000 m with section sizes ranging from 225 × 225 mm to 600 × 600 mm. They are easy to handle and can be driven by percussion with the minimum of experience. Most timber piles are fitted with an iron or steel driving shoe and have an iron ring around the head to prevent splitting due to driving. Although not particularly common they are used in sea defences such as groynes and sometimes as guide piles for large trestles in conjunction with steel sheet piling. Load bearing capacities can be up to 350 kN per pile depending upon section size and/or species.

Precast concrete piles: used on medium to large contracts where soft soils overlying a firm strata are encountered and at least 100 piles will be required. Lengths up to 18.000 m with section sizes ranging from 250 × 250 mm to 450 × 450 mm carrying loadings of up to 1 000 kN are generally economical for the conditions mentioned above. The precast concrete driven pile has little frictional bearing strength since the driving operation moulds the cohesive soils around the shaft which reduces the positive frictional resistance.

Problems can be encountered when using this form of pile in urban areas due to:

1. Transporting the complete length of pile through narrow and/or congested streets.
2. The driving process, which is generally percussion, can set up unacceptable noise and/or vibrations.
3. Many urban sites are in themselves restricted or congested thus making it difficult to manoeuvre the long pile lengths around the site.

Preformed concrete piles: available as reinforced precast concrete or prestressed concrete piles, but due to the problems listed above and the site difficulties which can be experienced in splicing or lengthening preformed piles their use has diminished considerably in recent years in favour of precast piles formed in segments or the partially preformed types of pile. Typical examples of the segmental type are West's 'Hardrive' and 'Segmental' piles. The 'Hardrive' pile is composed of standard interchangeable precast concrete units of 10.000, 5.000 and 2.500 m lengths designed to carry working loads up to 800 kN. The pile lengths are locked together with four H-section pins located at the corners of an aligning sleeve — see Fig. III.27. The 'Segmental' pile is designed for lighter loading conditions of up to 300 kN and is formed by joining the 1.000 m long standard lengths together with spigot and socket joints up to a maximum length of 15.000 m. Special half length head units are available to reduce wastage to a minimum — see Fig. III.28.

Steel preformed piles: used mainly in conjunction with marine structures and where overlying soils are very weak. Two forms are encountered, the box pile, which is made from welded rolled steel sections, and the BS4 universal bearing pile, which has the conventional 'H' section. These piles are relatively light and therefore are easy to handle and drive. Splicing can be carried out by site welding to form piles up to 15.000 m long with load bearing capacities up to 600 kN. Consideration must always be given as to the need to apply a protective coating to the pile to guard against corrosion.

Composite piles: sometimes referred to as partially preformed piles and are formed by a method which combines the use of precast and *in situ* concrete or steel and *in situ* concrete. They are used mainly on medium to large contracts where the presence of running water or very loose soils would render the use of bored or preformed piles as unsuitable. Composite piles provide a pile of readily variable length made from easily transported short lengths. Typical examples are 'Prestcore', West's 'Shell' and cased piles.

The 'Prestcore' pile is a composite pile formed inside a lined bored hole and is strictly speaking a replacement pile and is therefore described in more detail in the following section on replacement piles.

The 'Shell' pile is however a driven or displacement pile consisting of a series of precast shells threaded on to a mandrel and top driven to the required set. After driving and removing the mandrel the hollow core can be inspected, a cage of reinforcement can be inserted and the void filled with *in situ* concrete. Lengths up to 60.000 m with bearing capacities within the range of 500 to 1 200 kN are possible with this method. The precast concrete shells are reinforced by a patent system using fibrillated polypropylene film as a substitute for the traditional welded steel fabric — see Fig. III.29.

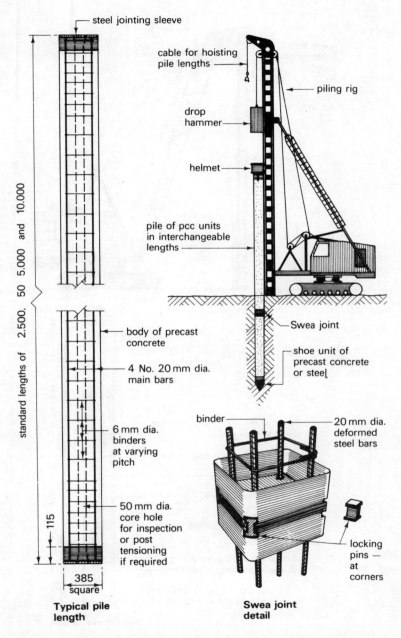

steel jointing sleeve

standard lengths of 2.500, 50 5.000 and 10.000

cable for hoisting pile lengths

piling rig

drop hammer

helmet

pile of pcc units in interchangeable lengths

Swea joint

shoe unit of precast concrete or steel

body of precast concrete

4 No. 20 mm dia. main bars

6 mm dia. binders at varying pitch

50 mm dia. core hole for inspection or post tensioning if required

115

385 square

Typical pile length

binder

20 mm dia. deformed steel bars

locking pins — at corners

Swea joint detail

Fig. III.27   West's hardrive precast modular piles

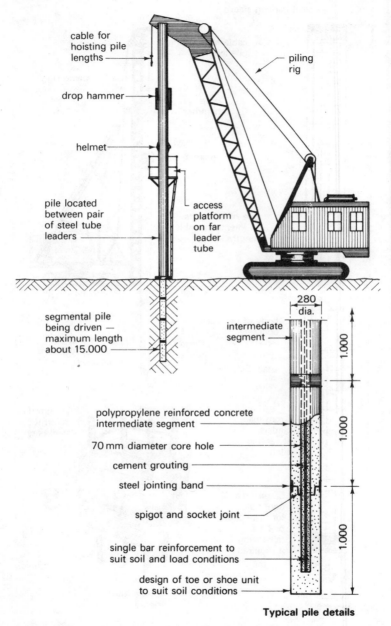

cable for
hoisting pile
lengths

piling
rig

drop hammer

helmet

pile located
between pair
of steel tube
leaders

access
platform
on far
leader
tube

segmental pile
being driven —
maximum length
about 15.000

280
dia.

intermediate
segment

1.000

polypropylene reinforced concrete
intermediate segment

1.000

70 mm diameter core hole

cement grouting

steel jointing band

spigot and socket joint

single bar reinforcement to
suit soil and load conditions

1.000

design of toe or shoe unit
to suit soil conditions

Typical pile details

Fig. III.28   West's segmental piles

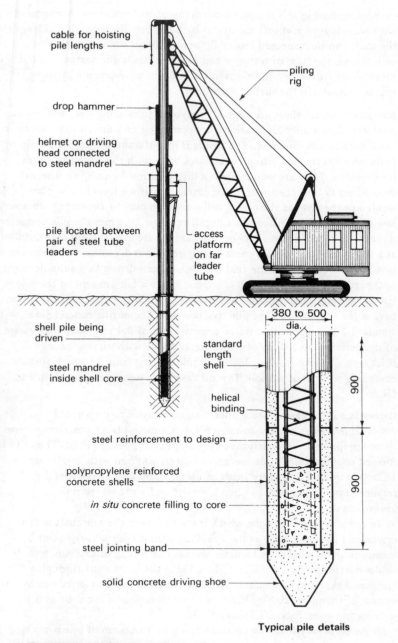

cable for hoisting pile lengths

piling rig

drop hammer

helmet or driving head connected to steel mandrel

access platform on far leader tube

pile located between pair of steel tube leaders

shell pile being driven

steel mandrel inside shell core

380 to 500 dia.

standard length shell

helical binding

steel reinforcement to design

polypropylene reinforced concrete shells

in situ concrete filling to core

steel jointing band

solid concrete driving shoe

900

900

Typical pile details

Fig. III.29 West's shell piles

Piles formed in this manner solve many of the problems encountered with waterlogged and soft substratas by being readily adaptable in length, the shaft can be inspected internally before the *in situ* concrete is introduced, the flow of water or soil into the pile is eliminated and the presence of corrosive conditions in the soil can be overcome by using special cements in the shell construction.

BSP cased piles: these are typical composite piles using steel and *in situ* concrete. Cased piles are bearing piles consisting of a driven tube which is filled with *in situ* concrete. The casing is manufactured from steel strip or plate which is formed into a continuous helix with the adjoining edges butt welded. They are usually driven into position by using an internal drop hammer operating within the casing. Usually a flat circular plate is welded to the base of the casing and a cushion plug of concrete with a very low water content is placed to a depth equal to 2½ times the pile diameter directly on top of the plate shoe. Pile lengths are available up to 24.000 m as a single tube but should extra length be required extension casings can be butt welded on after the first length has been driven to a suitable depth.

Apart from situations such as jetties, where a fair amount of the pile is left projecting, cased piles do not require reinforcement except for splice bars at the top to bond the pile to a pile cap. The *in situ* concrete is a standard 1:2:4 mix with a water/cement ratio of 0.4 to 0.5. A wide range of diameters from 250 to 600 mm are available with varying casing thicknesses to give working loads per pile ranging from 150 to 1 500 kN according to type of subsoil. Typical cased pile details are shown in Fig. III.30.

Driven *in situ* or cast in place piles: an alternative to preformed displacement piles and are suitable for medium and large contracts where there are likely to be variations in the lengths of piles required. They can be formed economically in diameters of 300 to 600 mm with lengths up to 18.000 m designed to carry loads of up to 1 300 kN. They generally require heavy piling rigs, an open level site and a site where noise is unrestricted.

In some systems the tube which is used to form the pile shaft is top driven and in others such as the Franki system driving is carried out by means of an internal drop hammer working on a plug of dry concrete. *In situ* concrete for the core is introduced into the lined shaft through a hopper or skip and consolidation of the concrete can be carried out by impact of the internal drop hammer or by vibration of the tube as it is withdrawn — see Figs. III.31 and III.32.

A problem which can be encountered with this form of pile is necking due to ground water movement washing away some of the concrete thus

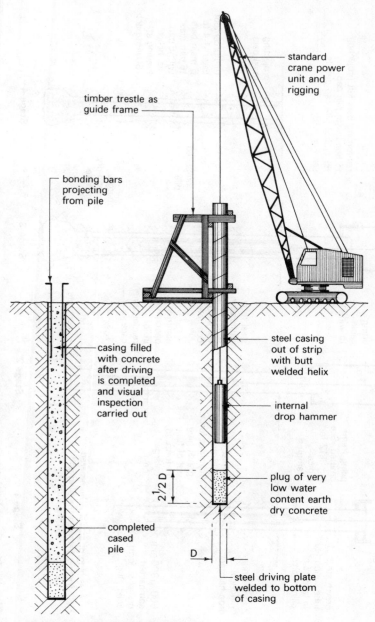

standard crane power unit and rigging

timber trestle as guide frame

bonding bars projecting from pile

casing filled with concrete after driving is completed and visual inspection carried out

steel casing out of strip with butt welded helix

internal drop hammer

$2\frac{1}{2}D$

plug of very low water content earth dry concrete

completed cased pile

D

steel driving plate welded to bottom of casing

Fig. III.30   BSP cased piles

211

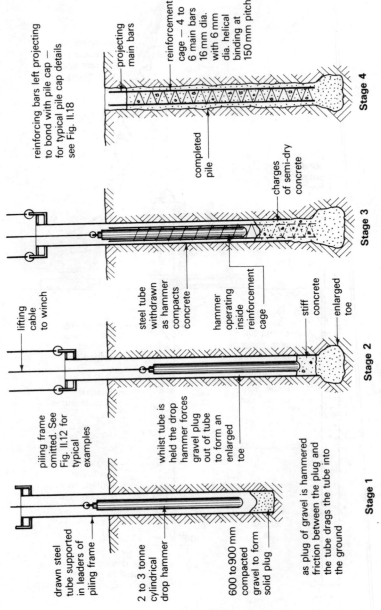

reinforcing bars left projecting
to bond with pile cap —
for typical pile cap details
see Fig. II.18

projecting
main bars

reinforcement
cage — 4 to
6 main bars
16 mm dia.
with 6 mm
dia. helical
binding at
150 mm pitch

Stage 4

completed
pile

charges
of semi-dry
concrete

Stage 3

lifting
cable
to winch

steel tube
withdrawn
as hammer
compacts
concrete

hammer
operating
inside
reinforcement
cage

piling frame
omitted. See
Fig. II.12 for
typical
examples

whilst tube is
held the drop
hammer forces
gravel plug
out of tube
to form an
enlarged
toe

stiff
concrete

enlarged
toe

Stage 2

drawn steel
tube supported
in leaders of
piling frame

2 to 3 tonne
cylindrical
drop hammer

600 to 900 mm
compacted
gravel to form
solid plug

as plug of gravel is hammered
friction between the plug and
the tube drags the tube into
the ground

Stage 1

Fig. III.31   Franki driven *in situ* piles

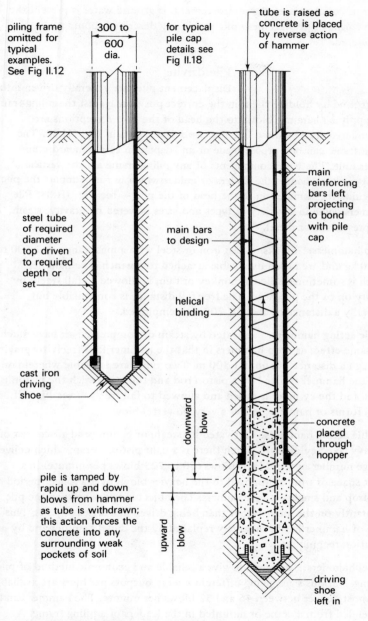

piling frame omitted for typical examples. See Fig II.12

300 to 600 dia.

for typical pile cap details see Fig II.18

tube is raised as concrete is placed by reverse action of hammer

steel tube of required diameter top driven to required depth or set

main bars to design

main reinforcing bars left projecting to bond with pile cap

helical binding

cast iron driving shoe

downward blow

pile is tamped by rapid up and down blows from hammer as tube is withdrawn; this action forces the concrete into any surrounding weak pockets of soil

upward blow

concrete placed through hopper

driving shoe left in

Fig. III.32 Vibro cast *in situ* pile

reducing the effective diameter of the pile shaft and consequently the cover of concrete over the reinforcement. If ground water is present the other forms of displacement pile previously described should be considered.

Pile driving

Displacement piles are generally driven into the ground by holding them in the correct position against the piling frame and applying hammer blows to the head of the pile. Exceptions are encountered such as those like the cased pile shown in Fig. III.30. The piling frame can be purpose made or an adaptation of a standard crane power unit. The basic components of any piling frame are the vertical member which houses the leaders or guides which in turn support the pile and guide the hammer on to the head of the pile — see Fig. III.33. Pile hammers come in a variety of types and sizes powered by gravity, steam, compressed air or diesel.

Drop hammers: blocks of cast iron or steel with a mass range of 1 500 to 8 000 kg and are raised by a cable attached to a winch. The hammer, which is sometimes called a monkey or ram, is allowed to fall freely by gravity on to the pile head. The free fall distance is controllable but generally a distance of about 1.200 m is employed.

Single acting hammers: activated by steam or compressed air have much the same effect as drop hammers in that the hammer falls freely by gravity through a distance of about 1.500 m. Two types are available wherein one case the hammer is lifted by a piston rod and those in which the piston is static and the cylinder is raised and allowed to fall freely — see Fig. III.33. Both forms of hammer deliver a very powerful blow.

Double acting hammers: activated by steam or compressed air consist of a heavy fixed cylinder in which there is a light piston or ram which delivers a large number of rapid light blows (90 to 225 blows per minute) in a short space of time as opposed to the heavier blows over a longer period of the drop and single acting hammers. The object is to try to keep the pile constantly on the move rather than being driven in a series of jerks. This type of hammer has been largely replaced by the diesel hammer and by vibration techniques.

Diesel hammers: designed to give a reliable and economic method of pile driving. Various sizes giving different energy outputs per blow are available but most deliver between 46 and 52 blows per minute. The hammer can be suspended from a crane or mounted in the leaders of a piling frame. A measured amount of liquid fuel is fed into a cup formed in the base of the

214

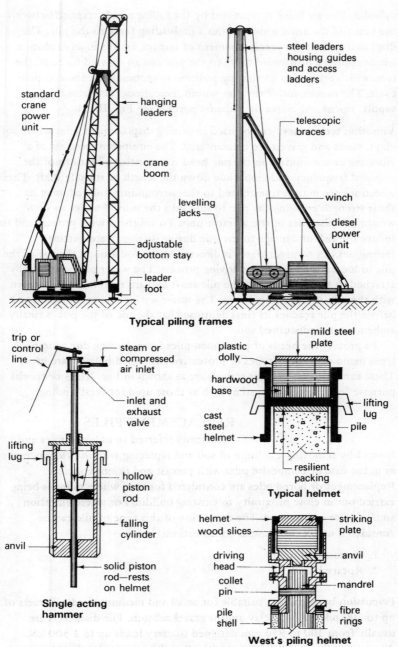

Fig. III.33 Piling frames and equipment

Labels within figure:

Typical piling frames

standard crane power unit

hanging leaders

crane boom

adjustable bottom stay

leader foot

steel leaders housing guides and access ladders

telescopic braces

winch

levelling jacks

diesel power unit

Typical piling frames

Single acting hammer:

trip or control line

steam or compressed air inlet

inlet and exhaust valve

lifting lug

hollow piston rod

falling cylinder

anvil

solid piston rod—rests on helmet

Single acting hammer

Typical helmet:

mild steel plate

plastic dolly

hardwood base

lifting lug

cast steel helmet

pile

resilient packing

Typical helmet

West's piling helmet:

helmet

wood slices

driving head

collet pin

pile shell

striking plate

anvil

mandrel

fibre rings

West's piling helmet

cylinder. The air being compressed by the falling ram is trapped between the ram and the anvil which applies a preloading force to the pile. The displaced fuel, at the precise moment of impact, results in an explosion which applies a downward force to the pile and an upward force on the ram, which returns to its starting position to recommence the complete cycle. The movement of the ram within the cylinder activates the fuel supply, opens and closes the exhaust ports — see Fig. III.34.

Vibration techniques: can be used in driving displacement piles where soft clays, sands and gravels are encountered. The equipment consists of a vibrating unit mounted on the pile head transmitting vibrations of the required frequency and amplitude down the length of the pile shaft. These vibrations are in turn transmitted to the surrounding soil, reducing its shear strength enabling the pile to sink into the subsoil under its own weight and also that of the vibrator unit. To aid the driving process and to reduce the risk of damage to the pile during driving, water jetting techniques can be used. Water is directed at the soil around the toe of the pile to loosen it and ease the driving process. The water pipes are usually attached to the perimeter of the pile shaft and are therefore taken down with the pile as it is being driven. The water jetting operation is stopped before the pile reaches its final depth so that the toe of the pile is finally embedded in undisturbed soil.

To protect the heads of preformed piles from damage due to impact from hammers various types of protective cushioned helmets are used. These can be either of a general nature as shown in Fig. III.33 or special purpose for a particular system such as those used for West's piling.

REPLACEMENT PILES

Sometimes referred to as bored piles and formed by removing a column of soil and replacing with *in situ* concrete or as in the case of composite piles with precast and *in situ* concrete. Replacement or bored piles are considered for sites where piling is being carried out in close proximity to existing buildings or where vibration and/or noise is restricted. The formation of this type of pile can be considered under two general classifications:

1. Percussion bored.
2. Rotary bored.

Percussion bored piles: suitable for small and medium sized contracts of up to 300 piles in both clay and/or gravel subsoils. Pile diameters are usually from 300 to 950 mm designed to carry loads up to 1 500 kN. Apart from the common factor with all replacement piles that the strata

216

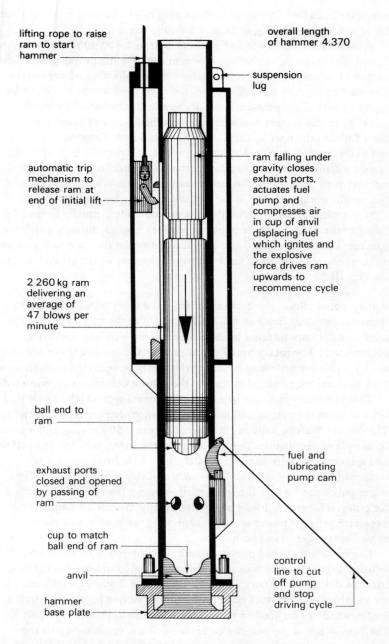

lifting rope to raise ram to start hammer

overall length of hammer 4.370

suspension lug

automatic trip mechanism to release ram at end of initial lift

ram falling under gravity closes exhaust ports, actuates fuel pump and compresses air in cup of anvil displacing fuel which ignites and the explosive force drives ram upwards to recommence cycle

2 260 kg ram delivering an average of 47 blows per minute

ball end to ram

fuel and lubricating pump cam

exhaust ports closed and opened by passing of ram

cup to match ball end of ram

anvil

control line to cut off pump and stop driving cycle

hammer base plate

Fig. III.34 Typical diesel hammer details

penetrated can be fully explored these piles can be formed by using a shear leg or tripod rig requiring as little as 1.800 m headroom.

A steel tube made up from lengths (1.000 to 1.400 m) screwed together is sunk by extracting the soil from within the tube liner using percussion cutters or balers according to the nature of the subsoil to be penetrated. The steel lining tube will usually sink under its own weight but it can be driven in with slight pressure normally applied by means of hydraulic jacks. When the correct depth has been reached a cage of reinforcement is placed within the liner and the concrete introduced. Tamping is carried out as the liner is extracted by using a winch or hydraulic jack operating against a clamping collar fixed to the top of the steel tube lining. An internal drop hammer can be used to tamp and consolidate the concrete but usually compressed air is the method employed — see Fig. III.35.

If waterlogged soil is encountered a pressure pile is usually formed by fixing to the head of the steel liner an air lock hopper through which the concrete can be introduced and consolidated whilst the bore hole remains under pressure in excess of the hydrostatic pressure of the ground water — see Fig. III.35.

Rotary bored piles: these can range from the short bored pile used in domestic dwellings (see Fig. III.2, Chapter 15) to the very large diameter piles used for concentrated loads in multi-storey buildings and bridge construction. The rotary bored pile is suitable for most cohesive soils such as clay and is formed using an auger which may be operated in conjunction with the steel tube liner according to the subsoil conditions encountered.

Two common augers are in use; the Cheshire auger which has 1½ to 2 helix turns at the cutting end and is usually mounted on a lorry or tractor. The turning shaft or kelly bar is generally up to 7.500 m long and is either telescopic or extendable. The soil is cut by the auger, raised to the surface and spun off the helix to the side of the bore hole from where it is removed from site — see Fig. III.36. Alternatively a continuous or flight auger can be used where the spiral motion brings the spoil to the surface for removal from site. Flight augers are usually mounted on an adapted excavator or crane power unit. Bucket boring tools, although not so common as augers, can also be used.

Large diameter bored piles are usually considered to be those over 750 mm and can be formed with diameters up to 2.600 m with lengths ranging from 24.000 to 60.000 m to carry loadings from 2 500 to 8 000 kN. They are suitable for use in stiff clays for structures having high concentrated loadings and can be lined or partially lined with steel tubes as required. The base or toe of the pile can be enlarged or underreamed up to three times the shaft diameter to increase the bearing capacity of the pile.

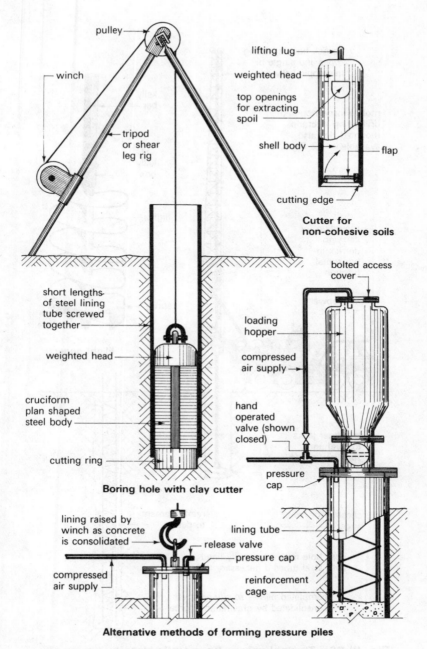

pulley

winch

tripod
or shear
leg rig

lifting lug

weighted head

top openings
for extracting
spoil

shell body

flap

cutting edge

**Cutter for
non-cohesive soils**

short lengths
of steel lining
tube screwed
together

weighted head

cruciform
plan shaped
steel body

cutting ring

Boring hole with clay cutter

bolted access
cover

loading
hopper

compressed
air supply

hand
operated
valve (shown
closed)

pressure
cap

lining tube

reinforcement
cage

lining raised by
winch as concrete
is consolidated

release valve

pressure cap

compressed
air supply

Alternative methods of forming pressure piles

Fig. III.35 Typical percussion bored pile details

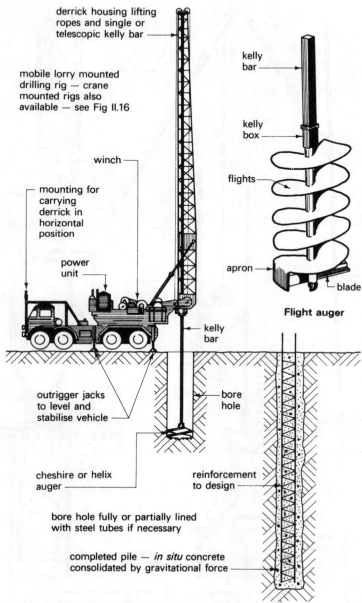

derrick housing lifting ropes and single or telescopic kelly bar

mobile lorry mounted drilling rig — crane mounted rigs also available — see Fig II.16

winch

mounting for carrying derrick in horizontal position

power unit

kelly bar

outrigger jacks to level and stabilise vehicle

cheshire or helix auger

bore hole fully or partially lined with steel tubes if necessary

completed pile — *in situ* concrete consolidated by gravitational force

kelly bar

kelly box

flights

apron

blade

Flight auger

bore hole

reinforcement to design

Fig. III.36 Typical rotary bored pile details

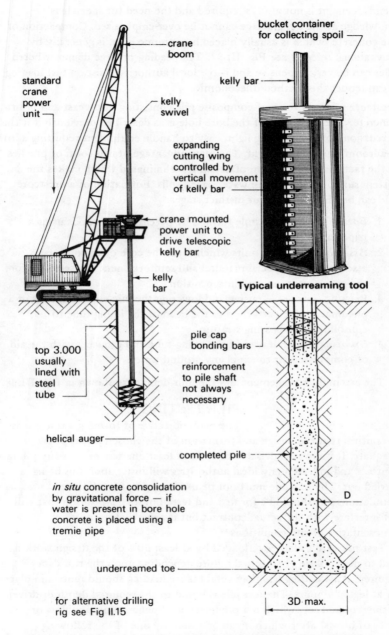

standard crane power unit

crane boom

kelly swivel

expanding cutting wing controlled by vertical movement of kelly bar

crane mounted power unit to drive telescopic kelly bar

kelly bar

bucket container for collecting spoil

kelly bar

Typical underreaming tool

top 3.000 usually lined with steel tube

pile cap bonding bars

reinforcement to pile shaft not always necessary

helical auger

completed pile

in situ concrete consolidation by gravitational force — if water is present in bore hole concrete is placed using a tremie pipe

D

underreamed toe

3D max.

for alternative drilling rig see Fig II.15

Fig. III.37   Typical large diameter bored pile details

Reinforcement is not always required and the need for specialists' knowledge at the design stage cannot be over-emphasised. Compaction of the concrete, which is usually placed by a tremie pipe, is generally by gravitational force — see Fig. III.37. Test loading of large diameter bored piles can be very expensive and if the local authority insist on test loading it can render this method uneconomic.

Prestcore piles: a form of composite pile consisting of precast and *in situ* concrete. The formation of the bore hole is as described previously for the percussion bored pile using light, easy to handle equipment requiring a low headroom or working height. The main advantage of this form of pile lies in the fact that the problem of necking is eliminated which makes the system suitable for piling in waterlogged soils. Formation of a prestcore pile can be divided into four distinct stages:

1. *Boring* — lined bore hole formed by percussion methods using a tripod rig.
2. *Assembly* — precast units which form the core of the pile are assembled on a special mandrel and reinforcement is inserted before the core unit is lowered into position.
3. *Pressing the core* — raising and lowering the pile core by means of a pneumatic winch attached to the head of the lining tube to consolidate the bearing stratum.
4. *Grouting* — withdrawal of the lining tube and grouting with the aid of compressed air to expel any ground water.

The assembly arrangement and the unit details are shown in Fig. III.38.

PILE TESTING

The main objective of forming a test pile is to confirm that the design and formation of the chosen pile type is adequate. It is always advisable to form at least one test pile on any piling contract and indeed many local authorities will insist upon this being carried out. The test pile must not be used as part of the finished foundations but should be formed and tested in such a position that will not interfere with the actual contract but is nevertheless truly representative of site conditions.

Test piles are usually overloaded by at least 50% of the design working load to near failure or to actual failure depending upon the test data required. Any loading less than total failure loading should remain in place for at least 24 hours. The test pile is bored to the required depth or driven to the required set (which is a predetermined penetration per blow or series of blows) after which it can be tested by one of the following methods:

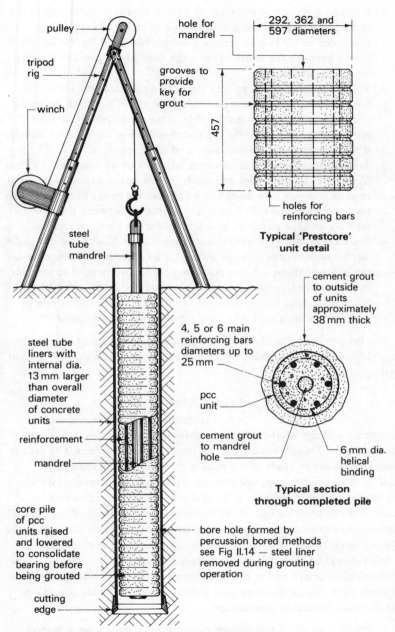

pulley

tripod
rig

winch

steel
tube
mandrel

hole for
mandrel

292, 362 and
597 diameters

grooves to
provide
key for
grout

457

holes for
reinforcing bars

**Typical 'Prestcore'
unit detail**

steel tube
liners with
internal dia.
13 mm larger
than overall
diameter
of concrete
units

reinforcement

mandrel

core pile
of pcc
units raised
and lowered
to consolidate
bearing before
being grouted

cutting
edge

4, 5 or 6 main
reinforcing bars
diameters up to
25 mm

pcc
unit

cement grout
to mandrel
hole

cement grout
to outside
of units
approximately
38 mm thick

6 mm dia.
helical
binding

**Typical section
through completed pile**

bore hole formed by
percussion bored methods
see Fig II.14 — steel liner
removed during grouting
operation

Fig. III.38 BSP prestcore bored pile

1. Forming a grillage or platform of steel or timber over the top of the test pile and loading the grillage with a quantity of kentledge composed of pig iron or precast concrete blocks. A hydraulic jack is placed between the kentledge and the head of the pile and the test load gradually applied.
2. Three piles are formed and the outer two piles are tied across their heads with a steel or concrete beam. The object is to jack down the centre or test pile against the uplift of the outer piles. Unless two outer piles are available for the test this method can be uneconomic if special outer piles have to be bored or driven.
3. Anchor stressing wires are secured into rock or by some other means to provide the anchorage and uplift the resistance to a cross beam of steel or concrete by passing the wires over the ends of the beam. The test load is applied by a hydraulic jack placed between the cross member and the pile head as described for the previous method.
4. Constant rate of penetration test is a method whereby the pile under test is made to penetrate the ground at a constant rate, generally in the order of about 0.8 mm per minute. The load needed to produce this rate of penetration is plotted against a deflection or timebase. When no further load is required to maintain this constant rate of penetration the ultimate bearing capacity has been reached.

It must be noted that the safe load for a single pile cannot necessarily be multiplied by the number of piles in a cluster to obtain the safe load of a group of piles.

PILE CAPS

Apart from the simple situations such as domestic dwellings or where large diameter piles are employed piles are not usually used singly but are formed into a group or cluster. The load is distributed over the heads of the piles in the group by means of a reinforced cast *in situ* concrete pile cap. To provide structural continuity the reinforcement in the piles is bonded into the pile cap; this may necessitate the breaking out of the concrete from the heads of the piles to expose the reinforcement. The heads of piles also penetrate the base of the pile cap some 100 to 150 mm to ensure continuity of the members.

Piles should be spaced at such a distance so that the group is economically formed and at the same time prevent an interaction between adjacent piles. Actual spacings must be selected upon subsoil conditions but the usual minimum spacings are:

1. *Friction piles* — 3 pile diameters or 1.000 m, whichever is greater.
2. *End bearing piles* — 2 pile diameters or 750 mm, whichever is greater.

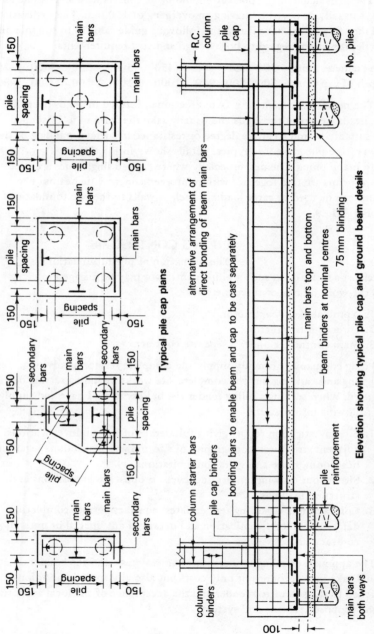

Typical pile cap plans

150 · pile spacing · 150

main bars

main bars

150 · 150 · pile spacing

150 · pile spacing · 150

main bars

main bars

150 · 150 · pile spacing

150 · pile spacing · 150

secondary bars

secondary bars

main bars

150 · 150 · pile spacing

150 · pile spacing · 150

main bars

secondary bars

150 · 150 · pile spacing

R.C. column

pile cap

4 No. piles

alternative arrangement of direct bonding of beam main bars

main bars top and bottom

beam binders at nominal centres

75 mm blinding

column starter bars

pile cap binders

bonding bars to enable beam and cap to be cast separately

column binders

pile reinforcement

main bars both ways

100

Elevation showing typical pile cap and ground beam details

Fig. III.39   Typical pile cap and ground beam details

225

The plan shape of the pile cap should be as conservative as possible and this is usually achieved by having an overhang of 150 mm. The Federation of Piling Specialists have issued the following guide table as to suitable pile cap depths having regard to both design and cost requirements:

Pile diameter (mm)	300	350	400	450	500	550	600	750
Depth of cap (mm)	700	800	900	1 000	1 100	1 200	1 400	1 800

The main reinforcement is two-directional, formed in bands over the pile heads to spread the loads and usually take the form of a 'U' shaped bar suitably bound to give a degree of resistance to surface cracking of the faces of the pile cap — see typical details shown in Fig. III.39.

In many piling schemes, especially where capped single piles are used, the pile caps are tied together with reinforced concrete tie beams. The beams can be used to carry loadings such as walls to the pile foundations — see Fig. III.39.

PILING CONTRACTS

The formation of piled foundations is a specialist's task and as such a piling contractor may be engaged to carry out the work by one of three methods:

1. Nominated subcontractor.
2. Direct subcontractor.
3. Main contractor under a separate contract.

Piling companies normally supply the complete service of advising, designing and carrying out the complete site works including setting out if required. When seeking a piling tender the builder should have and supply the following information:

1. Site investigation report giving full details of subsoil investigations, adjacent structures, topography of site and any restrictions regarding headroom, noise and vibration limitations.
2. Site layout drawings indicating levels, proposed pile positions and structural loadings.
3. Contract data regarding tender dates, contract period, completion dates, a detailed specification and details of any special or unusual contract clauses.

The appraisal of piling tenders is not an easy task and the builder should take into account not only costs but also any special conditions attached to the submitted tender and the acceptance of the local authority to the proposed scheme and system.

23
Underpinning

The main objective of underpinning is to transfer the load carried by an existing foundation from its present bearing level to a new level at a lower depth. It can also be used to replace an existing weak foundation.

Underpinning may be necessary for one or more of the following reasons:

1. (a)   uneven loading;
   (b)   unequal resistance of the subsoil;
   (c)   action of tree roots;
   (d)   action of subsoil water;
   (e)   cohesive soil settlement.

2. To increase the load-bearing capacity of a foundation, which may be required to enable an extra storey to be added to the existing structure or if a change of use would increase the imposed loadings.

3. As a preliminary operation to lowering the adjacent ground level when constructing a basement at a lower level than the existing foundations of the adjoining structure or when laying deep services near to or below the existing foundations.

SITE SURVEY AND PRELIMINARY WORKS

Before any underpinning is commenced the following surveying and preliminary work should be carried out:

1. Notice should be served to the adjoining owners setting out in detail the intention to proceed with the proposed works and giving full details of any proposed temporary supports such as shoring.
2. A detailed survey of the building to be underpinned should be made recording any defects, cracks, supplemented by photographs and agreed with the building owner where possible.
3. Glass slips or 'tell tales' should be fixed across any vertical and lateral cracks to give a visual indicator of any movement taking place.
4. A series of check levels should be taken against a reliable datum or alternatively metal studs can be fixed to the external wall and their levels noted. These levels should be checked periodically as the work proceeds to enable any movements to be recorded and the necessary remedial action taken.
5. Permission should be obtained, from the adjoining owner, to stop up all flues and fireplaces to prevent the nuisance and damage which can be caused by falling soot.
6. If underpinning is required to counteract unacceptable settlement of the existing foundations an investigation of the subsoil should be carried out to determine the cause and to forecast any future movement so that the underpinning design will be adequate.
7. The loading on the structure should be reduced as much as possible by removing imposed floor loads and installing any shoring that may be necessary.

WALL UNDERPINNING

Traditional underpinning to walls is carried out by excavating in stages alongside and underneath the existing foundation, casting a new foundation, building up to the underside of the existing foundation in brickwork or concrete and finally pinning between the old and new work with a rich dry mortar.

To prevent the dangers of fracture or settlement the underpinning stages or bays should be kept short and formed to a definite sequence pattern so that no two bays are worked consecutively. This will enable the existing foundation and wall to arch or span the void created underneath prior to underpinning. The number and length of the bays will depend upon the following factors:

1. Total length of wall to be underpinned.
2. Width of existing foundation.
3. General condition of existing substructure.
4. Superimposed loading of existing foundation.

5. Estimated spanning ability of existing foundation.
6. Subsoil conditions encountered.

The generally specified maximum length for bays used in the underpinning of traditional wall construction is 1.500 m with the proviso that at no time should the sum total of unsupported lengths exceed 25% of the total wall length.

Bays are excavated and timbered as necessary after which the bottom of the excavation is prepared to receive the new foundation. To give the new foundation strip continuity, dowel bars are inserted at the end of each bay. Brick underpinning is toothed at each end to enable the bonding to be continuous whereas concrete underpinning usually has splice bars or dowels projecting to provide the continuity. Brickwork would normally be in a class 'B' brick bedded in 1:3 cement mortar laid in English bond for strength. Concrete used in underpinning is usually specified as a 1:2:4/20 mm aggregate mix using rapid hardening cement. The final pinning mix should consist of 1 part rapid hardening cement to 3 parts of well graded fine aggregate from 10 mm down to fine sand with a water/cement ratio of 0.35. In both methods the projection of the existing foundation is cut back to the external wall line so that the loads are transmitted to the new foundation and not partially dissipated through the original foundation strip on to the backfill material — see Fig. III.40.

PRETEST METHOD OF UNDERPINNING

This method is designed to prevent further settlement of foundations after underpinning has been carried out by consolidating the soil under the new foundation before the load from the underpinning is applied. The perimeter of the wall to be underpinned is excavated in stages as described for wall underpinning, the new foundation strip is laid and a hydraulic jack supporting a short beam is placed in the centre of the bay under the existing foundation. A dry mortar mix is laid between the top of the beam and the existing foundation and before it has finally set the jack is extended to give a predetermined load on the new foundation, thus pretesting the soil beneath.

This process is repeated along the entire underpinning length until the whole wall is being supported by the hydraulic jacks. Underpinning is carried out using brickwork or concrete walling between the jacks which are later removed and replaced with underpinning to complete the operation.

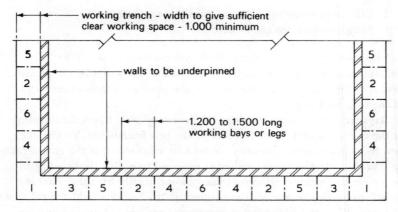

working trench - width to give sufficient
clear working space - 1.000 minimum

walls to be underpinned

1.200 to 1.500 long
working bays or legs

Typical underpinning schedule

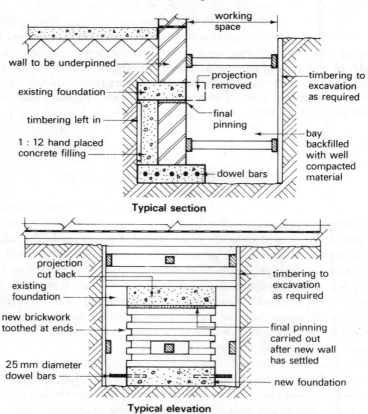

working space

wall to be underpinned

existing foundation

timbering left in

1 : 12 hand placed
concrete filling

projection removed

final pinning

dowel bars

timbering to excavation as required

bay backfilled with well compacted material

Typical section

projection cut back

existing foundation

new brickwork toothed at ends

25 mm diameter dowel bars

timbering to excavation as required

final pinning carried out after new wall has settled

new foundation

Typical elevation

Fig. III.40 Traditional brick underpinning

230

JACK OR MIGA PILE
UNDERPINNING

This is a method which can be used in the following circumstances:

1. Depth of suitable bearing capacity subsoil is too deep to make traditional wall underpinning practical or economic.
2. Where a system giving no vibration is required. It is worth noting that this method is also practically noiseless.
3. If a system of flexible depth is required.

The system consists of short precast concrete pile lengths jacked into the ground until a suitable subsoil is reached — see Fig. III.41. When the jack pile has reached the required depth the space between the top of the pile and underside of the existing foundation is filled with a pinned concrete cap. The existing foundation must be in a good condition since in the final context it will act as a beam spanning over the piles. The condition and hence the spanning ability of the existing strip foundation will also determine the spacing of the piles.

NEEDLE AND PILES

If the wall to be underpinned has a weak foundation that is considered unsuitable for spanning over the heads of jack piles an alternative method giving the same degree of flexibility can be used. This method uses pairs of jacks or usually bored piles in conjunction with an *in situ* reinforced concrete beam or needle placed above the existing foundation. The system works on the same principle as a dead shoring arrangement relying on the arching effect of bonded brickwork. If water is encountered when using bored piles a pressure pile can be used as an alternative. The formation of both types of pile is described in the following chapter on piling. Typical arrangements to enable the work to be carried out from both sides of the wall or from the external face only are shown in Fig. III.42.

Pynford Stooling Method

The Pynford method of underpinning enables walls to be underpinned in continuous runs without the use of needles or raking shoring. The procedure is to cut away portions of brickwork, above the existing foundation, to enable precast concrete or steel stools to be inserted and pinned. The intervening brickwork can be removed, leaving the structure entirely supported on the stools. Reinforcing bars are threaded between and around the stools and caged to form the ring beam reinforcement. After the formwork has been placed

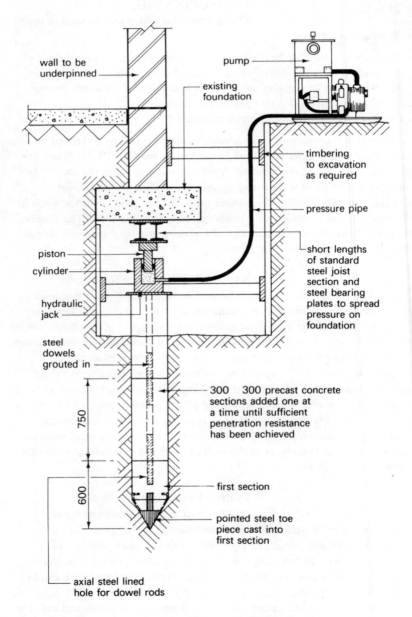

wall to be underpinned

pump

existing foundation

timbering to excavation as required

pressure pipe

piston

cylinder

short lengths of standard steel joist section and steel bearing plates to spread pressure on foundation

hydraulic jack

steel dowels grouted in

300 300 precast concrete sections added one at a time until sufficient penetration resistance has been achieved

750

600

first section

pointed steel toe piece cast into first section

axial steel lined hole for dowel rods

Fig. III.41 Jack or miga pile underpinning

232

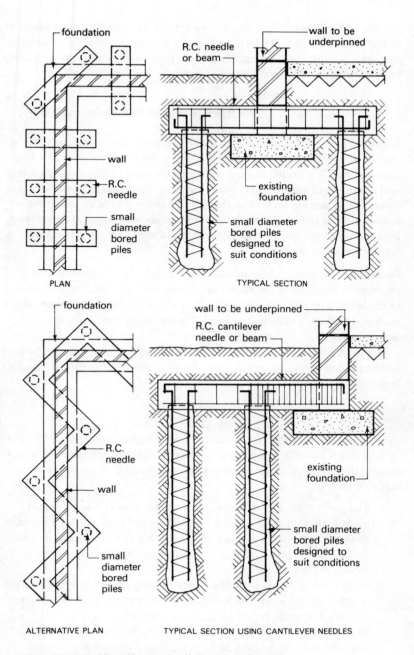

foundation

wall to be underpinned

R.C. needle or beam

wall

R.C. needle

small diameter bored piles

PLAN

wall to be underpinned

existing foundation

small diameter bored piles designed to suit conditions

TYPICAL SECTION

foundation

wall to be underpinned

R.C. cantilever needle or beam

R.C. needle

wall

small diameter bored piles

ALTERNATIVE PLAN

existing foundation

small diameter bored piles designed to suit conditions

TYPICAL SECTION USING CANTILEVER NEEDLES

Fig. III.42   Needle and pile underpinning

233

and the beam cast, final pinning can be carried out using a well rammed dry mortar mix — see Fig. III.43. This method replaces the existing foundation strip with a reinforced concrete ring beam from which other forms of deep underpinning can be carried out if necessary.

Other forms of underpinning using beams

Stressed Steel: This consists of standard universal beam sections in short lengths of 600 to 1 500 mm long with a steel diaphragm plate welded to each end which is drilled to take high tensile torque bolts. Short lengths of wall are removed and the steel beam inserted. The joints between adjacent diaphragm plates are formed so that a small space occurs on the lower or tension side to give a predetermined camber when the bolts are tightened. Final pinning between the top of the stressed steel beam and the wall completes the operation.

Prestressed concrete: short precast concrete blocks are inserted over the existing foundations as the brickwork is removed. The blocks are formed to allow for post tensioning stressing tendons to be inserted, stressed and anchored to form a continuous beam. Final pinning completes the underpinning.

It should be noted that all forms of beam underpinning can also be used to form a lintel or beam, in any part of a wall, prior to the formation of a large opening.

FINAL PINNING

Although final pinning is usually carried out by ramming a stiff dry cement mortar mix into the space between the new underpinning work and the existing structure, alternative methods are available such as:

1. *Flat jacks* — circular or rectangular hollow plates of various sizes made from thin sheet metal which can be inflated with high pressure water for temporary pinning or, if work is to be permanent, with a strong cement grout. The increase in thickness of the flat jacks is approximately 25 mm.
2. *Wedge bricks* — special bricks of engineering quality of standard face length but with a one brick width and a depth equal to two courses. The brick is made in two parts, the lower section having a wide sloping channel in its top bed surface to receive the wedge shaped and narrower top section. Both parts have a vertical slot through which the bedding grout passes to key the two sections together.

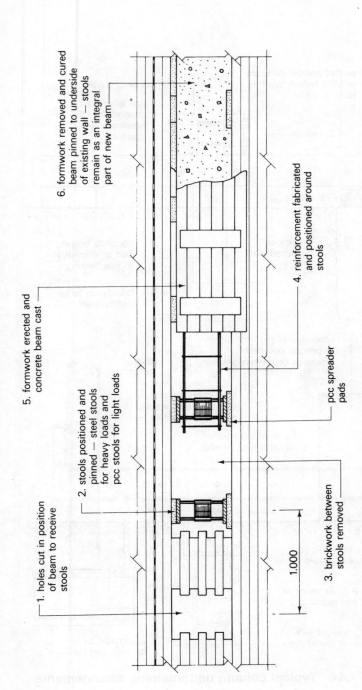

1. holes cut in position of beam to receive stools

2. stools positioned and pinned — steel stools for heavy loads and pcc stools for light loads

3. brickwork between stools removed

4. reinforcement fabricated and positioned around stools

5. formwork erected and concrete beam cast

6. formwork removed and cured beam pinned to underside of existing wall — stools remain as an integral part of new beam

pcc spreader pads

1.000

Fig. III.43 'Pynford' stooling method of underpinning

235

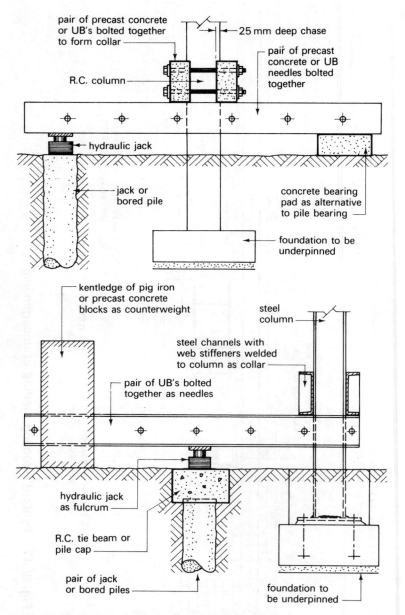

Fig. III.44 Typical column underpinning arrangements

UNDERPINNING COLUMNS

This is a more difficult task than underpinning a wall. It can be carried out on brick or stone columns by inserting a series of stools, casting a reinforced concrete base and then underpinning by the methods described above.

Structural steel or reinforced concrete columns must be relieved of their loading before any underpinning can take place. This can be achieved by variations of one basic method. A collar of steel or precast concrete members is fixed around the perimeter of the column. Steel collars are usually welded to the structural member whereas concrete columns are usually chased to a depth of 25 to 50 mm to receive the support collar. The column loading is transferred from the collar to cross beams or needles which in turn transmits the loads to the ground at a safe distance from the proposed underpinning excavations. Cantilever techniques which transfer the loadings to one side of the structural member are possible providing sufficient kentledge and anchorage can be obtained — see Fig. III.44. The underpinning of the column foundation can now be carried out by the means previously described.

Part IV
Drainage and roadworks

24
Simple domestic drainage

Drainage is a system of pipework, usually installed below ground level, to convey the discharge from sanitary fittings, rainwater gutters and downpipes to a suitable disposal installation. The usual method of disposal is to connect the pipework to the public sewer which will convey the discharges to a Local Authority sewage treatment plant. Alternatives are a small self contained treatment plant on site or a cesspool; the latter is a collection tank to hold the discharge until it can be collected in a special tanker lorry and taken to the Local Authority sewage treatment installation for disposal.

PRINCIPLES OF GOOD DRAINAGE

1. Materials should have adequate strength and durability.
2. Diameter of drain to be as small as practicable: for soil drains the minimum diameter allowed is 100 mm and for surface water the minimum diameter is 75 mm.
3. Every part of a drain should be accessible for the purposes of inspection and cleansing.
4. Drains should be laid in straight runs as far as possible.
5. Drains must be laid to a gradient which will render them efficient. The fall or gradient should be calculated according to the rate of flow, velocity required and the diameter of the drain. Individual domestic buildings have an irregular flow and Maguire's rule will give a gradient with a reasonable velocity. Maguire's rule:

gradient = diameter of pipe (mm)/2·5, therefore for a 100 mm diameter pipe the gradient is 1 in 40 with an approximate velocity of 9·6 l/s. Recommended minimum velocity for small diameter pipes is 4·86 l/s with a maximum velocity of 11·86 l/s. If domestic buildings are linked together with common drains the gradient of 1 in 40 can be considerably reduced by using other formulae for calculating the gradient—but such considerations are beyond the scope of this book.

6. Every drain inlet should be trapped to prevent the entry of foul air into the building, the minimum seal required is 50 mm. The trap seal is provided in many cases by the sanitary fitting itself, rain-water drains need not be trapped unless they connect with a soil drain or sewer.

7. Inspection chambers, manholes, rodding eyes or access fittings should be placed at changes of direction and gradient if these changes would prevent the drain from being readily cleansed.

8. Inspection chambers must also be placed at a junction, unless each run can be cleared from an access point.

9. Junctions between drains must be arranged so that the incoming drain joints at an oblique angle in the direction of the main flow.

10. Avoid drains under buildings if possible; if unavoidable they must be protected to ensure watertightness and to prevent damage. The usual protection methods employed are:
    (i) Encase the drain with 100 mm (minimum) of granular filling.
    (ii) Use cast iron pipes under the building.

11. Drains which are within 1 m of the foundations to the walls of buildings and below the foundation level must be backfilled with concrete up to the level of the underside of the foundations. Drains more than 1 m from the foundations are backfilled with concrete to a depth equal to the distance of the trench from the foundation less 150 mm.

12. Where possible the minimum invert level of a drain should be 450 mm to avoid damage by ground movement and 700 mm for traffic. The invert level is the lowest level of the bore of a drain.

Drainage schemes

The scheme or plan lay-out of drains will depend upon a number of factors:

(*a*) Number of discharge points.

(b) Relative positions of discharge points.

(c) Drainage system of the Local Authority sewers.

There are three drainage systems used by Local Authorities in this country and the method employed by any particular authority will determine the basic scheme to be used for the drain runs from individual premises.

COMBINED SYSTEM

All the drains discharge into a common or combined sewer. It is a simple and economic method since there is no duplication of drains. This method has the advantages of easy maintenance, all drains are flushed when it rains and it is impossible to connect to the wrong sewer. The main disadvantage is that all the discharges must pass through the sewage treatment installation, which could be costly and prove to be difficult with periods of heavy rain.

TOTALLY SEPARATE SYSTEM

The most common method employed by Local Authorities; two sewers are used in this method. One sewer receives the surface water discharge and conveys this direct to a suitable outfall such as a river where it is discharged without treatment. The second sewer receives all the soil or foul discharge from baths, basins, sinks, showers and toilets; this is then conveyed to the sewage treatment installation. More drains are required and it is often necessary to cross drains one over the other. There is a risk of connecting to the wrong sewer and the soil drains are not flushed during heavy rain, but the savings on the treatment of a smaller volume of discharge leads to an overall economy.

PARTIALLY SEPARATE SYSTEM

This is a compromise of the other two systems and is favoured by some Local Authorities because of its flexibility. Two sewers are used, one to carry surface water only and the other to act as a combined sewer. The amount of surface water to be discharged into the combined sewer can be adjusted according to the capacity of the sewage treatment installation.

Soakaways, which are pits below ground level designed to receive surface water and allow it to percolate into the soil, are sometimes used to lessen the load on the surface water sewers. Typical examples of the three drainage systems are shown in Fig. IV.1.

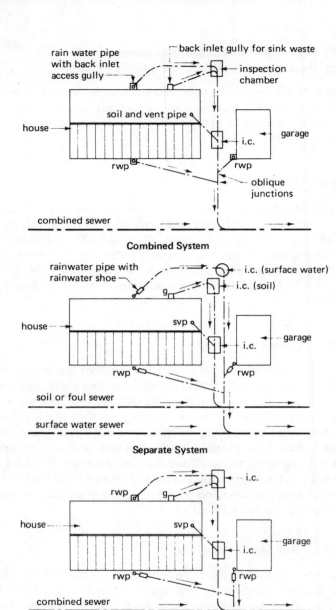

Fig. IV.1 Drainage systems

Drainage materials

Drain pipes are considered as either rigid or flexible according to the material used in their manufacture. Clay is a major material used for rigid drain pipes in domestic work, with cast iron as the main alternative; the usual materials for flexible drain pipes are pitch fibre and unplasticised PVC.

CLAY PIPES

This is the traditional material used for domestic drainage and is often termed 'salt glazed', although unglazed pipes are permitted in the recommendations of BS 65 for clay drains. The glazing of clay pipes can be obtained by the action of common salt, borax, boric acid or a combination of these, during the firing process in the kiln or alternatively a suitable ceramic glaze can be applied to the pipe before firing. Several qualities of pipes are produced ranging from standard pipes for general use, surface water pipes and pipes of extra strength to be used where heavy loadings are likely to be encountered. The type and quality of pipes are marked on the barrel so that they can be identified after firing.

Clay pipes are produced in a range of diameters from 75-900 mm with lengths from 600-1 500 mm, and can be obtained with sockets and spigots prepared for rigid or flexible jointing. A wide variety of fittings for use with clay pipes are manufactured to give flexibility when planning drainage lay-outs and means of access. Typical examples of clay pipes, joints and fittings are shown in Figs. IV.2 and IV.3.

Clay pipes are resistant to attack by a wide range of acids and alkalis; they are therefore suitable for all forms of domestic drainage.

CAST IRON PIPES

These pipes are generally only considered for domestic drainage in special circumstances such as sites with unstable ground, drains with shallow inverts and drains which pass under buildings. Like clay pipes cast iron pipes are made with a spigot and socket for rigid or flexible joints. The rigid joint is made with a tarred gaskin and caulked lead whereas the flexible joint has a sealing strip in the socket allowing a 5° deflection. Lengths, diameters and fittings available are similar to those produced for clay pipes but to the recommendations of BS 78, BS 437, and BS 4622, the latter being for grey iron metric pipes and fittings.

Cast iron pipes are given a protective coating of a hot tar composition or a cold solution of a naphtha and bitumen composition. This coating gives the pipes good protection against corrosion and reasonable durability in average ground conditions.

PITCH FIBRE PIPES

Pitch fibre pipes and fittings are made from preformed felted wood cellulose fibres thoroughly impregnated under vacuum and pressure, with at least 65% by weight of coal tar pitch or bituminous compounds. They are suitable for all forms of domestic drainage and because of the smooth bore with its high flow capacity they can generally be laid to lower gradients than most other materials. BS 2760 specifies the strength, composition and resistance requirements for pitch fibre pipes and fittings. Diameters available range from 50-225 mm with general lengths of 2 400 and 3 000mm.

The original joints had a machined 2° taper on the ends of the pipe which made a drive fit to machined pitched fibre couplings. These joints are watertight but do not readily accommodate axial or telescopic movement. The snap joint is formed by using a rubber 'D' ring in conjunction with a polypropylene coupling giving a flexible joint and is rapidly superseding the tapered joints (both methods are shown in Fig. IV.2).

UNPLASTICISED PVC PIPES

These pipes and fittings are made from polyvinyl chloride plus additives which are needed to facilitate the manufacture of the polymer and produce a sound, durable pipe. BS 3506 gives the requirements for pipes intended for industrial purposes where BS 4660 covers the pipes and fittings for domestic use. The pipes are obtainable with socket joints for either a solvent welded joint or a ring seal joint (see Fig. IV.2). Like pitch fibre pipes, UPVC pipes have a smooth bore, are light and easy to handle— long lengths reducing to a minimum the number of joints required; they can be jointed and laid in all weathers.

Drain laying

Domestic drains are laid in trenches which are excavated and if necessary timbered in a similar manner to that described in Part I for foundations, the main difference is that drain trenches are excavated to the required fall or gradient. It is good practice to programme the work to enable the activities of excavation, drain laying and backfilling to be carried out in quick succession so that the excavations remain open for the shortest possible time.

The technique used in the laying and bedding of drains will depend upon two factors:

1. Material—rigid or flexible.
2. Joint—rigid or flexible.

246

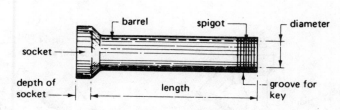

Typical B.S. 65 Clay Drain Pipe

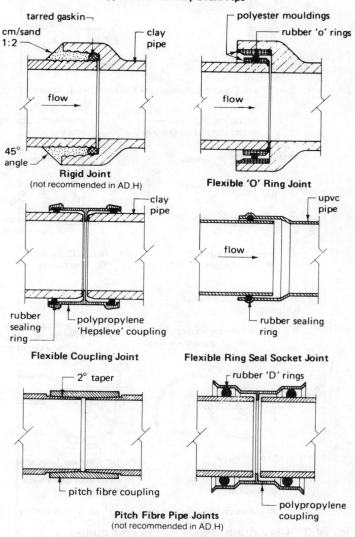

Rigid Joint
(not recommended in AD.H)

Flexible 'O' Ring Joint

Flexible Coupling Joint

Flexible Ring Seal Socket Joint

Pitch Fibre Pipe Joints
(not recommended in AD.H)

Fig. IV.2   Pipes and joints

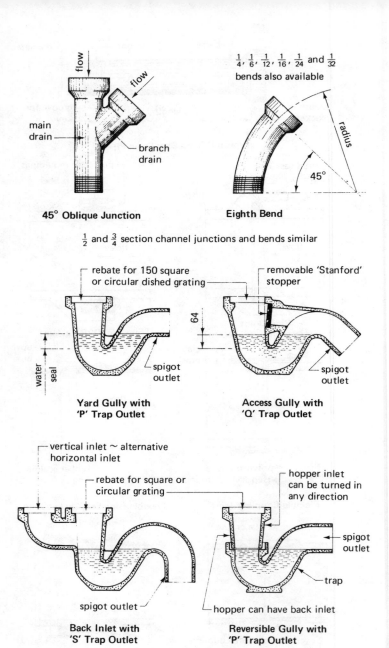

Fig. IV.3 Clay drain pipe fittings and gullies

Approved Document H recommends drains to be of sufficient strength, durability and so jointed that the drain remains watertight under all working conditions, including any differential movement between the pipe and ground.

Where a firm and stable ground is present many designers still prefer to specify the traditional rigid bed of concrete and haunching, used in conjunction with a rigid pipe such as clay, cast iron, concrete or asbestos cement. The main advantage is that the excavated spoil can be used as backfill which is not always the case when using a granular bedding. The use of flexible materials, such as pitch fibre and unplasticised PVC together with their flexible joints, is generally recommended since they give both axial flexibility and extensibility, but they will require a flexible bed to fulfil their function. Three bedding techniques are in general use and these are illustrated in Fig IV.4.

The selected material required for granular bedding and for tamping around pipes laid on a jointed concrete base must be of the correct quality. Pipes depend to a large extent upon the support bedding for their strength and must therefore be uniformly supported on all sides by a material which can be hard compacted. Generally a non-cohesive granular material with a particle size of 5-20 mm is suitable and if not present on site it will have to be 'imported'. Details of the suitability of materials for bedding and surrounding all types of pipes can be found in BS 8301—Code of Practice for Building Drainage.

Pipes with socket joints are laid from the bottom of the drain run with the socket end laid against the flow, each pipe being aligned and laid to the correct fall. The collar of the socket is laid in a prepared 'hollow' in the bedding and the bore is centralised. In the case of a rigid joint a tarred gaskin is used which also forms the seal, whereas the mechanical or flexible joints are self aligning. Most flexible joints require a special lubricant to ease the jointing process and those which use a coupling can be laid in any direction.

Inspection chambers

Deep inspection chambers are called manholes: they are a box containing half or three-quarter section round channels to enable the flow to be observed; at the same time providing an access point to the drain for the purpose of cleansing. Inspection chambers are positioned to comply with the access recommendations of Approved Document H (see Fig. IV.1).

Simple domestic drainage is normally only concerned with shallow inspection chambers up to an invert depth of 1 800 mm. The internal sizing is governed by the depth to invert, the number of branch drains, the diameter of branch drains and the space required for a man to work within

249

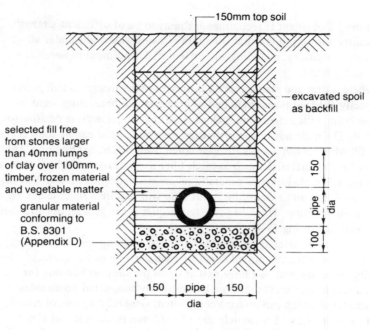

150mm top soil

excavated spoil as backfill

selected fill free from stones larger than 40mm lumps of clay over 100mm, timber, frozen material and vegetable matter

granular material conforming to B.S. 8301 (Appendix D)

150

pipe dia

100

150 | pipe dia | 150

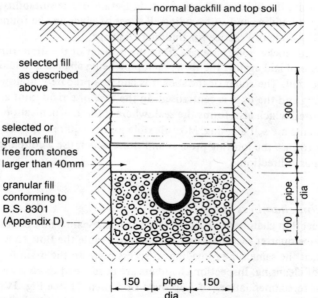

normal backfill and top soil

selected fill as described above

selected or granular fill free from stones larger than 40mm

granular fill conforming to B.S. 8301 (Appendix D)

300

100

pipe dia

100

150 | pipe dia | 150

Fig. IV.4 Typical pipe bedding details

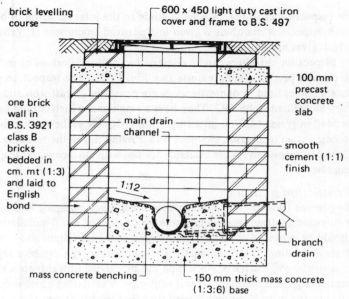

brick levelling course

600 x 450 light duty cast iron cover and frame to B.S. 497

100 mm precast concrete slab

one brick wall in B.S. 3921 class B bricks bedded in cm. mt (1:3) and laid to English bond

main drain channel

smooth cement (1:1) finish

1:12

branch drain

mass concrete benching

150 mm thick mass concrete (1:3:6) base

Shallow Brick Inspection Chamber

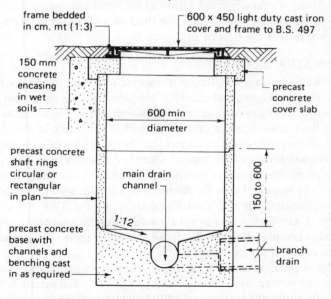

frame bedded in cm. mt (1:3)

600 x 450 light duty cast iron cover and frame to B.S. 497

150 mm concrete encasing in wet soils

precast concrete cover slab

600 min diameter

precast concrete shaft rings circular or rectangular in plan

main drain channel

150 to 600

precast concrete base with channels and benching cast in as required

1:12

branch drain

Precast Concrete Inspection Chamber (B.S. 5911)

Fig. IV.5 Typical shallow inspection chambers

251

the inspection chamber. A general guide to the internal sizing of brick built inspection chambers is given in Approved Document H, Table 9 which gives minimum sizes.

Inspection chambers can be constructed of brickwork or of rectangular or circular precast concrete units (see Fig. IV.5). The inspection chamber access covers used in domestic work are generally of cast iron and light duty as defined in BS 497. They have a single seal which should be bedded in grease to form an air-tight joint; double seal covers would be required if an inspection chamber was situated inside the building. Concrete access covers are available for use with surface water inspection chambers.

Ventilation of drains

To prevent foul air from soil and combined drains escaping and causing a nuisance all drains should be vented by a flow of air. A ventilating pipe should be provided at or near the head of each main drain and any branch drain exceeding 10·000 in length. The ventilating pipe can be a separate pipe or the soil discharge stack pipe can be carried upwards to act as a ventilating discharge stack or soil vent pipe. Ventilating pipes should be open to the outside air and carried up for at least 900 mm above the head of any window opening within a horizontal distance of 3·000 from the ventilating pipe which should be finished with a cage or cover which does not restrict the flow of air.

RAINWATER DRAINAGE

A rainwater drainage installation is required to collect the discharge from roofs and paved areas, and convey it to a suitable drainage system. Paved areas, such as garage forecourts or hardstands, are laid to fall so as to direct the rainwater into a yard gully which is connected to the surface water drainage system. A rainwater installation for a roof consists of a collection channel called a 'gutter' which is connected to vertical rainwater pipes. The rainwater pipe is terminated at its lowest point by means of a rainwater shoe for discharge to a surface water drain or a trapped gully if the discharge is to a combined drain (see Fig. IV.6). If a separate system of drainage or soakaways are used it may be possible to connect the rainwater pipe direct to the drains, providing there is an alternative means of access for cleansing.

The materials available for domestic rainwater installations are asbestos, galvanised pressed steel, cast iron and UPVC. The usual materials for domestic work are cast iron and UPVC, the latter being the usual specification for new work.

Cast iron rainwater goods

Cast iron rainwater pipes, gutters and fittings are generally made to the requirements of BS 460 which specifies a half round section gutter with a socket joint in diameters from 75-150 mm and an effective length of 1 800 mm. The gutter socket joint should be lapped in the direction of the flow and sealed with either red lead putty or an approved caulking compound before being bolted together. The gutter is supported at 1 000 to 1 800 mm centres by means of mild steel gutter brackets screwed to the feet of rafters for an open eaves or to the fascia board with a closed eaves.

Cast iron rainwater pipes are also produced to a standard effective length of 1 800 mm with a socket joint which is caulked with red lead putty, run lead or in many cases dry jointed—the pipe diameters range from 50-150 mm. The down pipes are fixed to the wall by means of pipe nails and spacers when the pipes are supplied with ears; or with split ring hinged holderbats when the pipes are supplied without ears cast on. A full range of fittings such as outlets, stopped ends, internal and external angles are available for cast iron half round gutters, and, for the downpipes, fittings such as bends, offsets and rainwater heads are produced.

Unplasticised PVC rainwater goods

The advantages of UPVC rainwater goods over cast iron are:

1. Easier jointing, gutter bolts are not required and the joint is self sealing, generally by means of a butyl or similar strip.
2. Corrosion is eliminated.
3. Decoration is not required, the two standard colours available are black and grey.
4. Breakages are reduced.
5. Better flow properties usually enables smaller sections and lower falls.

Half round gutters are supplied in standard effective lengths of 1 800 and 3 600 mm with diameter range of 100-110 mm; the pipes are supplied in two standard effective lengths of 2 000 and 4 000 mm with diameters of 63, 68 and 75 mm. The gutters, pipes and fittings are generally produced to the requirements of BS 4576. Typical details of domestic rainwater gutter and pipework is shown in Fig. IV.6.

Sizing of pipes and gutters

The sizing of the gutters and downpipes to effectively cater for the discharge from a roof will depend upon:

(a) The area of roof to be drained.
(b) Anticipated intensity of rainfall.
(c) Material of gutter and downpipe.

253

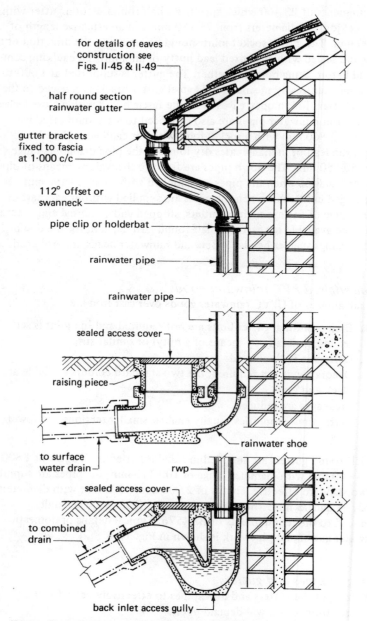

for details of eaves construction see Figs. II-45 & II-49

half round section rainwater gutter

gutter brackets fixed to fascia at 1·000 c/c

112° offset or swanneck

pipe clip or holderbat

rainwater pipe

rainwater pipe

sealed access cover

raising piece

to surface water drain

rainwater shoe

rwp

sealed access cover

to combined drain

back inlet access gully

Fig. IV.6   Rainwater pipework and drainage

(*d*) Fall within gutter, usually in the range of 1/150 to 1/600.

(*e*) Number, size and position of outlets.

The requirements for Building Regulation H3 concerning rainwater drainage can be satisfied by using the design guide tables contained in Approved Document H which gives guidance to sizing gutters, downpipes and selection of suitable materials.

25
Drainage

Drainage is a system of pipes, generally underground, used to convey the discharge from roofs, paved areas and sanitary fittings to a point of discharge or treatment. The discharges of rainwater and foul water can be conveyed together in a single drain or in separate drains to the public sewers according to the local authorities' directions based on their treatment facilities.

The fundamentals of drainage layouts, pipe materials, jointing techniques, bedding methods and simple inspection chambers construction together with the main requirements of the Building Regulations have been covered in Chapter 24. A reiteration of these basic principles is not considered necessary and therefore the emphasis of this study will be on amplification and consideration of further points such as sewer connections, testing and soakaways in the context of simple drainage.

The arrangement of any drainage scheme is governed by:
1. Internal layout of sanitary fittings.
2. External positions of rainwater pipes.
3. Relationship of one building to another.
4. Location of public sewers.
5. Topography of the area to be served.

Drainage systems must be designed within the limits of the terrain, so that the discharges can flow by gravity from the point of origin to the point of discharge. The pipe sizes and gradients must be selected to provide sufficient capacity to cater for maximum flows and at the same time give adequate self-cleansing velocities at minimum flows to prevent deposits. Economic and constructional factors control the depth to which drains can be laid and it may be necessary in flat areas to provide pumping stations to raise the discharge to a higher level.

Private sewers

A sewer can be defined as a means of conveying waste, soil or rainwater below the ground that has been collected from the drains and conveying it to the final disposal point. If the sewer is owned and maintained by the local authority it is generally called a public sewer whereas one owned by a single person or a group of people and maintained by them can be classed as a private sewer.

When planning the connection of houses to the main or public sewer one method is to consider each dwelling in isolation but important economies in design can be achieved by the use of a private sewer. A number of houses are connected to the single sewer which in turn is connected to the public sewer. Depending upon the number of houses connected to the private sewer and the distance from the public sewer the following savings are possible:

1. Total length of drain required.
2. Number of connections to public sewer.
3. Amount of openings in the roads.
4. Number of inspection chambers.

A comparative example is shown in Fig. IV.7.

CONNECTIONS TO SEWERS

It is generally recommended that all connections to sewers shall be made so that the incoming drain or private sewer is joined to the main sewer obliquely in the direction of flow and that the connection will remain watertight and satisfactory under all working conditions. Normally sewer connections are made by the local authority or under their direction and supervision.

The method of connection will depend upon a number of factors:

1. Relative sizes of sewer and connecting drain or private sewer.
2. Relative invert levels.
3. Position of nearest inspection chamber on the sewer run.
4. Whether the sewer is existing or being laid concurrently with the drains or private sewers.
5. Whether stopped or joinder junctions have been built into the existing sewer.
6. The shortest and most practicable route.

If the public sewer is of a small diameter, less than 225 mm, the practical method is to remove two or three pipes and replace with new

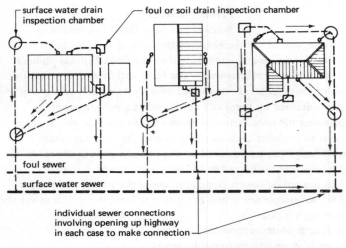

Individual drain and sewer connections

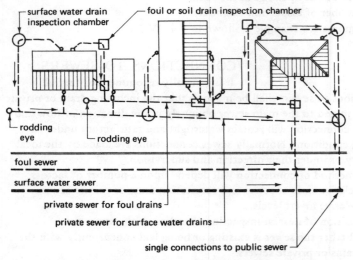

NB generally 20 houses can be connected to a 100 mm dia.
private sewer at a gradient of 1:70 and 100 houses
can be connected to a 150 mm dia. private sewer
laid to a fall of 1:150

Fig. IV.7 Example of a private sewer arrangement

pipes and an oblique junction to receive the incoming drain. If three pipes are removed it is usually possible to 'spring in' two new pipes and the oblique junction and joint in the usual manner, but if only two pipes are removed a collar connection will be necessary (see Fig. IV.8).

If new connections have been anticipated stopped junctions or joinder junctions may have been included in the sewer design. A stopped junction has a disc temporarily secured in the socket of the branch arm whereas the joinder has a cover cap as an integral part of the branch arm. In both cases careful removal of the disc or cap is essential to ensure that a clean undamaged socket is available to make the connection (see Fig. IV.8).

Connections to inspection chambers or manholes, whether new or existing, can take several forms depending mainly upon the differences in invert levels. If the invert levels of the sewer and incoming drain are similar the connection can be made in the conventional way using an oblique branch channel (see Fig. IV.5). Where there is a difference in invert levels the following can be considered:

1. A ramp formed in the benching within the inspection chamber.
2. A backdrop manhole or inspection chamber.
3. Increase in the gradient of the branch drain.

The maximum difference between invert levels which can be successfully overcome by the use of a ramp is a matter of conjecture. CP 2005 entitled 'Sewerage', gives a maximum difference of 1.800 m, whereas BS 8301, covering building drainage, gives 1.000 for external ramps at 45°. The generally accepted limit of invert level difference for the use of internal ramps is 700 mm, which approximates to the figure quoted in the first edition of CP 301. Typical constructional details are shown in Fig. IV.9.

Where the limit for ramps is exceeded a backdrop manhole construction can be considered. This consists of a vertical 'drop' pipe with access for both horizontal and vertical rodding. If the pipework is of clay or concrete the vertical pipe should be positioned as close to the outside face of the manhole as possible and encased in not less than 150 mm of mass concrete. Cast iron pipework is usually sited inside the chamber and fixed to the walls with holderbolts. Whichever material is used the basic principles are constant (see Fig. IV.9).

Changing the gradient of the incoming drain to bring its invert level in line with that of the sewer requires careful consideration and design. Although simple in conception the gradient must be such that a self-cleansing velocity is maintained and the requirements of Building Regulation Part H are not contravened.

Connections of small diameter drains to large diameter sewers can be made by any of the methods described above or by using a saddle connection. A saddle is a short socketed pipe with a flange or saddle curved to

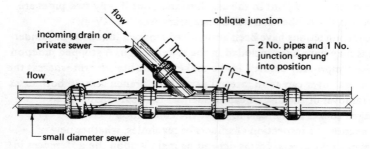

Removing 3 No. pipes and inserting oblique junction

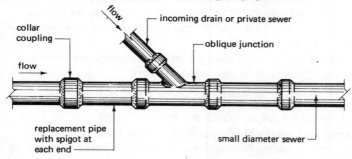

Removing 2 No. pipes and inserting oblique junction

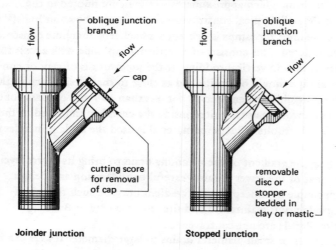

Joinder junction   Stopped junction

Fig. IV.8   Connections to small diameter sewers

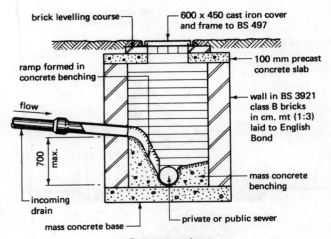

brick levelling course

600 x 450 cast iron cover
and frame to BS 497

ramp formed in
concrete benching

100 mm precast
concrete slab

flow

wall in BS 3921
class B bricks
in cm. mt (1:3)
laid to English
Bond

700 max.

mass concrete
benching

incoming
drain

private or public sewer

mass concrete base

Ramp connection

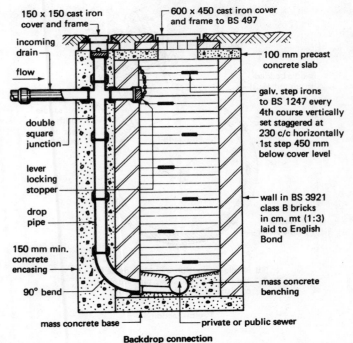

150 x 150 cast iron
cover and frame

600 x 450 cast iron cover
and frame to BS 497

incoming
drain

100 mm precast
concrete slab

flow

galv. step irons
to BS 1247 every
4th course vertically
set staggered at
230 c/c horizontally
1st step 450 mm
below cover level

double
square
junction

lever
locking
stopper

drop
pipe

wall in BS 3921
class B bricks
in cm. mt (1:3)
laid to English
Bond

150 mm min.
concrete
encasing

90° bend

mass concrete
benching

mass concrete base

private or public sewer

Backdrop connection

Fig. IV.9 Manhole and inspection chamber sewer connections

261

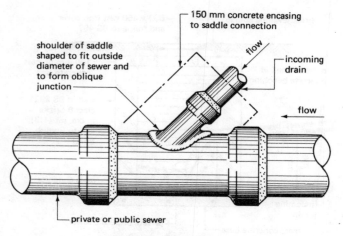

150 mm concrete encasing to saddle connection

shoulder of saddle shaped to fit outside diameter of sewer and to form oblique junction

flow

incoming drain

flow

private or public sewer

Connection arrangement

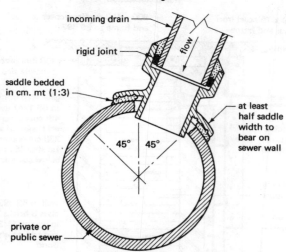

incoming drain

rigid joint

saddle bedded in cm. mt (1:3)

flow

at least half saddle width to bear on sewer wall

45° 45°

private or public sewer

NB saddle connection should be made in the crown of the sewer pipe within 45° on either side of the vertical axis

Typical section

Fig. IV.10   Saddle connections to sewers

suit the outer profile of the sewer pipe. To make the connection a hole must be cut in the upper part of the sewer to receive the saddle ensuring that little or no débris is allowed to fall into the sewer. A small pilot hole is usually cut first and this is enlarged to the required diameter by careful cutting and removing the débris outwards. The saddle connection is bedded on to the sewer pipe with a cement mortar and the whole connection surrounded with a minimum of 150 mm of mass concrete (see Fig. IV.10).

DRAIN TESTING

The Building Regulations 1985 make two references to the inspection and testing of drains. Regulation 14 requires that a person carrying out building work shall give the local authority notice in writing, or by such other means as they may agree, of the carrying out of any work of laying a drain or private sewer, including any necessary work of haunching or surrounding the drain and the backfilling of the trench. The required notice is to be given within not more than seven days after the work has been carried out.

Under Building Regulation 15 the local authority may make such tests of any drain or private sewer as may be necessary to establish whether it complies with the requirements of Part H (Drainage and waste disposal) of Schedule 1. Part H makes no direct reference to drain testing but the supporting Approved Document H recommends the water-testing of gravity drains and private sewers to establish watertightness and gives full details of the water-test requirements. The Approved Document also makes reference to the recommendations contained in BS 8301 which is the Code of Practice for building drainage.

The local authority will carry out drain testing after the backfilling of the drain trench has taken place, therefore it is in the contractor's interest to test drains and private sewers before the backfilling is carried out since the detection and repair of any failure discovered after backfilling can be time-consuming and costly.

Types of tests

There are three methods available for the testing of drains:

Water test: the usual method employed and is carried out by filling the drain run being tested with water under pressure and observing if there is any escape of water (see Fig. IV.11).

Smoke test: method used by some authorities by pumping smoke into the

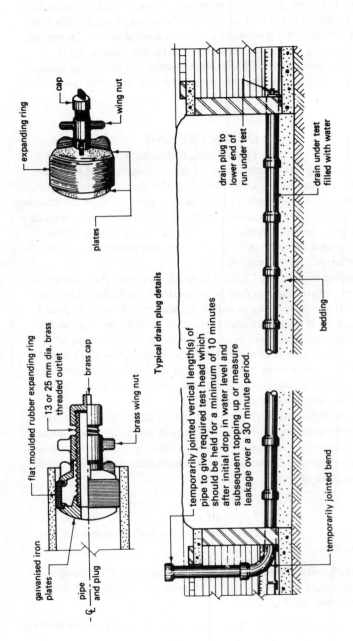

cap

wing nut

expanding ring

plates

Typical drain plug details

flat moulded rubber expanding ring

13 or 25 mm dia. brass threaded outlet

brass cap

brass wing nut

galvanised iron plates

pipe and plug

temporarily jointed vertical length(s) of pipe to give required test head which should be held for a minimum of 10 minutes after initial drop in water level and subsequent topping up or measure leakage over a 30 minute period.

temporarily jointed bend

drain plug to lower end of run under test

drain under test filled with water

bedding

Fig. IV.11 Water testing of drains

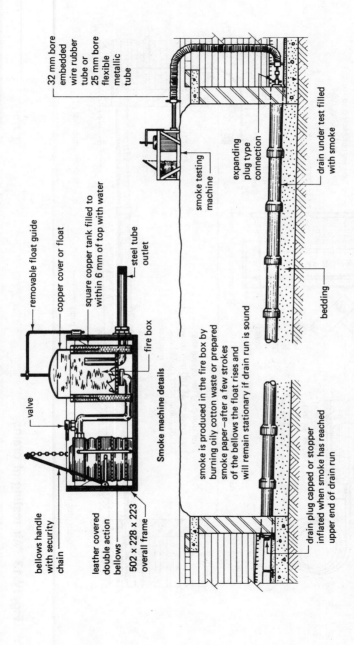

removable float guide

copper cover or float

square copper tank filled to
within 6 mm of top with water

steel tube
outlet

fire box

32 mm bore
embedded
wire rubber
tube or
25 mm bore
flexible
metallic
tube

valve

bellows handle
with security
chain

leather covered
double action
bellows

502 x 228 x 223
overall frame

Smoke machine details

smoke testing
machine

expanding
plug type
connection

drain under test filled
with smoke

bedding

smoke is produced in the fire box by
burning oily cotton waste or prepared
smoke paper—after a few strokes
of the bellows the float rises and
will remain stationary if drain run is sound

drain plug capped or stopper
inflated when smoke has reached
upper end of drain run

Fig. IV.12 Smoke testing of drains

265

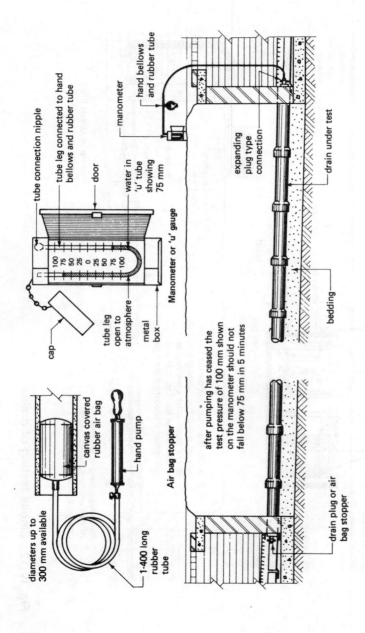

Fig. IV.13 Air testing of drains

266

sealed drain run under test and observing any fall in pressure as indicated by the fall of the float on the smoke machine (see Fig. IV.12).

Air test: not a particularly conclusive test but it is sometimes used in special circumstances such as large diameter pipes where a large quantity of water would be required. If a failure is indicated by an air test the drain should be retested using the more reliable water test (see Fig. IV.13).

The illustrations of drain testing have been prepared on the assumption that the test is being carried out by the contractor before backfilling and haunching has taken place.

In general the testing of drains should be carried out between manholes; manholes should be tested separately and short branches of less than 6.000 m should be tested with the main drain to which they are connected; long branches would be tested in the same manner as a main drain.

SOAKAWAYS

A soakaway is a pit dug in permeable ground which receives the rainwater discharge from the roof and paved areas of a small building and is so constructed that the water collected can percolate into the surrounding subsoil. To function correctly and efficiently a soakaway must be designed taking into account the following factors:

1. Permeability or rate of dispersion of the subsoil.
2. Area to be drained.
3. Storage capacity required to accept sudden inflow of water such as that encountered during a storm.
4. Local authority requirements as to method of construction and siting in relation to buildings.
5. Depth of water table.

Before any soakaway is designed or constructed the local authority should be contacted to obtain permission and ascertain its specific requirements. Some authorities will permit the use of soakaways as an outfall to a subsoil drainage scheme or to receive the effluent from a small sewage treatment plant.

The rate at which water will percolate into the ground depends mainly on the permeability of the soil. Generally clay soils are unacceptable for soakaway construction, whereas sands and gravels are usually satisfactory. An indication of the permeability of a soil can be ascertained by observing the rate of percolation. A bore hole 150 mm in diameter should be drilled to a depth of 1.000 m. Water to a depth of 300 m is poured into the hole and the time taken for the water to disperse is noted. Several tests should

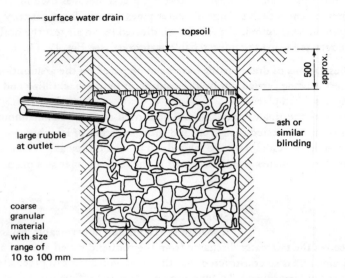

surface water drain

topsoil

500 approx.

large rubble at outlet

ash or similar blinding

coarse granular material with size range of 10 to 100 mm

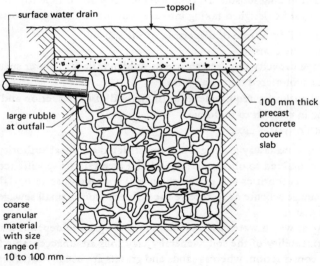

surface water drain

topsoil

large rubble at outfall

100 mm thick precast concrete cover slab

coarse granular material with size range of 10 to 100 mm

suitable coarse granular materials include broken bricks, crushed sound rock and hard clinker

Fig. IV.14 Filled soakaways

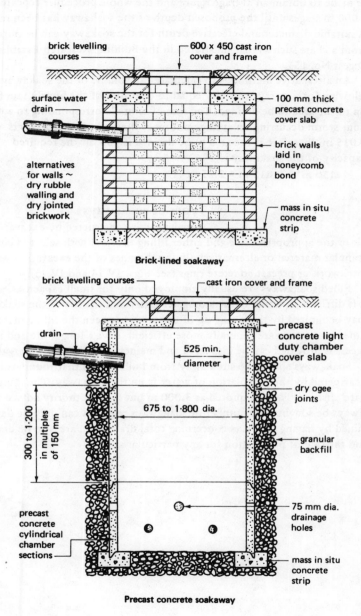

Fig. IV.15   Lined soakaways

269

be made to obtain an average figure and the whole procedure repeated at 1.000 m stages until the proposed depth of the soakaway has been reached. A suitable diameter and effective depth for the soakaway can be obtained from a chart such as that illustrated in the Building Research Establishment Digest No. 151.

An alternative method is to calculate the volume of the soakaway by allowing for a storage capacity equal to one-third of the hourly rain falling on to the area to be drained. The rate of rainfall corresponding to a two-hour storm occurring on average not more than once in ten years is 0.015 m; therefore if the area to be drained is 150 m^2 the required capacity of the soakaway is:

$$150 \text{ m}^2 \times 0.015 \text{ m} = 2.25 \text{ m}^3.$$

Types of soakaways

A soakaway is constructed by excavating a pit of the appropriate size and either filling the void with selected coarse granular material or alternatively lining the sides of the excavation with brickwork or precast concrete rings (see Figs. IV.14 and IV.15).

Filled soakaways are usually employed only for small capacities, since it is difficult to estimate the storage capacity and the life of the soakaway may be limited by the silting up of the voids between the filling material. Lined soakaways are generally more efficient, have a longer life and if access is provided can be inspected and maintained at regular intervals.

Soakaways should be sited away from buildings so that foundations are unaffected by the percolation of water from the soakaway. The minimum 'safe' distance is often quoted as 3.000 m but local authority advice should always be sought. The number of soakaways required can only be determined by having the facts concerning total drain runs, areas to be drained and the rate of percolation for any particular site.

26
Roads and pavings

A building contractor is not normally engaged to construct major roads or motorways as this is the province of the civil engineer. However, he can be involved in the laying of small estate roads, service roads and driveways and it is within this context that the student of construction technology would consider road works.

Before considering road construction techniques and types it is worth while considering some of the problems encountered by the designer when planning road layouts. The width of a road can be determined by the anticipated traffic flow which will use the road upon completion. The major layout problems occur at road junctions and at the termination of cul-de-sac roads. At right-angle junctions it is important that vehicles approaching the junction from any direction have a clear view of approaching vehicles intending to join the main traffic flow. Most planning authorities have layout restrictions at such junctions in the form of triangulated sight lines which give a distance and area in which an observer can see an object when both are at specific heights above the carriageway. Within this triangulated area street furniture or any other obstruction is not allowed — see Fig. IV.16. Angled junctions by virtue of their distinctive layout do not present the same problems. At any junction a suitable radius should be planned so that vehicles filtering into the main road should not have to apply a full turning lock. The actual radius required will be governed by the anticipated vehicle types which will use the road.

Terminations at the end of cul-de-sacs must be planned to allow vehicles to turn round. For service roads this is usually based on the length and turning circle specifications of refuse collection vehicles which are

271

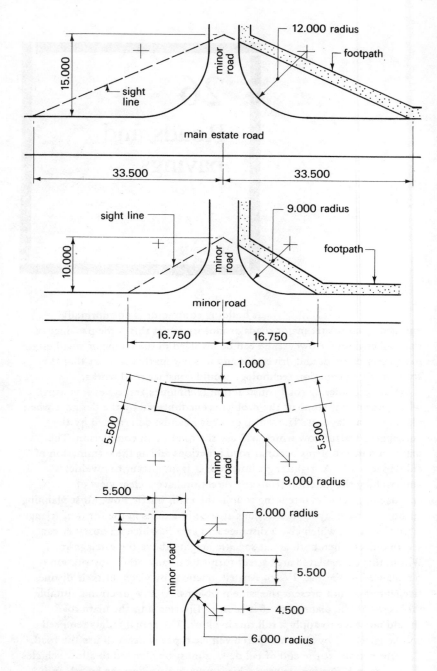

Fig. IV.16   Typical road junctions and terminations

probably the largest vehicles to use the road — typical examples are shown in Fig. IV.16.

The construction of roads can be considered under two headings:

1. Preparation or earthworks.
2. Pavement construction.

Before any roadwork is undertaken a thorough soil investigation should be carried out to determine the nature of the subgrade which is the soil immediately below the topsoil that will ultimately carry the traffic loads from the pavement above. Soil investigations should preferably be carried out during the winter period when subgrade conditions will be at their worst. Trial holes should be taken down to at least 1.000 below the proposed formation level. The information required from these investigations to ensure that a good pavement design can be formulated are the elasticity, plasticity, cohesion and internal friction properties of the subgrade.

EARTHWORKS

This will include removing topsoil, scraping and grading the exposed surface to the required formation level, preparation of the subgrade to receive the pavement and forming any embankments and/or cuttings. The strength of the subgrade will generally decrease as the moisture content increases. An excess of water in the subgrade can also cause damage by freezing, causing frost heave in fine sands, chalk and silty soils. Conversely thawing may cause a reduction in subgrade strength giving rise to failure of the pavement above. Tree roots, particularly those of fast-growing deciduous trees such as the poplar and willow, can also cause damage in heavy clay soils by extracting vast quantities of water from the subgrade down to a depth of 3.000.

The pavement covering will give final protection to the subgrade from excess moisture but during the construction period the subgrade should be protected by a waterproof surfacing such as a sprayed bituminous binder with a sand cover applied at a rate of 1 litre per square metre. If the subgrade is not to be immediately covered with the sub-base of the pavement it should be protected by an impermeable membrane such as 500 gauge plastic sheeting with 300 mm side and end laps.

PAVEMENT CONSTRUCTION

Pavement is a general term for any paved surface and is also the term applied specifically to the whole construction of a road. Road pavements can be classified as flexible pavements which for the purpose of design are assumed to have no tensile strength and consist of a series of layers of materials to distribute the wheel loads to the subgrade. The alternative form is the rigid pavement of which, for the purpose of design, the tensile strength is taken into account and consists of a concrete slab resting on a granular base.

Flexible pavements

The sub-base for a flexible pavement is laid directly onto the formation level and should consist of a well-compacted granular material such as a quarry overburden or crushed rocks. The actual thickness of sub-base required is determined by the cumulative number of standard axles to be carried (where a standard axle is taken as 8 200 kg) and the CBR of the subgrade. The CBR, or California bearing ratio, is an empirical method in which the thickness of the sub-base is related to the strength of the sub-grade and to the amount of traffic the road is expected to carry. Data regarding CBR values can be obtained from the design charts contained in Road Note 29 published by HM Stationery Office.

The subgrade is covered with a sub-base, a base course and a wearing course; the last two components are called collectively the surfacing. The sub-base can consist of any material which remains stable in water such as crushed stone, dry lean concrete and blast furnace slag. Compacted dry-bound macadam in a 75 to 125 mm thick layer with a 25 mm thick overlay of firmer material or a compacted wet mix macadam in 75 to 150 mm thick layers could also be used. The material chosen should also be unaffected by frost and have a CBR value of not less than 80% and should be well compacted in layers giving a compacted thickness of between 100 and 150 mm for each layer.

The base course of the surfacing can consist of rolled asphalt, dense tarmacadam, dense bitumen macadam or open-textured macadam and should be applied to a minimum thickness of 60 mm. Base courses are laid to the required finished road section providing any necessary gradients or crossfalls ready to receive the thinner wearing course which should be laid within three days of completing the base course. The wearing course is usually laid by machine and provides the water protection for the base layers. It should also have non-skid properties, reasonable resistance to glare, have good riding properties and have a good life expectancy. Materials which give these properties include hot rolled asphalt, bitumen macadam, dense tar surfacing and cold asphalt — see Fig. IV.17 for typical details. Existing flexible road surfaces can be renovated quickly and cheaply by the application of a hot tar or cut-back bitumen binder with a rolled layer of gravel, crushed stone or slag chippings applied immediately after the binder and before it sets.

The above treatments are termed bound surfaces but flexible roads or

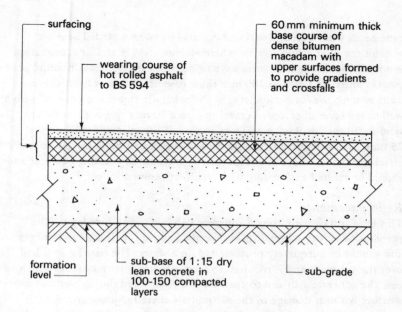

surfacing

wearing course of hot rolled asphalt to BS 594

60 mm minimum thick base course of dense bitumen macadam with upper surfaces formed to provide gradients and crossfalls

formation level

sub-base of 1:15 dry lean concrete in 100-150 compacted layers

sub-grade

Typical flexible pavement

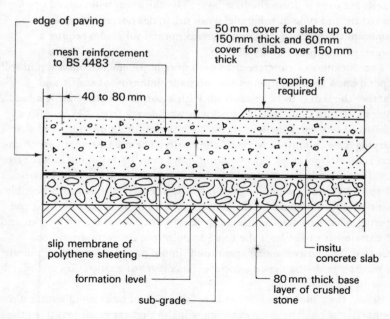

edge of paving

mesh reinforcement to BS 4483

40 to 80 mm

50 mm cover for slabs up to 150 mm thick and 60 mm cover for slabs over 150 mm thick

topping if required

slip membrane of polythene sheeting

formation level

sub-grade

insitu concrete slab

80 mm thick base layer of crushed stone

Typical rigid pavement

Fig. IV.17 Typical pavement details

275

pavements with unbound surfaces can also be constructed. These are suitable for light vehicle traffic where violent braking and/or acceleration is not anticipated such as driveways to domestic properties. Unbound pavements consist of a 100 to 200 mm thick base of clinker or hardcore laid directly onto the formation level of the subgrade and this is covered with a well-rolled layer of screeded gravel to pass a 40 mm ring with sufficient sand to fill the small voids to form an overall consolidated thickness of 25 mm. This will give a relatively cheap flexible pavement but to be really efficient it should have adequate falls to prevent the ponding of water and should be treated each spring with an effective weed killer.

Rigid pavements

This is a form of road using a concrete slab laid over a base layer. The preparation of the subgrade is as described above for flexible pavements and should be adequately protected against water. The base layer is laid over the subgrade and is required to form a working surface from which to case the concrete slab and to enable work to proceed during wet and frosty weather without damage to the subgrade. Generally, granular materials such as crushed concrete, crushed stone, crushed slag and suitably graded gravels are used to form the base layer. The thickness will depend upon the nature and type of subgrade; weak subgrades normally require a minimum thickness of 150 mm whereas normal subgrades require a minimum thickness of only 80 mm.

The thickness of concrete slabs used in rigid pavement construction will depend upon the condition of the subgrade, intensity of traffic and whether the slab is to be reinforced. With a normal subgrade using a base layer of 80 mm thick the slab thickness would vary from 125 mm for a reinforced slab carrying light traffic to 200 mm for an unreinforced slab carrying a medium to heavy traffic intensity. The usual strength specification is 28 MN/m^2 at 28 days with not more than 1% test cube failure rate; therefore the mix design should be based on a mean strength of between 40 and 50 MN/m^2, depending upon the degree of quality control possible on or off site. To minimise the damage which can be caused by frost and de-icing salts the water/cement ratio should not exceed 0.5 by weight, and air entrainment to at least the top 50 mm of the concrete should be specified. The air entraining agent used should produce 3 to 6% of minute air bubbles in the hardened concrete thus preventing saturation of the slab by capillary action.

Before the concrete is laid the base layer should be covered with a slip membrane of polythene sheet which will also prevent grout loss from the concrete slab. Concrete slabs are usually laid between pressed steel road forms which are positioned and fixed to the ground with steel stakes.

These side forms are designed to provide the guide for hand tamping or to provide for a concrete train consisting of spreaders and compacting units. Curved or flexible road forms have no top or bottom flange and are secured to the ground with an increased number of steel stakes — see Fig. IV.18 for typical road form examples.

Reinforcement generally in the form of a welded steel fabric complying with the recommendations of BS 4483 can be included in rigid pavement constructions to prevent the formation of cracks and to enable the number of expansion and contraction joints required to be reduced. If bar reinforcement is used instead of welded steel fabric it should consist of deformed bars at spacings not exceeding 150 mm. The cover of concrete over the reinforcement will depend on the thickness of concrete, for slabs under 150 mm thick the minimum cover should be 50 mm and for slabs over 150 mm thick the minimum cover should be 60 mm.

Joints used in rigid pavements may be either transverse or longitudinal and are included in the design to:

1. Limit the size of slab.
2. Limit the stresses due to subgrade restraint.
3. Make provision for slab movements such as expansion, contraction and warping.

The spacing of joints will be governed by a number of factors, namely slab thickness, presence of reinforcement, traffic intensity and the temperature at which the concrete is placed. Five types of joint are used in rigid road and pavement construction and are classed as follows:

1. *Expansion joints* — transverse joints at 36 to 72 m centres in reinforced slabs and at 27 to 54 m centres in unreinforced slabs.
2. *Contraction joints* — transverse joints placed between expansion joints at 12 to 24 m centres in reinforced slabs and at 4.5 to 7.5 m centres in unreinforced slabs to limit the size of slab bay or panel. It should be noted that every third joint should be an expansion joint.
3. *Longitudinal joints* — similar to contraction joints and are required where slab width exceeds 4.5 m.
4. *Construction joints* — the day's work should normally be terminated at an expansion or contraction joint, but if this is impossible a construction joint can be included. These joints are similar to contraction joints but with the two portions tied together with reinforcement. Construction joints should not be placed within 3.000 of another joint and should be avoided wherever possible.
5. *Warping joints* — transverse joints which are sometimes required in unreinforced slabs to relieve the stresses caused by vertical

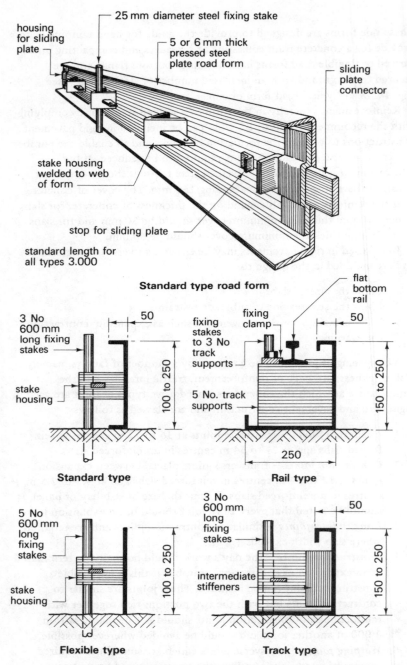

Fig. IV.18   Typical steel road form details

temperature gradients within the slab if they are higher than the contractional stresses. The detail is similar to contraction joints but it has a special arrangement of reinforcement.

Typical joint details are shown in Fig. IV.19.

Road joints can require fillers and/or sealers; the former needs to be compressible whereas the latter should protect the joint against the entry of water and grit. Suitable materials for fillers are soft knot-free timber, impregnated fibreboard, chipboard, cork and cellular rubber. The common sealing compounds used are resinous compounds, rubber-bituminous compounds and straight run bitumen compounds containing fillers. The sealed surface groove used in contraction joints to predetermine the position of a crack can be formed whilst casting the slab or be sawn into the hardened concrete using water-cooled circular saws. Although slightly dearer than the formed joint, sawn joints require less labour and generally give a better finish.

The curing of newly laid rigid roads and pavings is important if the concrete strength is to be maintained and the formation of surface cracks is to be avoided. Curing precautions should commence as soon as practicable after laying, preferably within 15 minutes of completion by covering the newly laid surface with a suitable material to give protection from the rapid drying effects of the sun and wind. This form of covering will also prevent unsightly pitting of the surface due to rain. Light covering materials such as waterproof paper and plastic film can be laid directly onto the concrete surface, ensuring that they are adequately secured at the edges. Plastic film can give rise to a smooth surface if the concrete is wet; this can be avoided by placing raised bearers over the surface to support the covering. Heavier coverings such as tarpaulin sheets will need to be supported on frames of timber or light metal work so that the covering is completely clear of the concrete surface. Coverings should remain in place for about seven days in warm weather and for longer periods in cold weather.

DRAINAGE

Road drainage consists of directing the surface water to suitable collection points and conveying the collected water to a suitable outfall. The surface water is encouraged to flow off the paved area by crossfalls which must be designed with sufficient gradient to cope with the volume of water likely to be encountered during a heavy storm to prevent vehicles skidding or aquaplaning. A minimum crossfall of 1 : 40 is generally specified for urban roads and motorways whereas crossfalls of between 1 : 40 and 1 : 60 are common specifications for service roads. The run-off water is directed towards the edges of the

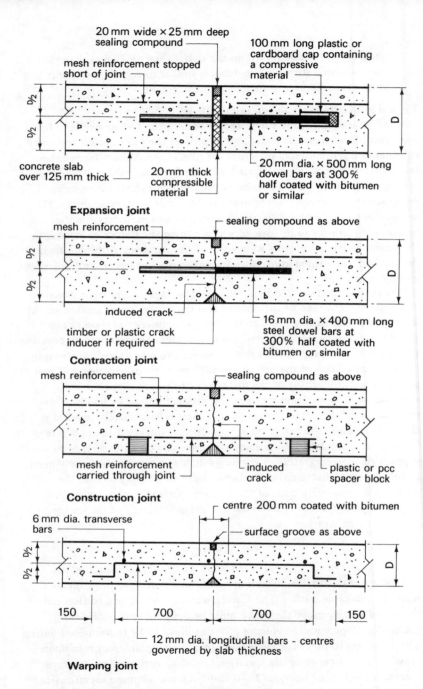

Fig. IV.19 Typical road joint details

road where it is in turn conveyed by gutters or drainage channels at a fall of about 1 : 200 in the longitudinal direction to discharge into road gullies and thence into the surface water drains.

Road gullies are available in clayware and precast concrete with or without a trapped outlet; if final discharge is to a combined sewer the trapped outlet is required and in some areas the local authority will insist upon a trapped outlet gully for all situations. Spacing of road gullies is dependent upon the anticipated storm conditions and crossfalls but common spacings are 25 to 30 m. The gratings are usually made from cast iron, slotted and hinged to allow easy flow into the collection chamber of the gully and to allow for access for suction cleaning — see Fig. IV.20. Roads which are not bounded by kerbs can be drained by having subsoil drains beneath the verge or drained directly into a ditch or stream running alongside the road. The sizing and layout design of a road drainage system is normally covered in the services syllabus of a typical building course of study. It is for this reason such calculations are not included in this text.

FOOTPATHS AND PEDESTRIAN AREAS

These can be constructed from a wide variety of materials or in the case of a large area they can consist of a mixture of materials to form attractive layouts. Widths of footpaths will be determined by local authority planning requirements but a width of 1.200 is usually considered to be the minimum in all cases. Roads are usually separated from the adjacent footpath by a kerb of precast concrete or natural stone which by being set at a higher level than the road not only marks the boundary of both road and footpath but also acts as a means of controlling the movement of surface water by directing it along the gutter into the road gullies — see Fig. IV.21.

Flexible footpaths, like roads, are those in which for design purposes no tensile strength is taken into account. They are usually constructed in at least two layers consisting of an upper wearing course laid over a base course of tarmacadam. Wearing courses of tarmacadam and cold asphalt are used, the latter being more expensive but having better durability properties — see Fig. IV.21 for typical details. Gravel paths similar in construction to unbound road surfaces are an alternative method to the layered tarmacadam footpaths. Loose cobble areas can make an attractive edging to a footpath as an alternative to the traditional grass verge. The 30 to 125 mm diameter cobbles are laid directly onto a hardcore or similar bed and are handpacked to the required depth.

Unit pavings are a common form of footpath construction consisting of a 50 to 75 mm thick base of well-compacted hardcore laid to a minimum

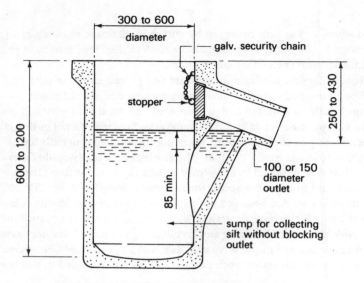

300 to 600
diameter

galv. security chain

stopper

250 to 430

600 to 1200

85 min.

100 or 150
diameter
outlet

sump for collecting
silt without blocking
outlet

BS 5911 Unreinforced concrete street gully

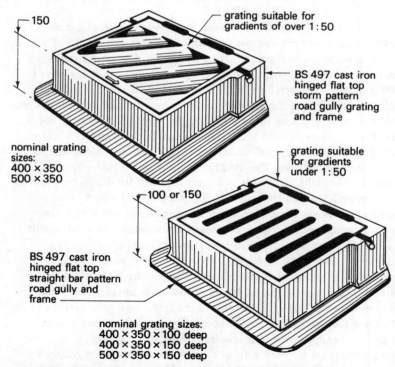

150

grating suitable for
gradients of over 1:50

BS 497 cast iron
hinged flat top
storm pattern
road gully grating
and frame

nominal grating
sizes:
400 × 350
500 × 350

grating suitable
for gradients
under 1:50

100 or 150

BS 497 cast iron
hinged flat top
straight bar pattern
road gully and
frame

nominal grating sizes:
400 × 350 × 100 deep
400 × 350 × 150 deep
500 × 350 × 150 deep

Fig. IV.20 Typical road gully and grating details

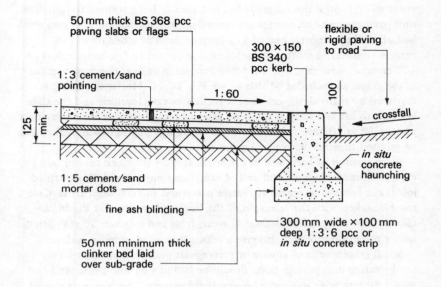

50 mm thick BS 368 pcc paving slabs or flags

1:3 cement/sand pointing

1:60

300 × 150 BS 340 pcc kerb

flexible or rigid paving to road

100

crossfall

125 min.

in situ concrete haunching

1:5 cement/sand mortar dots

fine ash blinding

50 mm minimum thick clinker bed laid over sub-grade

300 mm wide × 100 mm deep 1:3:6 pcc or in situ concrete strip

Paving slabs on mortar dots

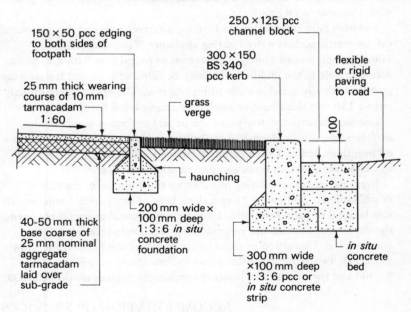

150 × 50 pcc edging to both sides of footpath

250 ×125 pcc channel block

300 × 150 BS 340 pcc kerb

flexible or rigid paving to road

25 mm thick wearing course of 10 mm tarmacadam

1:60

grass verge

100

haunching

200 mm wide × 100 mm deep 1:3:6 in situ concrete foundation

40-50 mm thick base coarse of 25 mm nominal aggregate tarmacadam laid over sub-grade

300 mm wide ×100 mm deep 1:3:6 pcc or in situ concrete strip

in situ concrete bed

Flexible footpath with grass verge

Fig. IV.21   Typical footpath details

283

crossfall of 1 : 60 if the subgrade has not already been formed to falls. The unit pavings can be of precast concrete flags or slabs laid on a 25 mm thick bed of sand or a mortar bed of 1 : 5 cement : sand or a bed of 1 : 1 : 6 cement : lime : sand mortar or each unit can be laid on five mortar dots of 1 : 5 cement : sand mix, one dot being located in each corner and one dot in the centre of each flag or slab — see Fig. IV.21. Mortar dot fixing is favoured by many designers since it facilitates easy levelling and the slabs are easy to lift and relay if the need arises. Paving flags can have a dry butt joint, a 12 to 20 mm wide soil joint to encourage plant growth or they can be grouted together with a 1 : 3 grout mix.

Brick pavings of hard well-burnt bricks laid on their bed face or laid on edge and set in a bed of sand or 1 : 4 sand : lime mortar with dry or filled joints can be used to create attractive patterned and coloured areas. Care must be taken with the selection of the bricks to ensure that the bricks chosen have adequate resistance to wear, frost and sulphate attack. Bricks with a rough texture will also give a reasonably good non-slip surface.

Small granite setts of square or rectangular plan format make a very hard wearing unit paving. Setts should be laid in a 25 mm thick sand bed with a 10 mm wide joint to a broken bond pattern. The laid setts should be well rammed and the joints should be filled with chippings and grouted with a cement : sand grout.

Firepath pots are suitable for forming a surface required for occasional vehicle traffic such as a fire-fighting appliance. Firepaths consist of 100 mm deep precast concrete hexagonal or round pots with a 175 mm diameter hole in the middle which may be filled with topsoil for growing grass or with any suitable loose filling material. The pots are laid directly onto a 150 mm thick base of ash blinded compacted hardcore.

Cobbled pavings and footpaths can be laid to form a loose cobble surface as previously described or the oval cobbles can be hand set into a 50 mm thick bed of 1 : 2 : 4 concrete having a small maximum aggregate size laid over a 50 mm thick compacted sand base layer.

Rigid pavements consisting of a 75 mm thick unreinforced slab of *in situ* concrete laid over a 75 mm thick base of compacted hardcore can also be used to form footpaths. Like their road counterparts these pavings should have expansion and contraction joints incorporated into the construction. Formation of these joints would be similar to those shown in Fig. IV.19 and for expansion joints the maximum centres would be 27.000 and for contraction joints the maximum centres would be 3.000.

ACCOMMODATION OF SERVICES

The services which may have to be accommodated under a paved area could include any or all of the following:

1. Public or private sewers.
2. Electrical supply cables.
3. Gas mains.
4. Water mains.
5. Telephone cables.
6. Television relay cables.
7. District heating mains.

In planning the layout of these services it is essential that there is adequate co-ordination between the various undertakings and bodies concerned if a logical and economical plan and installation programme is to be formulated.

Sewers are not generally grouped with other services and due to their lower flexibility are given priority of position. They can be laid under the carriageway or under the footpath or verge, the latter position creating less disturbance should repairs be necessary. The specification as to the need for ducts, covers and access positions for any particular service will be determined by the undertaking or board concerned. Most services are laid under the footpath or verge so that repairs will cause the minimum of disturbance and to take advantage of the fact that the reinstatement of a footpath is usually cheaper and easier than that of the carriageway.

Services which can be grouped together are very often laid in a common trench commencing with the laying of the lowest service and backfilling until the next service depth is reached and then repeating the procedure until all the required services have been laid. The selected granular back-filling materials should be placed in 200 to 250 mm well-compacted layers. All services should be kept at least 1.500 clear of tree trunks, any small tree roots should be cut, square trimmed and tarred. Typical common service trench details are shown in Fig. IV.22.

INTERNAL SLABS AND PAVINGS

The design and construction of a large paved area to act as a ground floor slab is similar to that already described in the context of rigid pavings. The investigation and preparation of the subgrade is similar in all aspects to the preparatory works for roads. A sub-base of well-compacted graded granular material to a thickness of 150 mm for weak subgrades and 80 mm thick for normal subgrades should be laid over the formation level. If the sub-base is to be laid before the roof covering has been completed the above thicknesses should be increased by 75 mm to counteract the effects of any adverse weather conditions. A slip membrane of 500 gauge plastic sheeting or similar material should be laid over the sub-base as described for rigid pavings for roads.

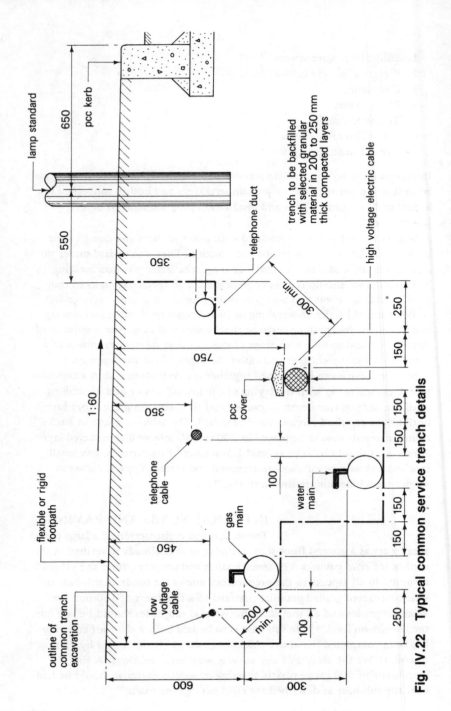

Fig. IV.22 Typical common service trench details

lamp standard

pcc kerb

650

550

350

flexible or rigid footpath

1:60

outline of common trench excavation

telephone duct

trench to be backfilled with selected granular material in 200 to 250 mm thick compacted layers

high voltage electric cable

300 min.

250

150

750

350

pcc cover

150

150

telephone cable

150

100

water main

150

450

gas main

150

low voltage cable

200 min.

100

250

600

300

286

The *in situ* concrete slab thickness is related to the load intensity, required life of the floor and the classification of the subgrade. Floors with light loadings of up to 5 kN/m^2 would require a minimum thickness of 175 mm for weak subgrades and a minimum thickness of 150 mm for normal subgrades, whereas heavier slab loadings would require minimum slab thicknesses of 200 mm for weak subgrades and 175 mm for normal subgrades. The grade of concrete specified would range from 20 N/mm^2 for offices and shops to 40 N/mm^2 for heavy industrial usages. The need, design, detail and spacing of the various types of joints is as described for rigid pavings and detailed in Fig. IV.19.

Large internal pavings or slabs are laid in bays to control the tensile stresses due to the thermal movement and contraction of the slab. Laying large areas of paving in bays is also a convenient method of dividing the work into practicable sizes. Bay widths of 4.500 will enable a two-man tamping beam to be used, and will facilitate the easy placing and finishing of the slab. This is also an ideal width for standard sheet of welded steel fabric reinforcement. Two basic bay layouts are possible, namely chequered board and long strip. Chequered board layout is where alternate bays in all directions are cast with joints formed to their perimeters. The intermediate bays are laid some seven days later to allow for some shrinkage to take place. Although this is the traditional method it has two major disadvantages in that access to the intermediate or infill bays is poor and control over shrinkage is suspect.

The long strip method of internal paving construction provides an excellent alternative and is based on established rigid road-paving techniques. The 4.500 wide strips are cast alternately which gives good access; expansion joints if required are formed along the edges; transverse contraction joints can be formed as the work proceeds or the surface groove can be sawn in at a later time. With this method it may be necessary to cast narrow edge strips some 600 to 1.000 wide at the commencement of the operation if perimeter columns or walls would hinder the use of a tamping board or beam across the full width of the first strip.

The concrete paving must be fully compacted during laying and this can be achieved by using a single or double tamping beam fitted with a suitable vibration unit. The finish required to the upper surface will depend upon the usage of the building and/or any applied finishes which are to be laid. Common methods employed are hand trowelling using steel trowels, power floating and power trowelling. The latter methods will achieve a similar result to hand trowelling but in a much shorter space of time. None of the above finishing methods can be commenced until the concrete has cured sufficiently to accept the method being used.

Vacuum dewatering is a method of reducing the time delay before power floating can take place. The object is to remove the excess water from the slab immediately after the initial compaction and levelling has taken place. The slab is covered with a fine filter sheet and a rigid or flexible suction mat to which is connected a transparent flexible plastic pipe attached to a vacuum generator. The vacuum created will compress the concrete slab and force the water to flow out up to a depth of 300 mm. The dewatering process will cause a reduction of about 2% in the slab depth and therefore a surcharge should be provided by means of packing strips on the side forms or at the ends of the tamping boards. The filter sheet will ensure that very little of the cement fines of the mix are carried along in suspension by the water being removed. The vacuum should be applied for about three minutes for every 25 mm of concrete depth which will generally mean that within approximately 20 minutes of casting the mats can be removed and the initial power floating operation commenced and followed by the final power trowelling operation. This method enables the laying of long strips of paving in a continuous operation. It is possible for a team consisting of six operatives and a ganger to complete 200 m^2 of paving per day by using this method.

Part V
Builders' plant

27
Builders' plant – general considerations

The general aim of building is to produce a structure of reasonable cost and sound workmanship within an acceptable time period. To achieve this time period and in many cases to overcome a shortage of suitable manpower the mechanisation of many building activities must be considered. The items of plant now available to building contractors is very extensive ranging from simple hand tools to very expensive equipment undertaking tasks beyond the capabilities of manual labour. In a text of this nature it is only possible to consider the general classes of plant and their uses; for a full analysis of the many variations with the different classifications, students are advised to consult the many text-books and catalogues devoted entirely to contractors' plant.

The main reasons for electing to use items of plant can be enumerated as follows:

1. Increase rate of output.
2. Reduce overall building costs.
3. Carry out activities which cannot be done manually or to do them more economically.
4. Eliminate heavy manual work thus reducing fatigue and increasing the productivity of manual workers.
5. Maintain a planned rate of production where there is a shortage of either skilled or unskilled labour.
6. Maintain the high standards often required by present-day designs and specifications especially when concerned with structural engineering works.

It must not be assumed that the introduction of plant to a contract will always reduce costs. This may well be true with large contracts but when carrying out small contracts such as a traditionally built one off house it is usually cheaper to carry out the constructional operations by traditional manual methods. The mixing of concrete and cement mortar using a small mobile batch mixer being the main exception.

The type of plant to be considered for selection will depend upon the tasks involved, the time element and the staff available. The person who selects the plant must be competent, the plant operator must be a trained man to obtain maximum efficiency, the manufacturer's recommended maintenance schedule for the plant must be followed and above all the site layout and organisation must be planned with a knowledge of the capabilities and requirements of the plant.

Having taken the decision to use a piece or pieces of plant the contractor now has the choice of buying, hiring or a combination of the two. The advantages of buying plant can be listed as follows:

1. Plant is available when required.
2. Cost of idle time caused by inclement weather, work being behind planned programme or delay in deliveries of materials will generally be less on owned plant than hired plant.
3. Builder can apportion the plant costs to the various contracts using the plant by his own chosen method.

The advantages of hiring plant can be enumerated as follows:

1. Plant can be hired as required and for short periods.
2. Hire firms are responsible for repairs and replacements.
3. Contractor is not left with expensive plant items on his hands after the completion of the contract.
4. Hire rates can include operator, fuel and oil.

Quotations and conditions of hiring plant can be obtained from a plant hiring company, a full list of companies belonging to the Contractors' Plant Association is contained in the CPA Annual Handbook. This Association was formed in 1941 to represent the plant hire industry in the United Kingdom to negotiate general terms and conditions of hiring plant, to give advice and to promote a high standard of efficiency in the services given by its members. Against plant hire rates and conditions a contractor will have to compare the cost of buying and owning a similar piece of plant. A comparison of costs can be calculated by the simple straight line method or by treating the plant as an investment and charging interest on the capital outlay.

Straight line method:

Capital cost of plant	£4 500.00
Expected useful life	5 years
Yearly working, say 75% of total year's working hours	$= 50 \text{ weeks} \times 40 \text{ hours} \times \dfrac{75}{100}$
	$= 1\ 500$ hours per year

Assuming a resale value at the end of the 5-year period of £750.00

$$\text{Annual depreciation} = \frac{4\ 500 - 750}{5} = £750.00$$

$$\text{Therefore hourly depreciation} = \frac{750}{1\ 500} = 50\text{p}$$

Net cost per hour	= 50p
Add 2% for insurance, etc.	= 1p
Add 10% for maintenance	= 5p
Total	56p per hour

To the above figure must be added the running costs which would include fuel, operator's wages and overheads.

Interest on capital outlay method:

Capital cost of plant	£4 500.00
Interest on capital − 6% for 5 years	1 350.00
	£5 850.00
Deduct resale value	750.00
	£5 100.00
Add 2% of capital cost for insurance, etc.	90.00
Add 10% of capital cost for maintenance	450.00
	£5 640.00

$$\text{Therefore cost per hour} = \frac{5\ 640}{5 \times 1\ 500} = 75\text{p}$$

To the above hourly rate must be added the running costs as given for the straight line method. This second method gives a more accurate figure to the actual cost of owning an item of plant than the straight line method and for this reason it is widely used.

Vehicles such as lorries and vans are usually costed on a straight annual depreciation of the yearly book value thus:

Cost of vehicle	£2 500.00
Estimated useful life, 5 years	
Annual depreciation, 30%	
Capital cost	£2 500.00
30% depreciation	750.00

Value after 1st year	1 750.00
30% depreciation	525.00
Value after 2nd year	1 225.00
30% depreciation	367.50
Value after 3rd year	857.50
30% depreciation	257.25
Value after 4th year	600.25
30% depreciation	180.08
Value at 5th year	£420.17

The percentages of insurance and maintenance together with the running costs can now be added on a yearly basis taking the new book values for each year, or alternatively the above additional costs could be averaged over the five-year period.

To be an economic proposition large items of plant need to be employed continuously and not left idle for considerable periods of time. Careful maintenance of all forms of plant is of the utmost importance not only to increase the working life of a piece of plant but if a plant failure occurs on site it can cause serious delays and disruptions of the programme and this in turn can affect the company's future planning. To reduce the risk of plant breakdown a trained and skilled operator should be employed to be responsible for the running, cleaning and daily maintenance of any form of machinery. Time for the machine operator to carry out these tasks must be allowed for in the site programme and the daily work schedules.

On a large contract where a number of machines are to be employed a full-time skilled mechanic could be engaged to be responsible for running repairs and recommended preventive maintenance. Such tasks would include:

1. Checking oil levels – daily.
2. Greasing – daily or after each shift.
3. Checking engine sump levels – after 100 hours running time.
4. Checking gearbox levels – after 1 200 to 1 500 hours running time.
5. Checking tyre pressures – daily.
6. Inspecting chains and ropes – daily.

As soon as a particular item of plant has finished its work on site it should be returned to the company's main plant yard so that it can be re-allocated to another contract. On its return to the main plant yard an item of plant should be inspected and tested so that any necessary repairs, replacements and maintenance can be carried out before it is re-employed on another site. A record of the machine's history should be accurately kept and should accompany the machine wherever it is employed so that the record can be kept up-to-date.

The soil conditions and modes of access to a site will often influence the choice of plant items which could be considered for a particular task. Congested town sites may severely limit the use of many types of machinery and/or plant. If the proposed structure occupies the whole of the site it could eliminate the use of large batch concrete mixers, dumpers and cement storage silos. Wet sites usually require plant equipped with caterpillar tracks whereas dry sites are suitable for tracked and wheeled vehicles or power units. On housing sites it is common practice to construct the estate roads at an early stage in the contract to provide the firm access routes for mobile plant and hardstanding for static plant such as cement mixers. Sloping sites are usually unsuitable for rail-mounted cranes but these cranes operating on the perimeter of a building are more versatile than the static cranes. The heights and proximity of adjacent structures or buildings may limit the use of a horizontal jib crane and may even dictate the use of a crane with a luffing jib.

For accurate pricing of a Bill of Quantities careful consideration of all plant requirements must be undertaken at the pre-tender stage taking into account plant types, plant numbers and personnel needed. If the tender is successful a detailed programme should be prepared in liaison with all those to be concerned in the supervision of the contract so that the correct sequence of operations is planned and an economic balance of labour and machines is obtained.

Apart from the factors discussed above consideration must also be given to safety and noise emission requirements when selecting items of plant for use on a particular contract. The aspects of safety which must be legally provided are contained in various Acts of Parliament and Statutory Instruments such as the Health and Safety at Work, etc., Act 1974 and the Construction Regulations. These requirements will be considered in the following chapters devoted to various classifications of plant.

Although reaction to noise is basically subjective excessive noise can damage a person's health and/or hearing, it can also cause disturbance to working and living environments. Under the Health and Safety at Work, etc., Act 1974 provision is made for the protection of workers against noise. The maximum safe daily dosages of noise for the unprotected human ear are given in the recommendations of the relevant Department of Employment Code of Practice for reducing the exposure of employed persons to noise. If these daily dosages are likely to be exceeded the remedies available are the issue of suitable ear protectors to the workers or to use quieter plant or processes.

Local authorities have powers under the Control of Pollution Act 1974 to protect the community against noise. Part III of this Act gives the local authority the power to specify its own requirements as to the limit of construction noise acceptable by serving a notice which may specify:

1. Plant or machinery which is, or is not, to be used.
2. Hours during which the works may be carried out.
3. Level of noise emitted from the premises in question or from any specific point on these premises or the level of noise which may be emitted during specified hours.

The local authority is also allowed to make provisions in these notices for any change of circumstance.

A contractor will therefore need to know the local authority requirements as to noise restrictions at the pre-tender stage to enable him to select the right plant and/or process to be employed. Methods for predicting site noise are given in BS 5228 Code of Practice, Noise Control on Construction and Demolition sites. This Code outlines the working of the controlling Act, gives noise outputs of some 150 plant items and also gives the procedure for predicting site noise in terms of equivalent continuous sound levels as well as maximum sound levels. These are the levels which local authorities use when specifying construction noise limits.

28
Small powered plant

A precise definition of builders' small powered plant is not possible since the term 'small' is relative. For example, it is possible to have small cranes but these when compared with a hand-held electric drill would be considered as large plant items. Generally therefore small plant can be considered to be hand held or operated power tools with their attendant power sources such as a compressor for pneumatic tools, one of the main exceptions being the small static pumps used in conjunction with shallow excavations.

Most hand-held power tools are operated by electricity or compressed air either to rotate the tool or drive it by percussion. Some of these tools are also designed to act as rotary/percussion tools. Generally the pneumatic tools are used for the heavier work and have the advantage that they will not burn out if a rotary tool stalls under load. Electrically driven tools are however relatively quiet since there is no exhaust noise and can be used in confined spaces because there are no exhaust fumes.

ELECTRIC HAND TOOLS
The most common hand-held tool is the electric drill for boring holes into timber, masonry and metals using twist drills. A wide range of twist drill capacities are available with single- or two-speed motors for general purpose work, the low speed being used for boring into or through timber. Chuck capacities generally available range from 6 to 30 mm for twist drills suitable for metals. Dual purpose electric drills are very versatile in that the rotary motion can be combined with or converted into a powerful but rapid percussion motion making the tool

297

suitable for boring into concrete providing that special tungsten carbide-tipped drills are used — see Fig. V.1.

A variation of the basic electric motor power units is the electric hammer which is used for cutting and chasing work where the hammer delivers powerful blows at a slower rate than the percussion drill described above. Another variation is the electric screwdriver which has an adjustable and sensitive clutch which will only operate when the screwdriver bit is in contact with the screw head and will slip when a predetermined tension has been reached when the screw has been driven in. Various portable electric woodworking tools such as circular saws, jigsaws, sanders, planes and routers are also available and suitable for site use.

Electric hand-held tools should preferably operate off a reduced voltage supply of 110 V and should conform to the recommendations of BS 2769. All these tools should be earthed unless they bear the 'two squares' symbol indicating that they are 'All Insulated' or 'Double Insulated' and therefore have their own built-in safety system. Plugs and couplers should comply with BS 4343 so that they are not interchangeable and cannot be connected to the wrong voltage supply. Protective guards and any recommended protective clothing such as goggles and ear protection should be used as instructed by the manufacturers and as laid down in the Construction (General Provisions) Regulations 1961 and in accordance with the Protection of Eyes Regulations 1974. Electric power tools must never be switched off whilst under load since this could cause the motor to become overstrained and burnt out. If electrical equipment is being used on a site the Electricity Regulations and relevant first-aid placards should be displayed in a prominent position.

PNEUMATIC TOOLS

These tools need a supply of compressed air as their power source and on building sites this is generally in the form of a mobile compressor powered by a diesel, petrol or electric motor, the most common power unit being the diesel engine. Compressors for building works are usually of the piston or reciprocating type where the air is drawn into a cylinder and compressed by a single stroke of the piston; alternatively two-stage compressors are available where the air is compressed to an intermediate level in a large cylinder before passing to a smaller cylinder where the final pressure is obtained. Air receivers are usually incorporated with and mounted on the chassis to provide a constant source of pressure for the air lines and to minimise losses due to pressure fluctuations of the compressor and/or frictional losses due to the air pulsating through the distribution hoses.

One of the most common pneumatic tools used in building is the

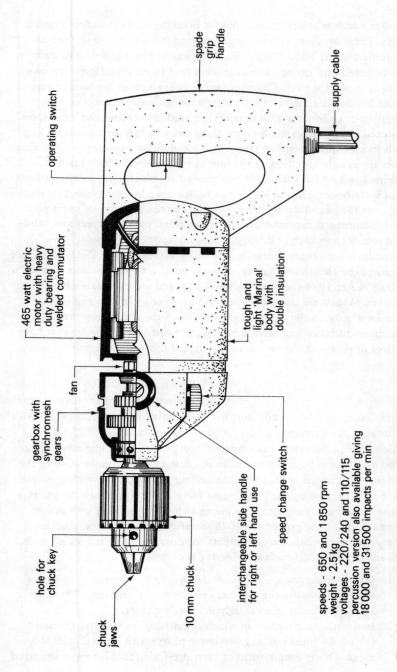

Fig. V.1 Typical electric drill (Stanley-Bridges Ltd)

spade grip handle

supply cable

operating switch

465 watt electric motor with heavy duty bearing and welded commutator

tough and light 'Marinal' body with double insulation

gearbox with synchromesh gears

fan

hole for chuck key

chuck jaws

10 mm chuck

interchangeable side handle for right or left hand use

speed change switch

speeds - 650 and 1850 rpm
weight - 2.5 kg
voltages - 220/240 and 110/115
percussion version also available giving
18 000 and 31 500 impacts per min

breaker which is basically intended for breaking up hard surfaces such as roads. These breakers vary in weight ranging from 15 to 40 kg with air consumptions of 10 to 20 m^3/min. A variety of breaker points or cutters can be fitted into the end of the breaker tool to tackle different types of surfaces — see Fig. V.2. Chipping hammers are a small lightweight version of the breaker described above having a low air consumption of 0.5 m^3/min or less. Backfill tampers are used to compact the loose spoil returned as backfill in small excavations and weigh approximately 23 kg with an air consumption of 10 m^3/min. Compressors to supply air to these tools are usually specified by the number of air hoses which can be attached and by the volume of compressed air which can be delivered per minute. Other equipment which can be operated by compressed air include vibrators for consolidating concrete, small trench sheeting or sheet pile driving hammers, concrete spraying equipment, paint sprayers and hand-held rotary tools such as drills, grinders and saws.

Pneumatic tools are generally very noisy and in view of the legal requirements of the Health and Safety at Work, etc., Act 1974 and the Control of Pollution Act 1974 these tools should be fitted with a suitable muffler or silencer. Models are being designed and produced with built-in silencers fitted not only on the tool holder but also on the compressor unit. The mufflers which can be fitted to pneumatic tools such as the breaker have no loss of power effect on the tool provided the correct muffler is used.

CARTRIDGE HAMMERS

Cartridge hammers or guns are used for the quick fixing together of components or for firing into a surface a pin with a threaded head to act as a bolt fixing. The gun actuates a 0.22 cartridge which drives a hardened austempered steel pin into an unprepared surface. Holding power is basically mechanical, caused by the compression of the material penetrated against the shank of the pin, although with concrete the heat generated by the penetrating force of the pin causes the silicates in the concrete to fuse into glass giving a chemical bond as well as the mechanical holding power. BS 4078 specifies the design, construction, safety and performance requirements for cartridge-operated fixing tools, this standard also defines two basic types of tool:

1. Direct-acting tools — in which the driving force on the pin comes directly from the compressed gases from the cartridge. These tools are high velocity guns with high muzzle energy.
2. Indirect-acting tools — in which the driving force is transmitted to the pin by means of an intervening piston with limited axial movement. This common form of cartridge-fixing tool is trigger operated

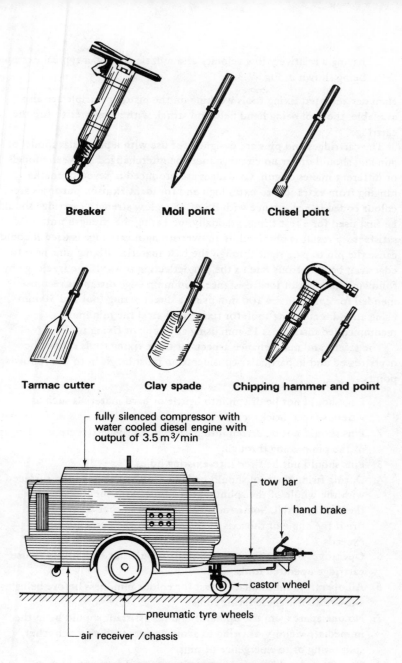

Breaker **Moil point** **Chisel point**

Tarmac cutter **Clay spade** **Chipping hammer and point**

fully silenced compressor with
water cooled diesel engine with
output of 3.5 m³/min

tow bar

hand brake

castor wheel

pneumatic tyre wheels

air receiver /chassis

Typical 2 tool silenced compressor

Fig. V.2 Typical pneumatic tools and compressor

301

having a relatively low velocity and muzzle energy, a typical example being shown in Fig. V.3.

Hammer-actuated fixing tools working on the piston principle are also available, the tool being hand held and struck with a hammer to fire the cartridge.

The cartridges and pins are designed for use with a particular model of gun and should under no circumstances be interchanged between models or different makes of gun. Cartridges are produced in seven strengths ranging from extra low to extra high and for identification purposes are colour coded in accordance with BS 4078. A low strength cartridge should be first used for a test firing, gradually increasing the strength until a satisfactory result is obtained. If an over-strength cartridge is used it could cause the pin to pass right through the base material. Fixing pins near to edges can be dangerous due to the pin deflecting towards the free edge by following the path of low resistance. Minimum edge distances recommended for concrete are 100 mm using a direct-acting tool and 50 mm using an indirect-acting tool; for fixing into steel the minimum recommended distance is 15 mm using any type of fixing tool.

The safety and maintenance aspects of these fixing tools cannot be overstressed and in particular consideration must be given to the following points:

1. Pins should not be driven into brittle or hard materials such as vitreous-faced bricks, cast iron and marble.
2. Pins should not be driven into base materials where there is a danger of the pin passing through.
3. Pins should not be fired into existing holes.
4. During firing the tool should be held at right angles to the surface with the whole of the splinter guard flush with the surface of the base material. Some tools are designed so that they will not fire if the angle of the axis of the gun with the perpendicular exceeds 7°.
5. Operatives under the age of 18 years should not be allowed to use cartridge-operated tools.
6. All operators should have a test for colour blindness before being allowed to use these fixing tools.
7. No one apart from the operator and his assistant should be in the immediate vicinity of firing to avoid accidents due to richochet, splintering or re-emergence of pins.
8. Operators should receive instructions as to the manufacturers' recommended method of loading, firing and the action to be taken in cases of misfiring.

302

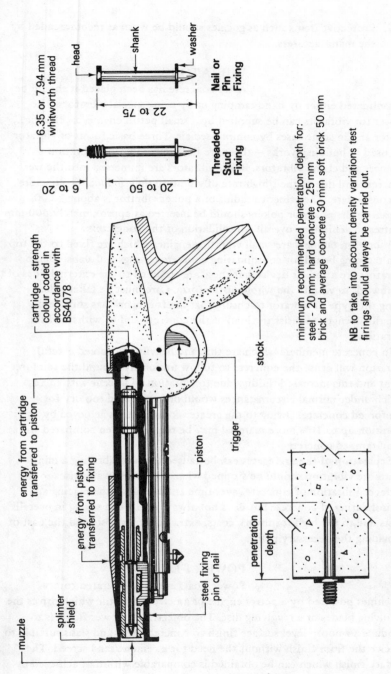

Fig. V.3 Typical cartridge hammer (Douglas Kane Group Ltd)

head

shank

washer

6.35 or 7.94 mm whitworth thread

22 to 75

Nail or Pin Fixing

20 to 50

6 to 20

Threaded Stud Fixing

cartridge - strength colour coded in accordance with BS4078

minimum recommended penetration depth for:
steel - 20 mm; hard concrete - 25 mm
brick and average concrete 30 mm soft brick 50 mm

NB to take into account density variations test firings should always be carried out.

stock

energy from cartridge transferred to piston

energy from piston transferred to fixing

trigger

piston

steel fixing pin or nail

muzzle

splinter shield

penetration depth

9. Protective items such as goggles should be worn as recommended by the manufacturers.

VIBRATORS

After concrete has been placed it should be consolidated either by hand tamping or by using special vibrators. The power for vibrators can be supplied by a small petrol engine, an electric motor and in some cases by compressed air. Three basic forms of vibrator are used in building works — these are the poker vibrator, vibration tampers and clamp vibrators. Poker vibrators are immersed into the wet concrete and due to their high rate of vibration they induce the concrete to consolidate. The effective radius of a poker vibrator is about 1.000, therefore the poker or pokers should be inserted at approximately 600 mm centres to achieve an overall consolidation of the concrete.

Vibration tampers are small vibrating engines which are fixed to the top of a tamping board for consolidating concrete pavings and slabs. Clamp vibrators are a similar device but these are attached to the external sides of formwork to vibrate the whole of the form. Care must be taken when using this type of vibrator to ensure that the formwork has sufficient in-built strength to resist the load of the concrete and to withstand the vibrations.

In concrete members which are thin and heavily reinforced careful vibration will cause the concrete to follow uniformly around the reinforcement and this increased fluidity due to vibration will occur with mixes which under normal circumstances would be considered too dry for reinforced concrete. Owing to the greater consolidation achieved by vibration up to 10% more material may be required when compared with hand-tamped concrete.

Separation of the aggregates can be caused by over vibrating a mix; therefore vibration should be stopped when the excess water rises to the surface. Vibration of concrete saves time and labour in the placing and consolidating of concrete but does not always result in a saving in overall costs due to the high formwork costs, extra materials costs and the cost of providing the necessary plant.

POWER FLOATS

Power floats are hand-operated rotary machines powered by a petrol engine or an electric motor which drives the revolving blades or a revolving disc. The objective of power floats is to produce a smooth level surface finish to concrete beds and slabs suitable to receive the floor finish without the need for a cement/sand screed. The surface finish which can be obtained is comparable with that achieved by craftsmen using hand trowels but takes only one-sixth of the time giving a considerable saving in both time and money. Most power floats can be fitted with either a revolving disc or blade head and are generally interchangeable.

The surfacing disc is used for surface planing after the concrete has been vibrated and will erase any transverse tamping line marks left by a vibrator beam as well as filling in any small cavities in the concrete surface. The revolving blades are used after the disc planing operation to provide the finishing and polishing which can usually be achieved with two passings. The time at which disc planing can be started is difficult to specify, depending on factors such as the workability of the concrete, temperature, relative humidity and the weight of the machine to be used. Experience is usually the best judge but as a guide if imprints of not more than 2 to 4 mm deep are made in the concrete when walked upon it is generally suitable for disc planing. It should be noted that if a suitable surface can be produced by traditional concrete placing method the disc planing operation prior to rotary blade finishing is often omitted. Generally blade finishing can be commenced once the surface water has evaporated, a typical power float being shown in Fig. V.4. Power floats can also be used for finishing concrete floors with a granolithic or similar topping.

PUMPS

Pumps are one of the most important items of small plant for the building contractor since they must be reliable in all conditions, easy to maintain, easily transported and efficient. The basic function of a pump is to move liquids vertically or horizontally or in a combination of the two directions. Before selecting a pump a builder must consider what task the pump is to perform and this could be any of the following:

1. Keeping excavations free from water.
2. Lowering the water table to a reasonable depth.
3. Moving large quantities of water such as the dewatering of a cofferdam.
4. Supplying water for general purposes.

Having defined the task the pump is required to carry out, the next step is to choose a suitable pump taking into account the following factors:

1. Volume of water to be moved.
2. Rate at which water is to be pumped.
3. Height of pumping which is the vertical distance from the level of the water to the pump and is usually referred to as 'suction lift' or

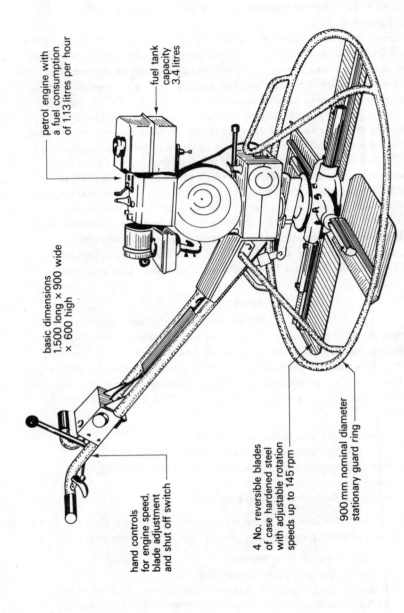

petrol engine with
a fuel consumption
of 1.13 litres per hour

fuel tank
capacity
3.4 litres

basic dimensions
1.500 long × 900 wide
× 600 high

hand controls
for engine speed,
blade adjustment
and shut off switch

4 No. reversible blades
of case hardened steel
with adjustable rotation
speeds up to 145 rpm

900 mm nominal diameter
stationary guard ring

Fig. V.4 Typical power float (Construction Equipment and Machinery (Gt. Briatin) Ltd)

head and should be the shortest distance practicable to obtain economic pumping.

4. Height and distance to outfall or discharge point and is usually called the 'delivery head'.
5. Loss due to friction in the length of hose or pipe which increases as the diameter decreases. In many pumps the suction and delivery hoses are marginally larger in diameter than the pump inlet to reduce these frictional losses.
6. Power source for pump which can be a petrol engine, diesel engine or an electric motor. Pumps powered by compressed air are available but these are unusual on general building contracts.

Pumps in common use for general building works can be classified as follows:

1. Centrifugal.
2. Displacement.
3. Submersible.

Centrifugal pumps: classed as normal or self-priming and consist of a rotary impeller which revolves at high speed forcing the water to the sides of the impeller chamber thus creating a vortex which sucks air out of the suction hose. Atmospheric pressure acting on the surface of the water to be pumped causes the water to rise into the pump initiating the pumping operation. Normal centrifugal pumps are easy to maintain but they require priming with water at the commencement of each pumping operation. Where continuous pumping is required such as in a basement excavation a self-priming pump should be specified. These pumps have a reserve supply of water in the impeller chamber so that if the pump runs dry the reserve water supply will remain in the chamber to reactivate the pumping sequence if the water level rises in the area being pumped.

Displacement pumps: either reciprocating or diaphragm pumps. Reciprocating pumps work by the action of a piston or ram moving within a cylinder. The action of the piston draws water into the cylinder with one stroke and forces it out with the return stroke, resulting in a pulsating delivery. Pumps of this type can have more than one cylinder, forming what is called a duplex (two-cylinder) or a triplex (three-cylinder) pump. Some reciprocating pumps draw water into the cylinder in front of the piston and discharge at the rear of the piston and are called double-acting pumps as opposed to the single-acting pumps where the water moves in one direction only with the movement of the piston. Although highly efficient and capable of increased capacity with increased engine speed these pumps have the disadvantage of being unable to handle water containing solids.

Displacement pumps of the diaphragm type can however handle liquids containing 10 to 15% of solids which makes them very popular. They work on the principle of raising and lowering a flexible diaphragm of rubber or rubberised canvas within a cylinder by means of a pump rod connected via a rocker bar to an engine crank. The upward movement of the diaphragm causes water to be sucked into the cylinder through a valve; the downward movement of the diaphragm closes the inlet valve and forces the water out through another valve into the delivery hose. Diaphragm or lift and force pumps are available with two cylinders and two diaphragms giving greater output and efficiency — typical pump examples are shown in Fig. V.5.

Submersible pumps: used for extracting water from deep wells and sumps (see Fig. II.41) and are suspended in the water to be pumped. The power source is usually an electric motor to drive a centrifugal unit which is housed in a casing with an annular space to allow the water to rise upwards into the delivery pipe or rising main. Alternatively an electric submersible pump with a diaphragm arrangement can be used where large quantities of water are not involved.

ROLLERS
Rollers are designed to consolidate filling materials and to compact surface finishes such as tarmacadam for paths and pavings. The roller equipment used by building contractors is basically a smaller version of the large rollers used by civil engineering contractors for roadworks. Rollers generally rely upon deadweight to carry out the consolidating operation or by vibration as in the case of lightweight rollers. Deadweight rollers are usually diesel powered and driven by a seated operator within a cab. These machines can be obtained with weights ranging from 1 to 16 tonnes which is distributed to the ground through two large diameter rear wheels and a wider but small front steering-wheel. Many of these rollers carry water tanks to add to the dead load and to supply small sparge or sprinkler pipes fixed over the wheels to dampen the surfaces thus preventing the adhesion of tar or similar material when being rolled. These rollers are also available fitted with a scarifier to the rear of the vehicle for ripping up the surfaces of beds or roads — see Fig. V.6.

Vibrating rollers which depend mainly upon the vibrations produced by the petrol- or diesel-powered engine can be hand guided or towed and are available with weights ranging from 500 kg to 5 tonnes — see Fig. V.6. These machines will give the same degree of consolidation and compaction as their heavier deadweight counterparts, but being lighter and smaller they

308

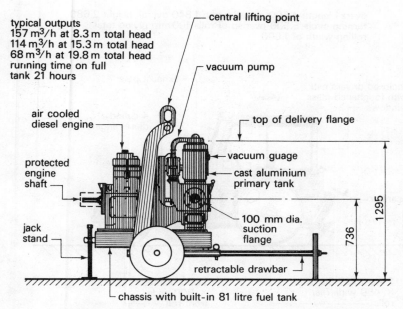

typical outputs
157 m³/h at 8.3 m total head
114 m³/h at 15.3 m total head
68 m³/h at 19.8 m total head
running time on full
tank 21 hours

central lifting point

vacuum pump

top of delivery flange

air cooled
diesel engine

vacuum guage

cast aluminium
primary tank

protected
engine
shaft

100 mm dia.
suction
flange

jack
stand

1295

736

retractable drawbar

chassis with built-in 81 litre fuel tank

Typical self priming centrifugal pump (Sykes Pumps Ltd)

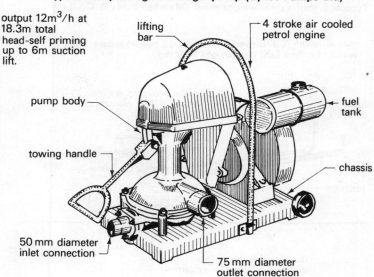

output 12m³/h at
18.3m total
head-self priming
up to 6m suction
lift.

lifting
bar

4 stroke air cooled
petrol engine

pump body

fuel
tank

towing handle

chassis

50 mm diameter
inlet connection

75 mm diameter
outlet connection

Typical diaphragm pump (William R Selwood Ltd)

Fig. V.5   Typical pumps

overall length 4.500 overall width 1.840 overall height 2.680
turning circle 5.500 overlap of rolls 100 mm giving total
rolling width of 1.600

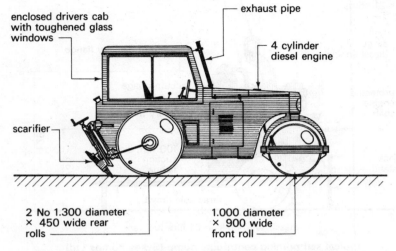

enclosed drivers cab
with toughened glass
windows

exhaust pipe

4 cylinder
diesel engine

scarifier

2 No 1.300 diameter
× 450 wide rear
rolls

1.000 diameter
× 900 wide
front roll

Typical 6 tonne deadweight roller (Marshall Sons & Co. Ltd)

overall length 3.376 overall width 1.092 overall height 1.092
width of rollers 890 deadweight 1 250 kg

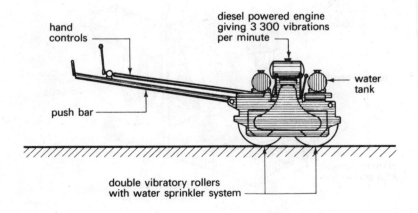

hand
controls

diesel powered engine
giving 3 300 vibrations
per minute

water
tank

push bar

double vibratory rollers
with water sprinkler system

Typical vibrating roller (Duomat R90)

Fig. V.6   Typical rollers

can be manoeuvred into buildings for consolidating small areas of hardcore or similar bed material. Single or double rollers are available with or without water sprinkler attachments and with vibrations within the region of 3 000 vibrations per minute. Vibrating rollers are particularly effective for the compaction and consolidation of granular soils.

29
Earth-moving and excavation plant

The selection, management and maintenance of builders' plant is particularly important when considered in the context of earth-moving and excavation plant. Before deciding to use any form of plant for these activities the site conditions and volume of work entailed must be such that it will be an economic venture. The difference between plant which is classified as earth-moving equipment and excavating machines is very narrow since a piece of plant which is designed primarily to excavate will also be capable of moving the spoil to an attendant transporting vehicle and likewise machines basically designed to move loose earth will also be capable of carrying out to some degree excavation works.

To browse through the catalogues of plant manufacturers and hirers to try and select a particular piece of plant is a bewildering exercise because of the wide variety of choice available for all classes of plant. Final choice is usually based upon experience, familiarity with a particular manufacturer's machines, availability or personal preference. There are many excellent works of reference devoted entirely to the analysis of the various machines to aid the would-be buyer or hirer; therefore in a text of this nature it is only necessary to consider the general classes of plant, pointing out their intended uses and amplifying this with typical examples of the various types without claiming that the example chosen is the best of its type but only representative.

BULLDOZERS AND ANGLEDOZERS

These machines are primarily a high-powered tractor with caterpillar or crawler tracks fitted with a mould board or

312

blade at the front for stripping and oversite excavations up to a depth of 400 mm (depending upon machine specification) by pushing the loosened material ahead of the machine. For back-filling operations the angledozer with its mould board set at an angle, in plan, to the machine's centre line can be used. Most mould boards can be set at an angle either in the vertical or horizontal plane to act as an angledozer and on some models the leading edge of the mould board can be fitted with teeth for excavating in hard ground. These machines can be very large with mould boards of 1.200 to 4.000 in width x 600 mm to 1.200 in height with a depth of cut up to 400 mm. Most bulldozers and angledozers are mounted on crawler tracks, although small bulldozers with a wheeled base are available. The control of the mould board on most models is hydraulic, the alternative being a winch and wire cable control system − for typical example see Fig. V.7. In common with other tracked machines one of the disadvantages of this arrangement is the need for a special transporting vehicle such as a low loader to move the equipment between sites.

Before any earth-moving work is started a drawing should be produced indicating the areas and volumes of cut and fill required to enable a programme to be prepared to reduce machine movements to a minimum. When large quantities of earth have to be moved on a cut and fill basis to form a predetermined level or gradient it is good practice to draw up a mass haul diagram indicating the volumes of earth to be moved, the direction of movement and the need to import more spoil or alternatively cart away the surplus − see Fig. V.8 for typical example.

SCRAPERS

This piece of plant consists of a power unit and a scraper bowl and is used to excavate and transport soil where surface stripping, site levelling and cut and fill activities are planned, particularly where large volumes are involved. These machines are capable of producing a very smooth and accurate formation level and come in three basic types:

1. Crawler-drawn scraper.
2. Two-axle scraper.
3. Three-axle scraper.

The design and basic operation of the scraper bowl is similar in all three types, consisting of a shaped bowl with a cutting edge which can be lowered to cut the top surface of the soil up to a depth of 300 mm. As the bowl moves forward the loosened earth is forced into the container and when full the cutting edge is raised to seal the bowl. To ensure that a full load is obtained many contractors use a bulldozer to act as a pusher over

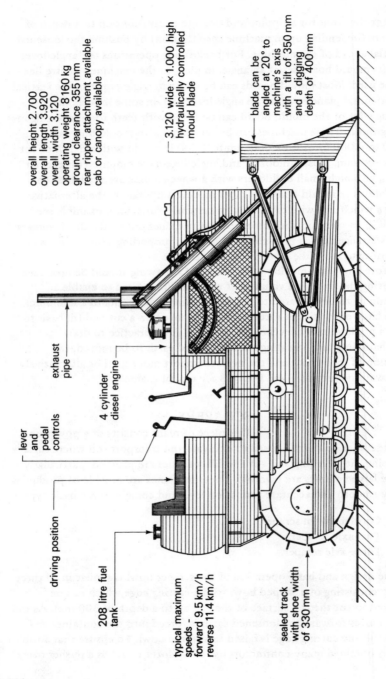

overall height 2.700
overall length 3.920
overall width 3.120
operating weight 8 160 kg
ground clearance 355 mm
rear ripper attachment available
cab or canopy available

3.120 wide × 1.000 high
hydraulically controlled
mould blade

blade can be
angled at 20° to
machine's axis
with a tilt of 350 mm
and a digging
depth of 400 mm

exhaust
pipe

lever
and
pedal
controls

4 cylinder
diesel engine

driving position

208 litre fuel
tank

typical maximum
speeds -
forward 9.5 km/h
reverse 11.4 km/h

sealed track
with shoe width
of 330 mm

Fig. V.7 Typical tractor powered bulldozer details (Caterpiller Tractor Co.)

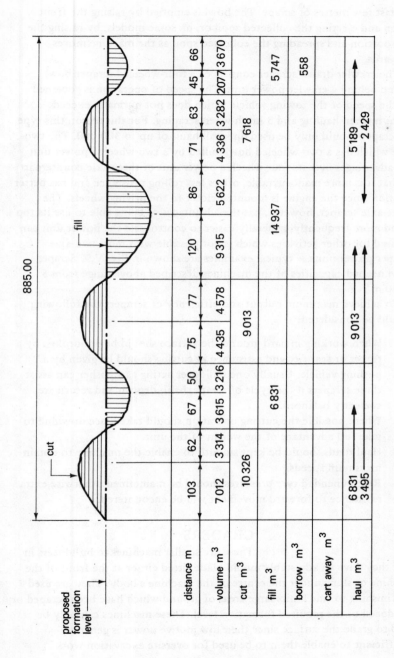

Fig. V.8 Typical mass haul diagram

the last few metres of scrape. The bowl is emptied by raising the front apron and ejecting the collected spoil or, on some models, by raising the rear portion and spreading the collected spoil as the machine moves forwards.

The crawler-drawn scraper consists of a four-wheeled scraper bowl towed behind a crawler power unit. The speed of operation is governed by the speed of the towing vehicle which does not normally exceed 8 km/h when hauling and 3 km/h when scraping. For this reason this type of scraper should only be used on small hauls of up to 300.000. The two-axle which has a two-wheeled bowl pulled by a two-wheeled power unit has advantages over its four-wheeled power unit or three-axle counterpart in that it is more manoeuvrable, offers less rolling resistance and has better traction since the engine is mounted closer to the driving wheels. The three-axle scraper, however, has the advantages of being able to use its top speed more frequently, generally easier to control and the power unit can be used for other activities which is not possible with most two-axle scraper power units — typical examples are shown in Fig. V.9. Scraper bowl heaped capacities of the machines described above range from 5 to 50 m^3.

To achieve maximum output and efficiency of scrapers the following should be considered:

1. When working in hard ground the surface should be pre-broken by a ripper or scarifier and assistance in cutting should be given by a pushing vehicle. Usually one bulldozer acting as a pusher can assist three scrapers if the cycle of scrape, haul, deposit and return are correctly balanced.
2. Where possible the cutting operation should take place downhill to take full advantage of the weight of the unit.
3. Haul roads should be kept smooth to enable the machine to obtain maximum speeds.
4. Recommended tyre pressures should be maintained otherwise extra resistance to forward movement will be encountered.

GRADERS

These are similar machines to bulldozers in that they have an adjustable mould blade fitted either at the front of the machine or slung under the centre of the machine's body. They are used for finishing to fine limits large areas of ground which have been scraped or bulldozed to the required formation level. These machines can only be used to grade the surface since their low motive power is generally insufficient to enable them to be used for oversite excavation work.

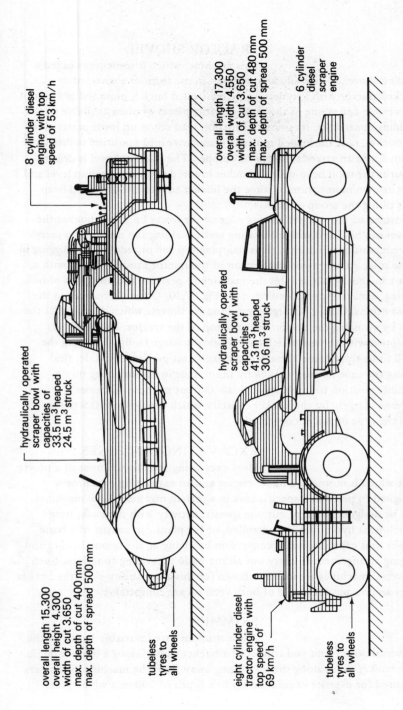

8 cylinder diesel engine with top speed of 53 km/h

hydraulically operated scraper bowl with capacities of 33.5 m³ heaped 24.5 m³ struck

overall length 15.300
overall height 4.300
width of cut 3.650
max. depth of cut 400 mm
max. depth of spread 500 mm

eight cylinder diesel tractor engine with top speed of 69 km/h

tubeless tyres to all wheels

6 cylinder diesel scraper engine

overall length 17.300
overall width 4.550
width of cut 3.650
max. depth of cut 480 mm
max. depth of spread 500 mm

hydraulically operated scraper bowl with capacities of 41.3 m³ heaped 30.6 m³ struck

tubeless tyres to all wheels

Fig. V.9 Typical 2 and 3 axle scraper details (Caterpiller Tractor Co.)

TRACTOR SHOVEL

This machine, which is sometimes called a loading shovel, is basically a power unit in the form of a wheeled or tracked tractor with a hydraulically controlled bucket mounted in front of the vehicle and is one of the most versatile pieces of plant available to the building contractor. Its primary function is to scoop up loose material in the bucket, raise the loaded spoil and manoeuvre into a position to discharge its load into an attendant lorry or dumper. The tractor shovel is driven towards the spoil heap with its bucket lowered almost to ground level and uses its own momentum to force the bucket to bite into the spoil heap thus filling the scoop or bucket.

Instead of the straight cutting edge to the lower lip of the bucket the shovel can be fitted with excavating teeth enabling the machine to carry out excavating activities such as stripping top soil or reduce level digging in loose soils. Another popular version of the tractor shovel is fitted with a 4-in-1 bucket which enables the machine to perform the functions of bulldozing, excavating and loading — see Fig. V.10. Other alternatives to the conventional front-discharging machine are shovels which discharge at the rear by swinging the bucket over the top of the tractor, and machines equipped with shovels which have a side discharge facility enabling the spoil to be tipped into the attendant haul unit parked alongside, thus saving the time normally taken by the tractor in manoeuvring into a suitable position to discharge its load. Output of these machines is governed largely by the bucket capacity which can be from 0.5 to 4 m^3 and the type of soil encountered.

EXCAVATING MACHINES

Most excavating machines consist of a power unit which is normally a diesel engine and an excavating attachment designed to perform a specific task in a certain manner. These machines can be designed to carry out one specific activity with the excavating attachment hydraulically controlled, or the plant can consist of a basic power unit capable of easy conversion by changing the boom, bucket and rigging arrangement to carry out all the basic excavating functions. Such universal machines are usually chosen for this adaptability since the bucket sizes and outputs available of both versions are comparable.

SKIMMER

These machines are invariably based on the universal power unit and consist of a bucket sliding along a horizontal jib. The bucket slides along the jib digging away from the machine. Skimmers are used for oversite excavation up to a depth of 300 mm where great

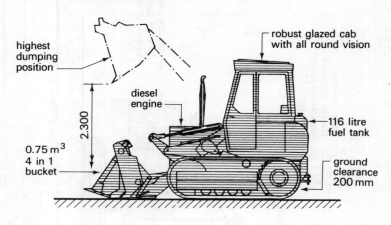

overall length - bucket on ground 4.300
overall width of bucket 1.800
maximum lifting height 4.675
top speeds - forwards 6.7 km/h reverse 8.2 km/h
width of tracks 300 mm

highest dumping position

diesel engine

robust glazed cab with all round vision

116 litre fuel tank

2.300

0.75 m³ 4 in 1 bucket

ground clearance 200 mm

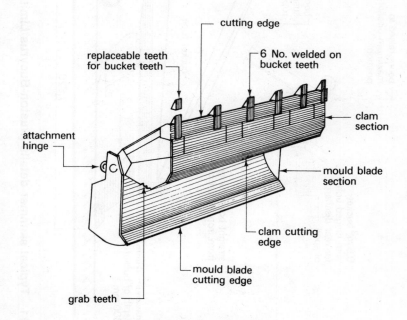

cutting edge

replaceable teeth for bucket teeth

6 No. welded on bucket teeth

clam section

attachment hinge

mould blade section

clam cutting edge

mould blade cutting edge

grab teeth

Typical 4 in 1 bucket details

Fig. V.10 Typical tractor shovel (International Harvester Co)

319

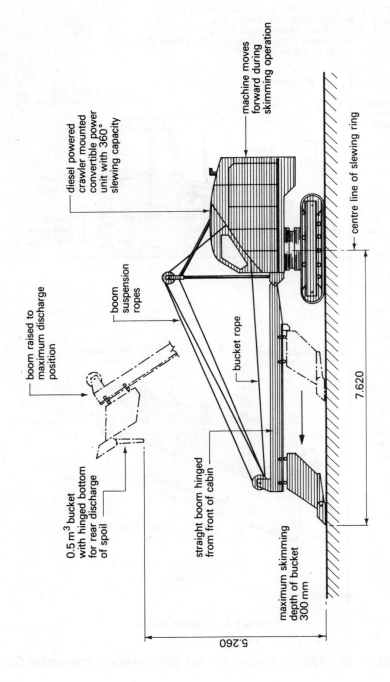

Fig. V.11 Typical skimmer details (Ruston-Bucyrus Limited)

diesel powered crawler mounted convertible power unit with 360° slewing capacity

machine moves forward during skimming operation

centre line of slewing ring

boom raised to maximum discharge position

boom suspension ropes

bucket rope

0.5 m³ bucket with hinged bottom for rear discharge of spoil

straight boom hinged from front of cabin

maximum skimming depth of bucket 300 mm

7.620

5.260

320

accuracy in level is required and they can achieve an output of some 50 bucket loads per hour. To discharge the spoil the boom or jib is raised and the power unit is rotated until the raised bucket is over the attendant haulage vehicle, enabling the spoil to be discharged through the opening bottom direct into the haul unit — see Fig. V.11.

FACE SHOVEL

This type of machine can be used as a loading shovel or for excavating into the face of an embankment or berm. Universal power unit or hydraulic machines are available with a wide choice of bucket capacities achieving outputs in the region of 80 bucket loads per hour. The discharge operation is similar to that described above for the skimmer except that in the universal machine the discharge opening is at the rear of the bucket whereas in the hydraulic machines discharge is from the front of the bucket — see Figs. V.10 and V.12. These machines are limited in the depth to which they can dig below machine level; this is generally within the range of 300 mm to 2.000.

BACKACTOR

This piece of plant is probably the most common form of excavating machinery used by building contractors for excavating basements, pits and trenches. Universal power unit and hydraulic versions are available, the latter often sacrificing bucket capacity to achieve a greater reach from a set position. Discharge in both types is by raising the bucket in a tucked position and emptying the spoil through the open front end into the attendant haul unit or alongside the trench. Outputs will vary from 30 to 60 bucket loads per hour, depending upon how confined is the excavation area. Typical details are shown in Figs. V.13 and V.14.

DRAGLINE

This type of excavator is essentially a crane with a long jib to which is attached a drag bucket for excavating in loose and soft soils below the level of the machine. This machine is for bulk excavation where fine limits are not of paramount importance since this is beyond the capabilities of the machine's design. The accuracy to which a dragline can excavate depends upon the skill of the operator. Discharge of the collected spoil is similar to that of a backactor, being through the open front end of the bucket — see Fig. V.15. A machine rigged as a dragline can be fitted with a grab bucket as an alternative for excavating in very loose soils below the level of the machine. Outputs of dragline excavators will vary according to operating restrictions from 30 to 80 bucket loads per hour.

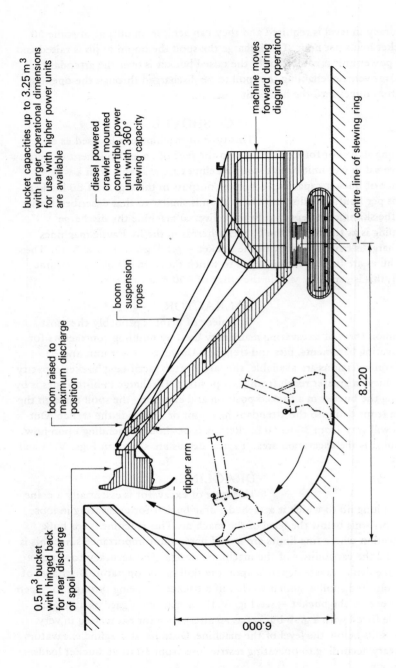

bucket capacities up to 3.25 m³
with larger operational dimensions
for use with higher power units
are available

diesel powered
crawler mounted
convertible power
unit with 360°
slewing capacity

machine moves
forward during
digging operation

centre line of slewing ring

boom
suspension
ropes

boom raised to
maximum discharge
position

dipper arm

0.5 m³ bucket
with hinged back
for rear discharge
of spoil

8.220

6.000

Fig. V.12 Typical face shovel details (Ruston-Bucyrus Limited)

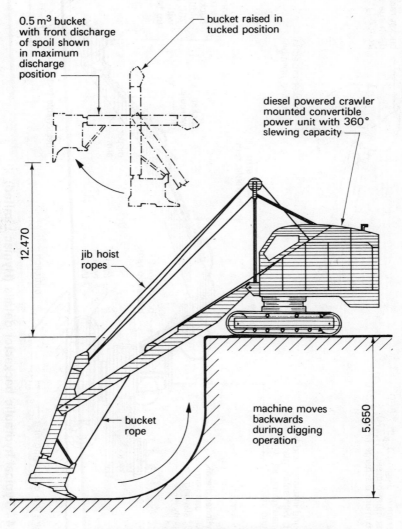

bucket capacities up to 1.53 m³ with larger operational dimensions for use with larger power machines are available

0.5 m³ bucket with front discharge of spoil shown in maximum discharge position

bucket raised in tucked position

diesel powered crawler mounted convertible power unit with 360° slewing capacity

jib hoist ropes

12.470

bucket rope

machine moves backwards during digging operation

5.650

maximum digging reach 9.600 measured from cutting edge of bucket to centre line of slewing ring

Fig. V.13   Typical backactor details (Ruston-Bucyrus Ltd)

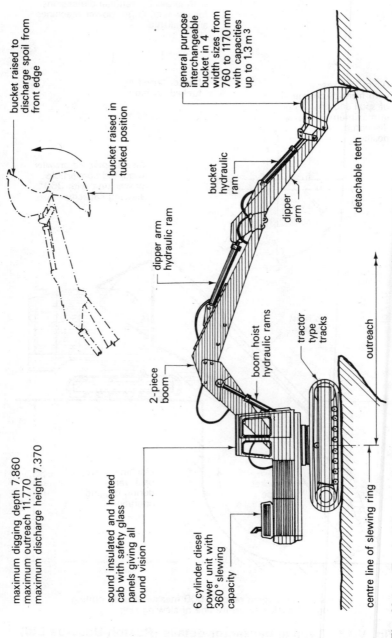

bucket raised to discharge spoil from front edge

bucket raised in tucked position

maximum digging depth 7.860
maximum outreach 11.770
maximum discharge height 7.370

sound insulated and heated cab with safety glass panels giving all round vision

6 cylinder diesel power unit with 360° slewing capacity

2-piece boom

boom hoist hydraulic rams

tractor type tracks

dipper arm hydraulic ram

bucket hydraulic ram

dipper arm

general purpose interchangeable bucket in 4 width sizes from 760 to 1170 mm with capacities up to 1.3 m³

detachable teeth

outreach

centre line of slewing ring

Fig. V.14 Typical hydraulic backactor details (Hymac Limited)

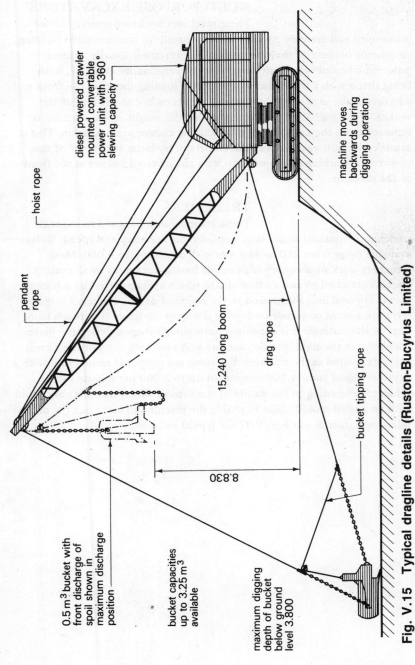

diesel powered crawler
mounted convertable
power unit with 360°
slewing capacity

hoist rope

pendant rope

15.240 long boom

drag rope

bucket tipping rope

machine moves
backwards during
digging operation

8.830

0.5 m³ bucket with
front discharge of
spoil shown in
maximum discharge
position

bucket capacities
up to 3.25 m³
available

maximum digging
depth of bucket
below ground
level 3.800

Fig. V.15 Typical dragline details (Ruston-Bucyrus Limited)

MULTI-PURPOSE EXCAVATORS

These machines are based upon a tractor power unit and are very popular with the small- to medium-sized building contractor because of their versatility. The tractor is usually a diesel-powered wheeled vehicle although tracked versions are available, both being fitted with a hydraulically controlled loading shovel at the front and a hydraulically controlled backacting bucket or hoe at the rear of the vehicle — see Fig. V.16. It is essential that the weight of the machine is removed from the axles during a backacting excavation operation. This is achieved by outrigger jacks at the corners or by jacks at the rear of the power unit working in conjunction with the inverted bucket at the front of the machine.

TRENCHERS

These are machines designed to excavate trenches of constant width with considerable accuracy and speed. Widths available range from 250 to 450 mm with depths up to 4.000. Most trenchers work on a conveyor principle having a series of small cutting buckets attached to two endless chains which are supported by a boom that is lowered into the ground to the required depth. The spoil is transferred to a cross conveyor to deposit the spoil alongside the trench being dug, or alternatively it is deposited onto plough-shaped deflection plates which direct the spoil into continuous heaps on both sides of the trench being excavated as the machine digs along the proposed trench run. With a depth of dig of some 1.500 outputs of up to 2.000 per minute can be achieved, according to the nature of the subsoil. Some trenchers are fitted with an angled mould blade to enable the machine to carry out the backfilling operation — see Fig. V.17 for typical example.

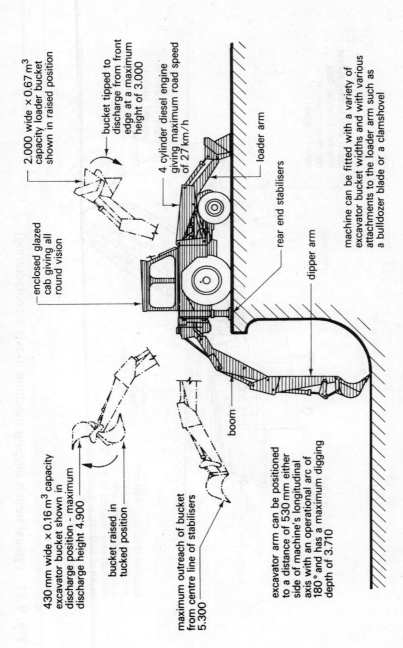

2.000 wide × 0.67 m³ capacity loader bucket shown in raised position

bucket tipped to discharge from front edge at a maximum height of 3.000

enclosed glazed cab giving all round vision

4 cylinder diesel engine giving maximum road speed of 27 km/h

loader arm

rear end stabilisers

dipper arm

boom

machine can be fitted with a variety of excavator bucket widths and with various attachments to the loader arm such as a bulldozer blade or a clamshovel

430 mm wide × 0.16 m³ capacity excavator bucket shown in discharge position – maximum discharge height 4.900

bucket raised in tucked position

maximum outreach of bucket from centre line of stabilisers 5.300

excavator arm can be positioned to a distance of 530 mm either side of machine's longitudinal axis with an operational arc of 180° and has a maximum digging depth of 3.710

Fig. V.16 Typical excavator/loader details (JCB Sales Limited)

327

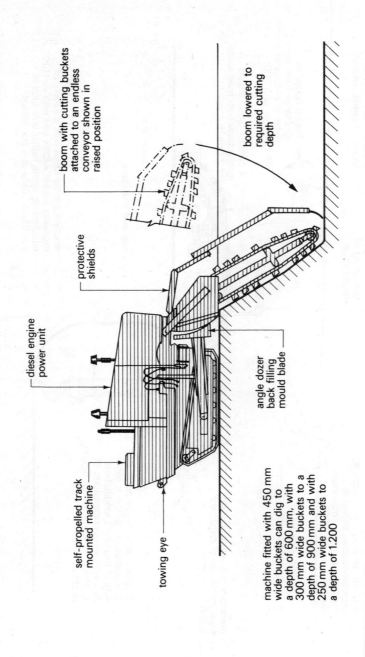

boom with cutting buckets attached to an endless conveyor shown in raised position

boom lowered to required cutting depth

protective shields

diesel engine power unit

self-propelled track mounted machine

towing eye

angle dozer back filling mould blade

machine fitted with 450 mm wide buckets can dig to a depth of 600 mm, with 300 mm wide buckets to a depth of 900 mm and with 250 mm wide buckets to a depth of 1.200

Fig. V.17 Typical trench digging machine (Davis Manufacturing)

30
Transporting plant

Movement of materials and/or personnel around and between building sites can be very time-consuming and non-productive; therefore wherever economically possible most contractors will use some form of mechanical transportation. The movement required can be horizontal, vertical or a combination of both directions. In the case of horizontal and vertical movement of large quantities of water the usual plant employed is a pump (already described in the chapter on small powered plant). Similarly the transportation of large quantities of concrete can be carried out by using special pumping equipment and this form of material transportation will be considered in the chapter on concreting plant.

LORRIES AND TRUCKS

Transportation between sites of men, machines and materials is usually carried out by using suitably equipped or adapted lorries or trucks ranging from the small 'pick-up' vehicle weighing less than 800 kg unladen to the very long, low loaders used to convey tracked plant such as cranes and bulldozers. The small 'pick-up' vehicle is usually based upon the manufacturer's private car range and has the advantages of lower road tax than heavier lorries and that the driver does not require a heavy goods vehicle licence for trucks weighing less than 3 000 kg unladen. Most lorries designed and developed for building contractors' use are powered by a diesel, which is more economical to operate than the petrol engine although they are heavier and dearer. But with mileages in excess of 32 000 km per year experienced by most contractors diesel engines usually prove to be a worth-while proposition. A vast range of lorries are produced by the leading motor manufacturers and are available with refinements such as tipping, tailhoist and self-loading facilities using hydraulic lifting gear. Since lorries, trucks and vans are standard forms of transportation encountered in all aspects of daily living they will not be considered in detail in this text but regulations made under the Road Traffic Act, Vehicles (Excise) Act and the Customs and Excise Act must be noted.

The above legislation is very extensive and complex, dealing in detail with such requirements as the minimum driving ages for various types of vehicles; limitations of hours of duty; maximum speed limits of certain classes of vehicles; vehicle lighting regulations; construction, weight and equipment of motor vehicles and trailers; testing requirements and the rear-marking regulations for vehicles over 13.000 long. Most of the statutory requirements noted above will be incorporated into the design and finish of the vehicle as purchased, but certain regulations regarding such matters as projection of loads, maximum loading of vehicles and notifications to be given to highway authorities, police forces and the Ministry of Transport are the direct concern of the building contractor. Precise information on these requirements can be found in the Motor Vehicles (Authorisation of Special Types) General Order 1969 together with any subsequent amendments. It should be noted that excise regulations and the use of rebated fuels are also the builder's responsibility.

Dumpers

These are one of the most versatile, labour-saving and misused pieces of plant available to the builder for the horizontal movement of materials ranging from bricks to aggregates, sanitary fittings to scaffolding and fluids such as wet concrete. These diesel-powered vehicles require only one operative, the driver, and can transverse the rough terrain encountered on many building sites. Many sizes and varieties are produced, giving options such as two- or four-wheel drive, hydraulic- or gravity-operated container, side or high level discharge, self-loading facilities and specially equipped dumpers for collecting and transporting crane skips. Specification for dumpers is usually given by quoting the container capacity in litres for heaped, struck and water levels — see Fig. V.18 for typical examples.

Fork lift trucks

Fork lift trucks for handling mainly palleted materials quickly and efficiently around building sites over the rough terrain normally encountered have rapidly gained in popularity since their

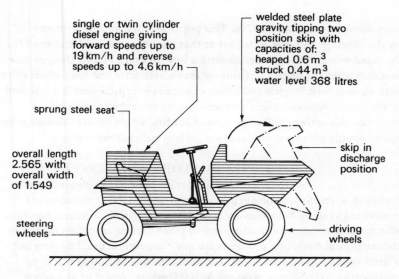

single or twin cylinder diesel engine giving forward speeds up to 19 km/h and reverse speeds up to 4.6 km/h

welded steel plate gravity tipping two position skip with capacities of: heaped 0.6 m³ struck 0.44 m³ water level 368 litres

sprung steel seat

overall length 2.565 with overall width of 1.549

skip in discharge position

steering wheels

driving wheels

Standard type dumper

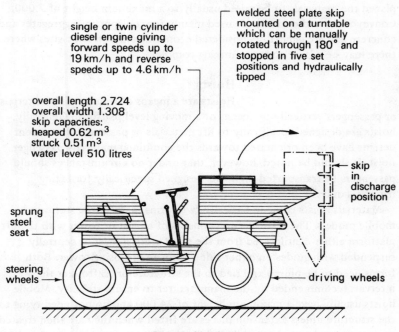

single or twin cylinder diesel engine giving forward speeds up to 19 km/h and reverse speeds up to 4.6 km/h

welded steel plate skip mounted on a turntable which can be manually rotated through 180° and stopped in five set positions and hydraulically tipped

overall length 2.724 overall width 1.308 skip capacities: heaped 0.62 m³ struck 0.51 m³ water level 510 litres

skip in discharge position

sprung steel seat

steering wheels

driving wheels

Swivel skip dumper

Fig. V.18   Typical diesel dumpers (Liner Concrete Machinery Co Ltd)

introduction in the early 1970s. This popularity was probably promoted by the shortage and cost of labour at that time together with the need for the rapid movement of materials with a low breakage factor. Designs now available offer the choice of front- or rear-wheel drive and four-wheel drive with various mast heights and lifting capacities — typical details are shown in Fig. V.19. Although these machines can carry certain unpalleted materials this activity will require hand loading which reduces considerably the economic advantages of machine loading palleted materials.

ELEVATORS AND CONVEYORS

The distinction between an elevator and a conveyor is usually one of direction of movement in that elevators are considered as those belts moving materials mainly in the vertical direction whereas conveyors are a similar piece of plant moving materials mainly in the horizontal direction. Elevators are not common on building sites but if used wisely can be economical for such activities as raising bricks or roofing tiles to the fixing position. Most elevators consist of an endless belt with raised transverse strips at suitable spacings against which can be placed the materials to be raised usually to a maximum height of 7.000. Conveyors or endless belts are used mainly for transporting aggregates and concrete and are generally considered economic only on large sites where there may be a large concrete-mixing complex.

Hoists

Hoists are a means of transporting materials or passengers vertically by means of a moving level platform. Generally, hoists are designed specifically to lift materials or passengers but recent designs have been orientated towards the combined materials/passenger hoist. It should be noted, however, that under no circumstances should passengers be transported on hoists designed specifically for lifting materials only.

Materials hoists come in basically two forms, namely the static and mobile models. The static version consists of a mast or tower with the lift platform either cantilevered from the small section mast or centrally suspended with guides on either side within an enclosing tower. Both forms need to be plumb and tied to the structure or scaffold at the intervals recommended by the manufacturer to ensure stability. Mobile hoists usually have a maximum height of 24.000 and do not need tying to the structure unless extension pieces are fitted when they are then treated as a cantilever hoist. All mobile hoists should be positioned on a firm level base and jacked to ensure stability — see Fig. V.20. The operation of a materials hoist should be entrusted to a trained driver who has a clear view

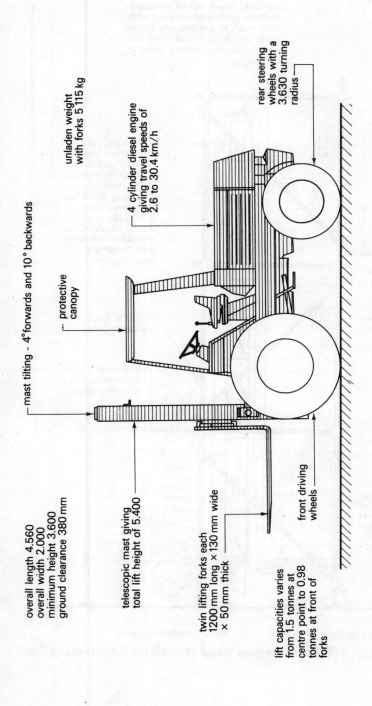

mast tilting - 4° forwards and 10° backwards

unladen weight with forks 5 115 kg

protective canopy

4 cylinder diesel engine giving travel speeds of 2.6 to 30.4 km/h

rear steering wheels with a 3.630 turning radius

overall length 4.560
overall width 2.000
minimum height 3.600
ground clearance 380 mm

telescopic mast giving total lift height of 5.400

twin lifting forks each 1200 mm long × 130 mm wide × 50 mm thick

front driving wheels

lift capacities varies from 1.5 tonnes at centre point to 0.98 tonnes at front of forks

Fig. V.19 Typical fork lift truck details (Manitou (Site Lift) Ltd)

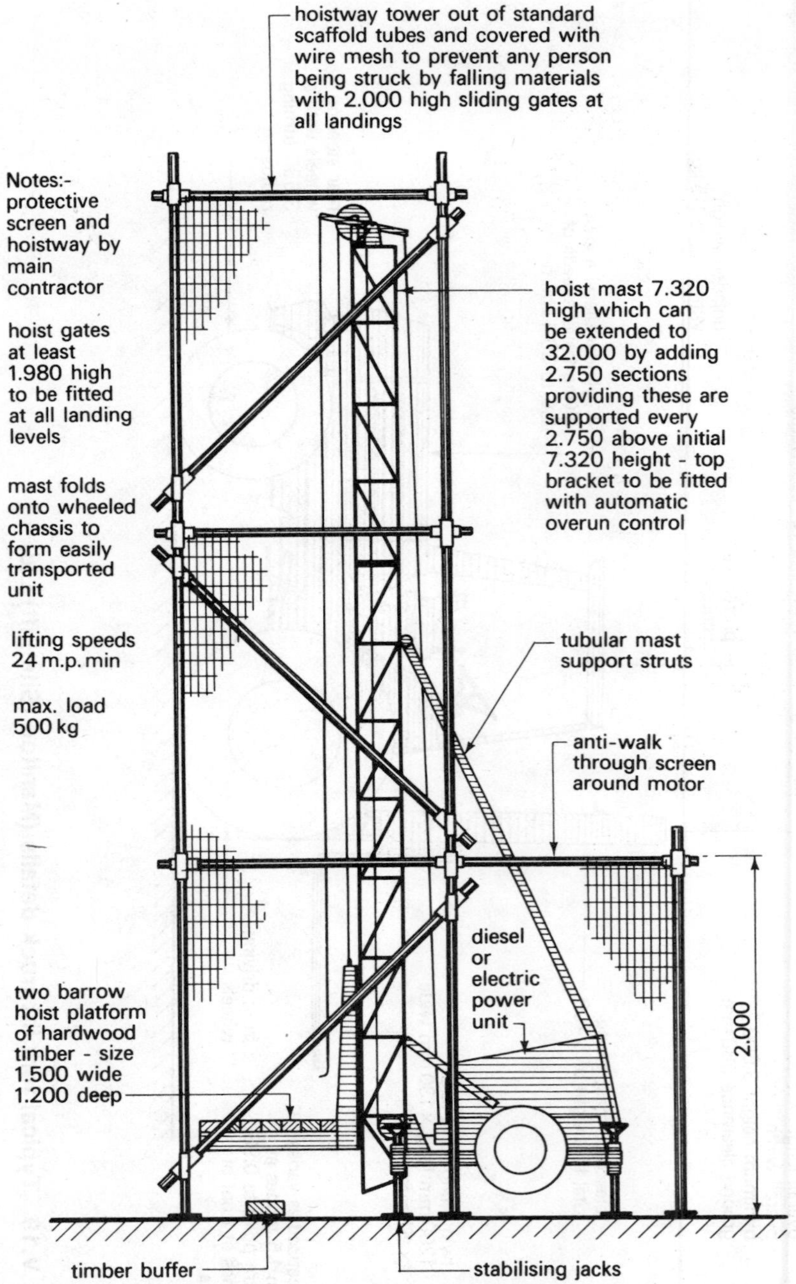

hoistway tower out of standard scaffold tubes and covered with wire mesh to prevent any person being struck by falling materials with 2.000 high sliding gates at all landings

Notes:-
protective screen and hoistway by main contractor

hoist gates at least 1.980 high to be fitted at all landing levels

mast folds onto wheeled chassis to form easily transported unit

lifting speeds 24 m.p. min

max. load 500 kg

hoist mast 7.320 high which can be extended to 32.000 by adding 2.750 sections providing these are supported every 2.750 above initial 7.320 height - top bracket to be fitted with automatic overrun control

tubular mast support struts

anti-walk through screen around motor

diesel or electric power unit

2.000

two barrow hoist platform of hardwood timber - size 1.500 wide 1.200 deep

timber buffer

stabilising jacks

Fig. V.20 Typical materials hoist (Wickham Engineering Co. Ltd)

334

from the operating position. Site operatives should be instructed as to the correct loading procedures, such as placing barrows onto the hoist platform at ground level with the handles facing the high level exit so that walking onto the raised platform is reduced to a minimum.

Passenger hoists, like the materials hoist, can be driven by a petrol, diesel or electric motor and can be of a cantilever or enclosed variety. The cantilever type consists of one or two passenger hoist cages operating on one or both sides of the cantilever tower; the alternative form consists of a passenger hoist cage operating within an enclosing tower. Tying back requirements are similar to those needed for materials hoist. Passenger hoists should conform to the recommendations of BS 4465 and materials hoists with the recommendations of BS 3125. Typical hoist details are shown in Fig. V.21.

THE CONSTRUCTION (LIFTING OPERATIONS) REGULATIONS 1961

This Statutory Instrument sets out in Parts V and VI the legal requirements regarding the use of hoists on construction sites.

Reg. 42: gives details regarding the need to enclose the hoistway wherever access can be gained and wherever anyone at ground level could be struck by the platform or counterweight and such enclosures and gates should be at least 2.000 high. Access gates must be kept closed at all times except for the necessary loading and unloading of the platform. The platform itself must be fitted with a device capable of supporting a fully loaded platform in the event of failure of the hoist ropes or hoisting gear; furthermore the hoist must be fitted with an automatic device to prevent the platform or cage over-running its highest point.

Reg. 43: deals with the operation of hoists, requiring that the controlling of the hoist is to be from one position only at all times if not controlled from the cage itself and that the driver must have a clear view of the hoist throughout its entire travel; if this is not possible a signalling system covering all landings must be installed and used.

Reg. 44: sets out the requirements for winches which must have an automatic braking system which is applied whenever the control lever, handle or switch is not in the operating position.

Reg. 45: deals with safe working loads in terms of materials and/or maximum number of passengers to be carried, and such safe working loads must be displayed on all platforms or cages.

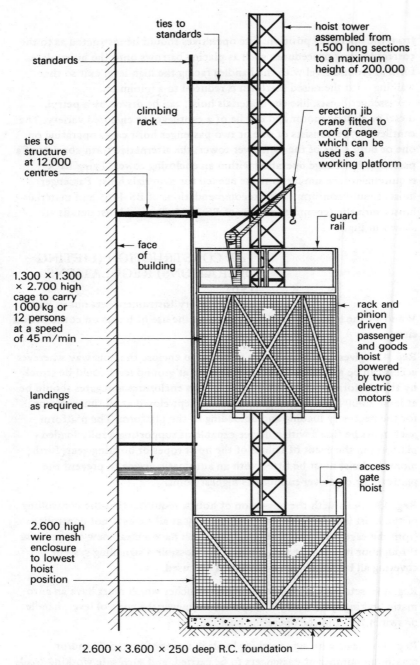

ties to standards

standards

climbing rack

ties to structure at 12.000 centres

hoist tower assembled from 1.500 long sections to a maximum height of 200.000

erection jib crane fitted to roof of cage which can be used as a working platform

guard rail

face of building

1.300 × 1.300 × 2.700 high cage to carry 1000 kg or 12 persons at a speed of 45 m/min

rack and pinion driven passenger and goods hoist powered by two electric motors

landings as required

access gate hoist

2.600 high wire mesh enclosure to lowest hoist position

2.600 × 3.600 × 250 deep R.C. foundation

Fig. V.21   Typical passenger hoist (Linden Alimark Ltd)

Reg. 46: sets out the testing and examination requirements for hoists which are:

1. Testing and thorough examination — before being used for the first time, after alterations to height and after repairs.
2. Thorough examination — at least every six months.
3. Inspection — weekly.

All tests, examinations and inspections are to be carried out by a competent person and recorded on the appropriate form 91 (Part 1).

Reg. 47: covers lifting devices which may be used to carry passengers. These include power-driven hoists, power-driven suspended scaffolds and, provided certain precautions are taken to stop passengers falling out, buckets or skips attached to a crane.

Reg. 48: deals specifically with passenger-carrying hoists and requires the cages to be constructed in such a manner that passengers cannot fall out, become trapped or struck by objects falling down the hoistway. Other requirements under this regulation include the need for gates which will prevent the hoists being activated until they are closed and which can only be opened at landing levels. Overrun devices must also be fitted at the bottom of the hoistway as well as those at the top in accordance with Regulation 42.

Reg. 49: is concerned with the security of loads being transported by a hoist, such as loose materials, which should be lifted in suitable containers, and wheelbarrows, which should be scotched or otherwise suitably secured to prevent movement or tipping over during transportation.

CRANES

A crane may be defined as a device or machine for lifting loads by means of a rope. The use of cranes has greatly increased in the construction industry due mainly to the need to raise the large and heavy prefabricated components often used in modern structures. The range of cranes available is very wide and therefore actual choice must be made on a basis of sound reasoning, overall economics, capabilities of cranes under consideration, prevailing site conditions and the anticipated utilisation of the equipment.

The simplest crane of all consists of a single-grooved wheel, over which the rope is passed, suspended from a scaffold or beam and is called a gin wheel. The gin wheel is manually operated and always requires more effort than the weight of the load to raise it to the required height. It is only suitable for light loads as, for example, a bucketful of mortar and is normally only used on very small contracts. To obtain some mechanical advantage the gin wheel can be replaced by a pulley block which contains more than one pulley or sheave; according to the number and pattern of sheaves used the lesser or greater is the saving in effort required to move any given load.

Another useful but simple crane which can be employed for small, low rise structures is the scaffold crane which consists of a short jib counter-balanced by the small petrol or electric power unit. The crane is fastened to a specially reinforced scaffold standard incorporated within the general scaffold framework with extra bracing to overcome the additional stresses as necessary. The usual maximum lifting capacity of this form of crane is 200 kg.

Apart from these simple cranes for small loads most cranes come in the more recognisable form. Subdivision of crane types can be very wide and varied but one simple method of classification is to consider cranes under three general headings:

1. Mobile cranes.
2. Static or stationary cranes.
3. Tower cranes.

Mobile cranes

Mobile cranes come in a wide variety of designs and capacities, generally with a 360° rotation or slewing circle, a low pivot and luffing jib, the main exception being the mast crane. Mobile cranes can be classed into five groups:

1. Self-propelled cranes.
2. Lorry-mounted cranes.
3. Track-mounted cranes.
4. Mast cranes.
5. Gantry cranes.

Self-propelled cranes: these are wheel-mounted mobile cranes which are generally of low lifting capacities of up to 10 tonnes. They can be distinguished from other mobile cranes by the fact that the driver has only one cab position for both driving and operating the crane. They are extremely mobile but to be efficient they usually require a hard level surface from which to work. Road speeds obtained are in the region of 30 km/h. The small capacity machines have a fixed boom or jib length, whereas the high capacity cranes can have a sectional lattice jib or a telescopic boom to obtain various radii and lifting capacities. In common with all cranes the shorter the lifting radius the greater will be the lifting capacity — see Fig. V.22 for typical example.

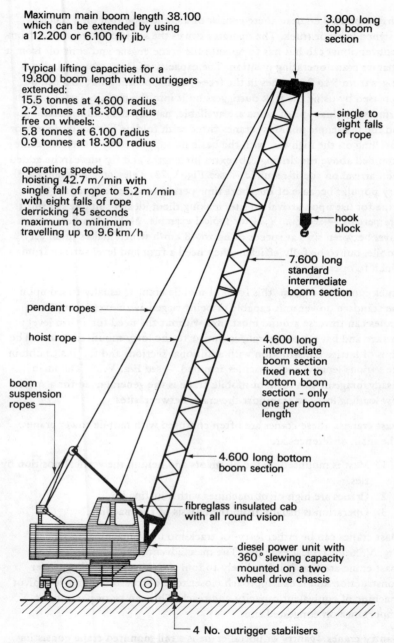

Maximum main boom length 38.100
which can be extended by using
a 12.200 or 6.100 fly jib.

Typical lifting capacities for a
19.800 boom length with outriggers
extended:
15.5 tonnes at 4.600 radius
2.2 tonnes at 18.300 radius
free on wheels:
5.8 tonnes at 6.100 radius
0.9 tonnes at 18.300 radius

operating speeds
hoisting 42.7 m/min with
single fall of rope to 5.2 m/min
with eight falls of rope
derricking 45 seconds
maximum to minimum
travelling up to 9.6 km/h

3.000 long
top boom
section

single to
eight falls
of rope

hook
block

7.600 long
standard
intermediate
boom section

pendant ropes

hoist rope

4.600 long
intermediate
boom section
fixed next to
bottom boom
section - only
one per boom
length

boom
suspension
ropes

4.600 long bottom
boom section

fibreglass insulated cab
with all round vision

diesel power unit with
360° slewing capacity
mounted on a two
wheel drive chassis

4 No. outrigger stabilisers

Fig. V.22   Typical self propelled crane (Jones Cranes Ltd)

Lorry-mounted cranes: these consist of a crane mounted on a specially designed lorry or truck. The operator drives the vehicle between sites from a conventional cab but has to operate the crane engine and controls from a separate crane operating position. The capacity of lorry-mounted cranes ranges from 5 to 20 tonnes in the free-standing position but this can be increased by using the jack outriggers built into the chassis. Two basic jib formats for this type of crane are available, namely the folding lattice jib and the telescopic jib. Most cranes fitted with folding jibs are designed for travelling on the highway with the basic jib supported by a vertical frame extended above the driving cab; extra jib lengths and fly jibs can be added upon arrival on site if required — see Fig. V.23. Telescopic jib cranes are very popular because of the short time period required to prepare the crane for use upon arrival on site, making them ideally suitable for short-hire periods — see Fig. V.24 for typical example. Mobile lorry cranes can travel between sites at speeds of up to 48 km/h which makes them very mobile, but to be fully efficient they need a firm and level surface from which to operate.

Track-mounted cranes: this form of mobile crane is usually based upon the standard power unit capable of being rigged as an excavator. These cranes can traverse around most sites without the need for a firm level surface and have capacity ranges similar to the lorry-mounted cranes. The jib is of lattice construction with additional sections and fly jibs to obtain the various lengths and capacities required — see Fig. V.25. The main disadvantage of this form of mobile crane is the general need for a special low-loading lorry to transport the crane between sites.

Mast cranes: these cranes are often confused with mobile tower cranes. The main differences are:

1. Mast is mounted on the jib pivots and held in the vertical position by ties.
2. Cranes are high pivot machines with a luffing jib.
3. Operation is usually from the chassis of the machine.

Mast cranes can be either lorry- or track-mounted machines — see Fig. V.26 for typical example. The main advantages of the high pivot mast crane are that it is less likely to foul the side of a building under construction and it can approach closer to the structure than a low pivot machine of equivalent capacity and reach. This can be of paramount importance on congested sites.

Gantry cranes: gantry or portal crane is a rail-mounted crane consisting of a horizontal transverse beam which carries a combined driver's cab and

340

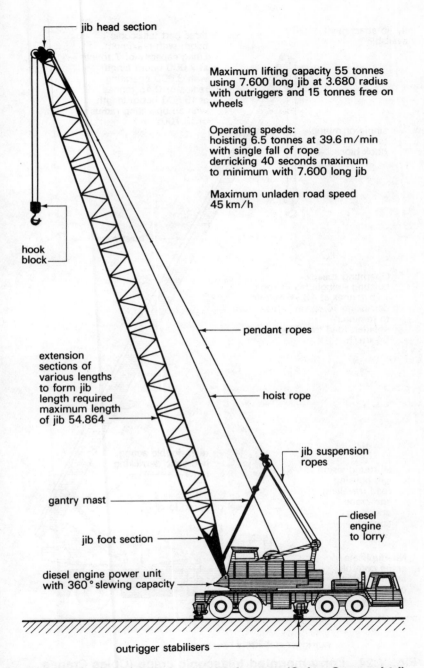

jib head section

Maximum lifting capacity 55 tonnes using 7.600 long jib at 3.680 radius with outriggers and 15 tonnes free on wheels

Operating speeds:
hoisting 6.5 tonnes at 39.6 m/min with single fall of rope
derricking 40 seconds maximum to minimum with 7.600 long jib

Maximum unladen road speed 45 km/h

hook block

pendant ropes

extension sections of various lengths to form jib length required maximum length of jib 54.864

hoist rope

jib suspension ropes

gantry mast

jib foot section

diesel engine to lorry

diesel engine power unit with 360° slewing capacity

outrigger stabilisers

Fig. V.23   Typical lorry mounted crane (Coles Cranes Ltd)

341

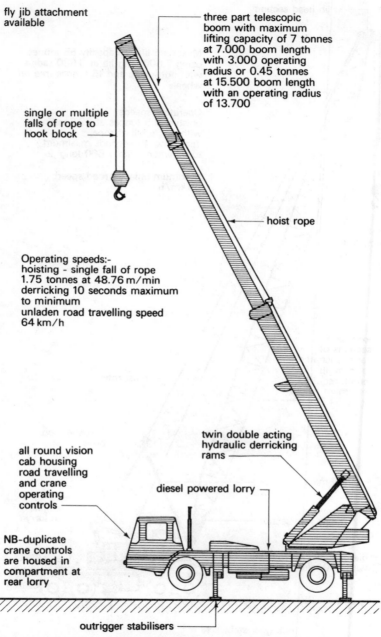

fly jib attachment
available

three part telescopic
boom with maximum
lifting capacity of 7 tonnes
at 7.000 boom length
with 3.000 operating
radius or 0.45 tonnes
at 15.500 boom length
with an operating radius
of 13.700

single or multiple
falls of rope to
hook block

hoist rope

Operating speeds:-
hoisting - single fall of rope
1.75 tonnes at 48.76 m/min
derricking 10 seconds maximum
to minimum
unladen road travelling speed
64 km/h

twin double acting
hydraulic derricking
rams

all round vision
cab housing
road travelling
and crane
operating
controls

diesel powered lorry

NB-duplicate
crane controls
are housed in
compartment at
rear lorry

outrigger stabilisers

**Fig. V.24 Lorry mounted telescopic crane (Coles Cranes
Ltd)**

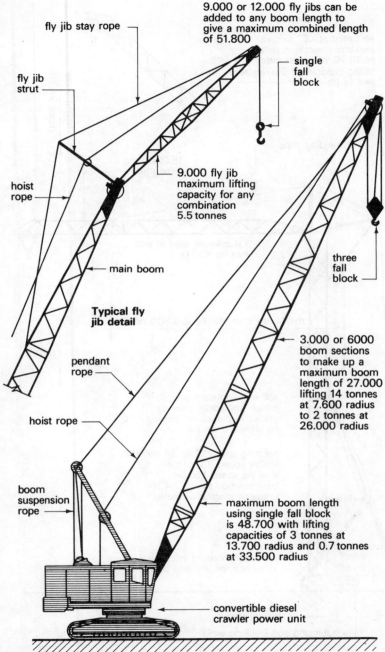

9.000 or 12.000 fly jibs can be added to any boom length to give a maximum combined length of 51.800

fly jib stay rope

fly jib strut

single fall block

hoist rope

9.000 fly jib maximum lifting capacity for any combination 5.5 tonnes

main boom

three fall block

Typical fly jib detail

3.000 or 6000 boom sections to make up a maximum boom length of 27.000 lifting 14 tonnes at 7.600 radius to 2 tonnes at 26.000 radius

pendant rope

hoist rope

boom suspension rope

maximum boom length using single fall block is 48.700 with lifting capacities of 3 tonnes at 13.700 radius and 0.7 tonnes at 33.500 radius

convertible diesel crawler power unit

Fig. V.25   Typical track mounted crane (Thomas Smith & Sons Ltd)

343

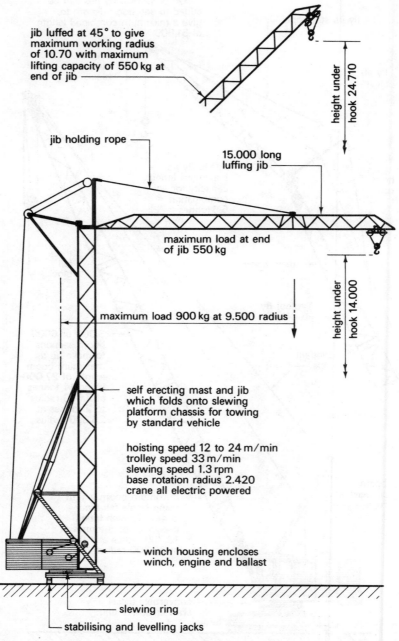

jib luffed at 45° to give maximum working radius of 10.70 with maximum lifting capacity of 550 kg at end of jib

height under hook 24.710

jib holding rope

15.000 long luffing jib

maximum load at end of jib 550 kg

height under hook 14.000

maximum load 900 kg at 9.500 radius

self erecting mast and jib which folds onto slewing platform chassis for towing by standard vehicle

hoisting speed 12 to 24 m/min
trolley speed 33 m/min
slewing speed 1.3 rpm
base rotation radius 2.420
crane all electric powered

winch housing encloses winch, engine and ballast

slewing ring

stabilising and levelling jacks

Fig. V.26   Typical mobile mast crane (Manitou (Site Lift) Ltd)

economic this form of crane needs to be centrally sited to give maximum site coverage.

Tower cranes

Since their introduction in 1950 by the then Department of Scientific and Industrial Research the tower crane has been universally accepted by the building industry as a standard piece of plant required for construction of medium- to high-rise structures. These cranes are available in several forms with a horizontal jib carrying a saddle or a trolley, or alternatively with a luffing or derricking jib with a lifting hook at its extreme end. Horizontal jibs can bring the load closer to the tower whereas luffing jibs can be raised to clear obstructions such as adjacent building, an advantage on confined sites. The basic types of tower cranes available are:

1. Self-supporting static tower cranes.
2. Supported static tower cranes.
3. Travelling tower cranes.
4. Climbing cranes.

Self-supporting static tower cranes: these cranes generally have a greater lifting capacity than other types of crane. The mast of the self-supporting tower crane must be firmly anchored at ground level to a concrete base with holding down bolts or alternatively to a special mast base section cast into a foundation. They are particularly suitable for confined sites and should be positioned in front or to one side of the proposed building with a jib of sufficient length to give overall coverage of the new structure. Generally these cranes have a static tower but types with a rotating or slewing tower and luffing jib are also available — see Fig. V.28 for typical self-supporting crane example.

Supported static tower cranes: these are similar in construction to self-supporting tower cranes but are used for lifting to a height in excess of that possible with self-supporting or travelling tower cranes. The tower or mast is fixed or tied to the structure using single or double steel stays to provide the required stability. This tying back will induce stresses in the supporting structure which must therefore be of adequate strength. Supported tower cranes usually have horizontal jibs since the rotation of a luffing jib mast renders it as unsuitable for this application — see Fig. V.29 for typical example.

Travelling tower cranes: to obtain better site coverage with a tower crane a rail-mounted or travelling crane could be used. The crane travels on heavy wheeled bogies mounted on a wide gauge (4.200) rail track with gradients

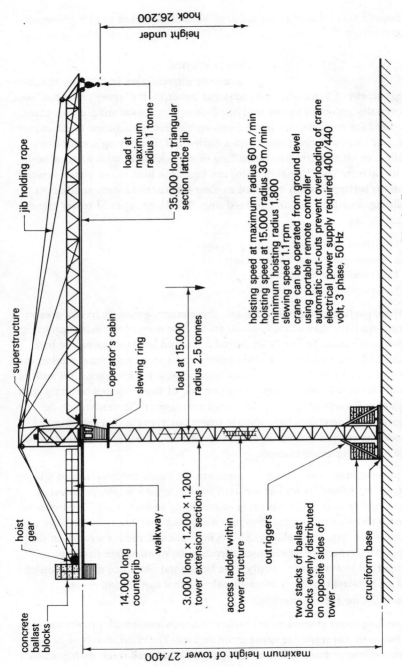

height under hook 26.200

load at maximum radius 1 tonne

35.000 long triangular section lattice jib

jib holding rope

superstructure

operator's cabin

slewing ring

load at 15.000 radius 2.5 tonnes

hoisting speed at maximum radius 60 m/min
hoisting speed at 15.000 radius 30 m/min
minimum hoisting radius 1.800
slewing speed 1.1 rpm
crane can be operated from ground level
using portable remote controller
automatic cut-outs prevent overloading of crane
electrical power supply required 400/440
volt, 3 phase, 50 Hz

hoist gear

walkway

14.000 long counterjib

3.000 long × 1.200 × 1.200 tower extension sections

access ladder within tower structure

two stacks of ballast blocks evenly distributed on opposite sides of tower

outriggers

cruciform base

concrete ballast blocks

maximum height of tower 27.400

Fig. V.28 Typical self supporting static tower crane (Stotherd & Pitt Ltd)

348

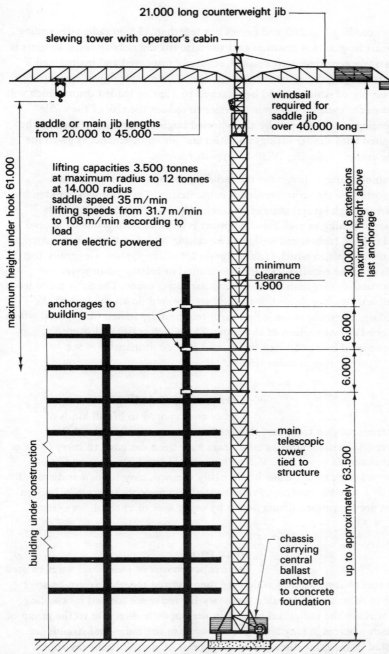

Fig. V.29 Typical supported static tower crane (Babcock Weitz)

The following labels appear on the figure:

21.000 long counterweight jib

slewing tower with operator's cabin

windsail required for saddle jib over 40.000 long

saddle or main jib lengths from 20.000 to 45.000

maximum height under hook 61.000

lifting capacities 3.500 tonnes at maximum radius to 12 tonnes at 14.000 radius
saddle speed 35 m/min
lifting speeds from 31.7 m/min to 108 m/min according to load
crane electric powered

minimum clearance 1.900

30.000 or 6 extensions maximum height above last anchorage

anchorages to building

6.000

6.000

main telescopic tower tied to structure

building under construction

chassis carrying central ballast anchored to concrete foundation

up to approximately 63.500

349

not exceeding 1 in 200 and curves not less than 11.000 radius depending on mast height. It is essential that the base for the railway track sleepers is accurately prepared, well drained, regularly inspected and maintained if the stability of the crane is to be ensured. The motive power is electricity, the supply of which should be attached to a spring loaded drum which will draw in the cable as the crane reverses to reduce the risk of the cable becoming cut or trapped by the wheeled bogies. Travelling cranes can be supplied with similar lifting capacities and jib arrangements as given for static cranes — see Fig. V.30 for typical example.

Climbing cranes: design for tall buildings being located within and supported by the structure under construction. The mast which extends down through several storeys requires only a small (1.500 to 2.000 square) opening in each floor. Support is given at floor levels by special steel collars, frames and wedges. The raising of the static mast is carried out using a winch which is an integral part of the system. Generally this form of crane requires a smaller horizontal or luffing jib to cover the construction area than a static or similar tower crane. The jib is made from small, easy-to-handle sections which are lowered down the face of the building, when the crane is no longer required, by means of a special winch attached to one section of the crane. The winch is finally lowered to ground level by hand when the crane has been dismantled — see Fig. V.31 for typical crane details.

Crane skips and slings

Cranes are required to lift all kinds of materials ranging from prefabricated components to loose and fluid materials. Various skips or containers have been designed to carry loose or fluid materials — see Fig. V.32. Skips should be of sound construction easy to attach to the crane hook, easily cleaned, easy to load and unload and of a suitable capacity. Prefabricated components are usually hoisted from predetermined lifting points by using wire or chain slings — see Fig. V.32.

Wire ropes

Wire ropes consist of individual wires twisted together to form strands which are then twisted together around a steel core to form a rope or cable. Ordinary lay ropes are formed by twisting the wires in the individual strands in the opposite direction to the group of strands whereas in lang lay ropes the wires in the individual strands are twisted in the same direction as the groups of strands. Lang lay ropes generally have better wearing properties due to the larger surface area of

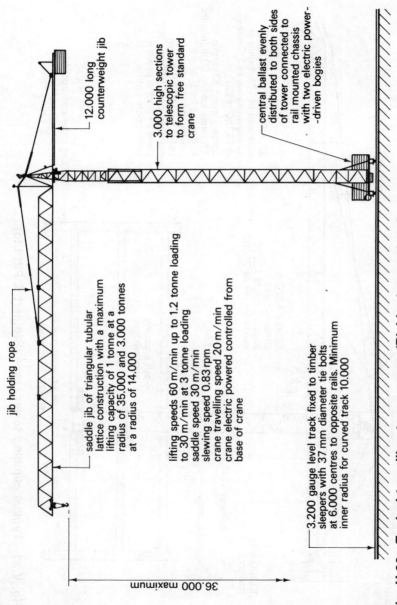

jib holding rope

12.000 long counterweight jib

3.000 high sections to telescopic tower to form free standard crane

central ballast evenly distributed to both sides of tower connected to rail mounted chassis with two electric power-driven bogies

saddle jib of triangular tubular lattice construction with a maximum lifting capacity of 1 tonne at a radius of 35.000 and 3.000 tonnes at a radius of 14.000

lifting speeds 60 m/min up to 1.2 tonne loading to 30 m/min at 3 tonne loading saddle speed 30 m/min slewing speed 0.83 rpm crane travelling speed 20 m/min crane electric powered controlled from base of crane

3.200 gauge level track fixed to timber sleepers with 37 mm diameter tie bolts at 6.000 centres to opposite rails. Minimum inner radius for curved track 10.000

36.000 maximum

Fig. V.30 Typical travelling tower crane (Richier International)

351

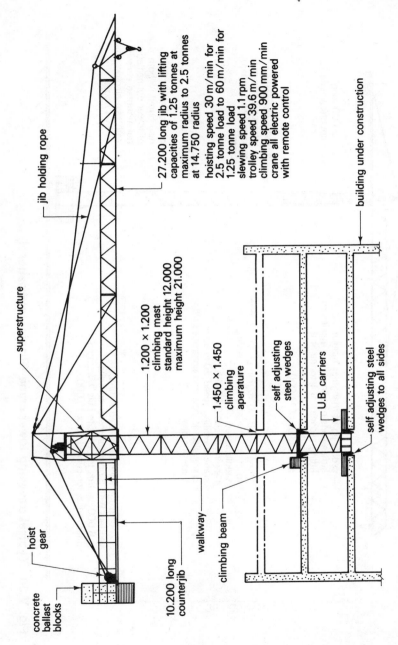

jib holding rope

superstructure

hoist gear

concrete ballast blocks

10.200 long counterjib

walkway

climbing beam

1.200 × 1.200 climbing mast standard height 12.000 maximum height 21.000

1.450 × 1.450 climbing aperature

self adjusting steel wedges

U.B. carriers

self adjusting steel wedges to all sides

building under construction

27.200 long jib with lifting capacities of 1.25 tonnes at maximum radius to 2.5 tonnes at 14.750 radius

hoisting speed 30 m/min for 2.5 tonne load to 60 m/min for 1.25 tonne load
slewing speed 1.1 rpm
trolley speed 39.6 m/min
climbing speed 900 mm/min
crane all electric powered with remote control

Fig. V.31   Typical climbing tower crane (Stothert & Pitt Ltd)

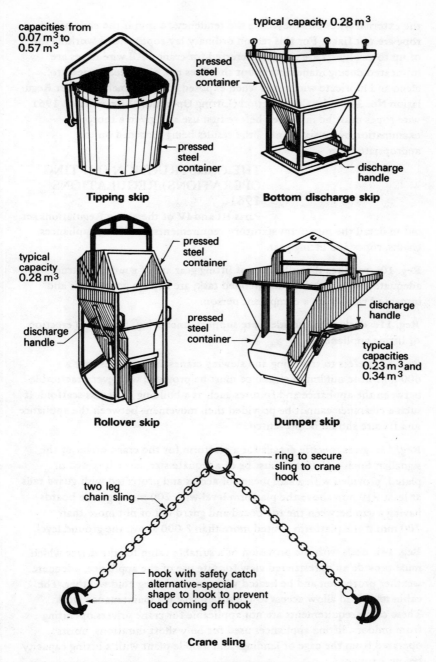

capacities from
0.07 m³ to
0.57 m³

pressed
steel
container

Tipping skip

typical capacity 0.28 m³

pressed
steel
container

discharge
handle

Bottom discharge skip

typical
capacity
0.28 m³

pressed
steel
container

discharge
handle

Rollover skip

pressed
steel
container

pressed
steel
container

discharge
handle

typical
capacities
0.23 m³ and
0.34 m³

Dumper skip

ring to secure
sling to crane
hook

two leg
chain sling

hook with safety catch
alternative-special
shape to hook to prevent
load coming off hook

Crane sling

Fig. V.32   Typical crane skips and sling

353

the external wires but they have the tendency to spin if the ends of the rope are not fixed. For this reason ordinary lay ropes with a working life of up to two years are usually preferred for cranes. All wire ropes are lubricated during manufacture but this does not preclude the need to clean and lubricate wire ropes when exposed to the elements. Under Regulation No. 34 of the Construction (Lifting Operations) Regulations 1961 wire ropes must be inspected before first use and given a thorough examination every six months, the results being recorded on the appropriate form.

THE CONSTRUCTION (LIFTING OPERATIONS) REGULATIONS 1961

Parts III and IV of the above Regulations set out in detail the minimum statutory requirements for lifting appliances, chains, ropes and lifting gear.

Reg. 10: requires that all forms of lifting gear are of sound construction, adequate in strength for the intended task, are kept in good order and inspected weekly by a competent person.

Reg. 11: deals with the adequate support, anchoring, fixing and erection of lifting appliances.

Reg. 12: refers to travelling and slewing cranes and requires that a 600 mm wide minimum clearance must be provided wherever practicable between the appliance and fixtures such as a building or access scaffold. If such a clearance cannot be provided then movement between the appliance and fixture should be prevented.

Reg. 13: gives specific details for a platform for the crane driver or the signaller. Such a platform must be of adequate size, close boarded or plated, provided with a safe means of access and protected with guard rails at least 910 mm above the platform level with 200 mm high toe boards having a gap between the toe board and guard rail of not more than 700 mm if the platform is sited more than 2.000 above the ground level.

Reg. 14: deals with the provision of a suitable cabin for the driver which must provide an unrestricted view for safe use of the appliance, adequate weather protection and be heated when in use during cold weather. The cabin must also allow access to the machinery for maintenance work. These cabin requirements are not applicable for crane drivers operating from indoors, lifting appliances used for only short durations, hoists operated from the cage or landings and mobile plant with a lifting capacity below 1 tonne.

Reg. 15: gives the requirements for the suitability of drums and pulleys.

Reg. 16: sets out the provisions for brakes, controls and safety devices, the need for clear marking of controls and designed to prevent accidental operation.

Reg. 17: deals with safe means of access for the purposes of examination, repair or lubrication, particularly where a person can fall more than 2.000.

Reg. 18: gives strength and fixing requirements for poles and beams supporting pulley blocks or gin wheels.

Reg. 19: deals with the stability of lifting appliances when used on soft ground, uneven surfaces and slopes. The crane must be either anchored to the ground or to a foundation, or suitably counterweighted to prevent overturning.

Reg. 20: is concerned with rail-mounted cranes and the need for the track to be laid and secured on a firm foundation to prevent the risk of derailment. This Regulation also deals with the requirements for buffers, effective braking systems and adequate maintenance of both track and equipment.

Reg. 21: sets out the strength requirements for the mounting of cranes on bogies, trolley or wheeled carriages.

Reg. 22: deals with cranes having a derricking jib operated through a clutch which must have an effective interlock arrangement between the derricking clutch and the pawl and the ratchet on the derricking drum.

Reg. 23: restricts the use of cranes to direct raising and lowering operations. Cranes with a derricking jib shall not be used with the jib at a radius greater than that specified on the test certificate.

Reg. 24: no crane which has any timber structural member shall be used.

Reg. 25: cranes must always be erected under the supervision of a competent person.

Regs. 26 and 27: covers the requirements of persons operating lifting appliances and signalling requirements. Drivers of lifting appliances must be trained, experienced and over 18 years of age. If the driver does not have a clear vision during the whole of the lifting operation an adequate signalling system must be used. A signaller must be over 18 years of age, capable of giving clear and distinct signals by hand, mechanical or electrical means.

Reg. 28: sets out the testing, examination and inspection requirements. Cranes, grabs and winches — testing and thorough examination every four years, thorough examination every 14 months and inspections to be carried out weekly. Pulley blocks, gin wheels and sheer legs — testing and thorough examination before first use, thorough examination every 14 months and weekly inspections.

Reg. 29: requires that all cranes are clearly marked with their safe maximum working loads relevant to lifting radius and maximum operating radius when fitted with a derricking jib.

Reg. 30: jib cranes must be fitted with an automatic safe load indicator approved by the Chief Inspector of Factories such as a warning light for the driver and a warning bell for persons nearby.

Reg. 31: except for testing purposes the safe working load must not be exceeded.

Reg. 32: when loads being lifted are approaching the safe maximum load the initial lift should be short. A check should then be made to establish safety and stability before proceeding to complete the lift.

Reg. 33: gives details of the stability requirements for Scotch and guy derricks.

Regs. 34 to 41: gives the special requirements for lifting gear such as chains, slings, ropes, hooks, chain shackles and eye bolts. Testing and examination requirements of before each use and thorough examination every six months are also set out in these Regulations.

Apart from the legal requirements summarised above commonsense precautions on site must be taken such as the clear marking of high voltage electric cables and leaving the crane in an 'out of service' position when unattended or if storm or high wind conditions prevail. Most tower cranes can operate in wind conditions of up to 60 km/h. The usual 'out of service' position for tower cranes is as follows:

1. Jibs to be left on free slew and pointed in the direction of the wind on the leeward side of the tower.
2. Fuel and power supplies switched off.
3. Load removed.
4. Hook raised to highest position.
5. Hook positioned close to tower.
6. Rail-mounted cranes should have their wheels chocked or clamped.

ERECTION OF CRANES

Before commencing to erect a crane careful consideration must be given to its actual position on the site. Like all forms of plant maximum utilisation is the ultimate aim, therefore a central position within reach of all storage areas, loading areas and activity areas is required. Generally output will be in the region of 18 to 20 lifts per hour therefore the working sequence of the crane needs to be carefully planned and co-ordinated if full advantage is to be made of the crane's capabilities.

The erection of mast and tower cranes varies with the different makes but there are several basic methods. Mast cranes are usually transported in a collapsed and folded position and are quickly unfolded and erected on site, using built-in lifting and erection gear. Tower cranes, however, have to be assembled on site. In some cases the superstructure which carries the jib and counterjib is erected on the base frame. The top section of the tower or pintle is raised by internal climbing gear housed within the superstructure; further 3.000 tower lengths can be added as the pintle is raised until the desired tower height has been reached. The jib and counterjib are attached at ground level to the superstructure which is then raised to the top of the pintle; this whole arrangement then slews around the static tower.

Another method of assembly and erection adopted by some manufacturers is to raise the first tower section onto a base, assemble the jib and counterjib and fix these to the first tower section. Using the facilities of the jib, further tower sections can be fitted inside the first section and elevated on a telescopic principle, this procedure being repeated until the desired height has been reached. A similar approach to the last method is to have the jib and top tower section fixed to a cantilever bracket arrangement so that it is offset from the main tower. Further sections can be added to the assembly until the required height is reached when the jib assembly can be transferred to the top of the tower.

31
Concrete mixers and pumps

The mixing and transporting of concrete and mortar mixes are important activities on most building sites from the very small to the very large contract. The choice of method for mixing and transporting the concrete or mortar must be made on the basis of the volume of mixed material required in any given time and also the horizontal and vertical transportation distances involved. Consideration must also be given to the use of ready mixed concrete especially where large quantities are required and/or site space is limited.

CONCRETE MIXERS

Most concrete mixers used on building sites are of the batch type conforming to the minimum recommendations of BS 1305 which defines two basic forms, namely the drum type or free-fall concrete mixer and the pan type or forced action concrete mixer. The drum mixers are subdivided into three distinct forms:

1. *Tilting drum* (T) — in which the single-compartment drum has an inclinable axis with loading and discharge through the front opening. This form of mixer is primarily intended for small batch outputs ranging from 100T to 200T litres. It should be noted that mixer output capacities are given in litres for sizes up to 1 000 litres and in cubic metres for outputs over 1 000 litres, a letter suffix designating the type being also included in the title. In common with all drum mixers tilting mixers have fixed blades inside the revolving drum which lift the mixture and at a certain point in each revolution allow

the mixture to drop towards the bottom of the drum to recommence the mixing cycle. The complete cycle time for mixing one batch from load to reload is usually specified as 2½ minutes. Typical examples of tilting drum mixers are shown in Fig. V.33.

2. *Non-tilting drum* (NT) − in which the single-compartment drum has two openings and rotates on a horizontal axis with output capacities ranging from 200 NT to 750 NT. Loading is through the front opening and discharge through the rear opening by means of a discharge chute collecting the mixture from the top of the drum. The chute should form an angle of not less than 40° with the horizontal axis of the drum.

3. *Reversing drum* (R) − a more popular version of a mixer with a drum rotating on a horizontal axis than the non-tilting drum mixer described above. Capacities of this type of mixer range from 200R to 500R. Loading is through a front opening and discharge from a rear opening carried out by reversing the rotation of the drum − see Fig. V.34.

Generally mixers with an output capacity exceeding 200 litres are fitted with an automatic or manually operated water system which will deliver a measured volume of water to the drum of the mixer. Table 1 of BS 1305 gives recommended minimum water tank capacities for the various mixer sizes.

Forced action mixers (P) are generally for larger capacity outputs than the drum mixers described above and can be obtained within the range of 200 P to P2.0. The mixing of the concrete is achieved by the relative movements between the mix, pan and blades or paddles. Usually the pan is stationary whilst the paddles or blades rotate but rotating pan models consisting of a revolving pan and a revolving mixer blade or star giving a shorter mixing time of 30 seconds with large outputs are also available. In general pan mixers are not easily transported and for this reason are usually only employed on large sites where it would be an economic proposition to install this form of mixer.

CEMENT STORAGE

Cement for the mixing of mortars or concrete can be supplied in 50 kg bags or in bulk for storage on site prior to use. Bagged cement requires a dry and damp-free store to prevent air setting taking place (see Chapter 2). If large quantities of cement are required an alternative method of storage is the silo which will hold cement supplied in bulk under ideal conditions. A typical cement silo consists of an elevated welded steel cylindrical container supported on four crossed braced

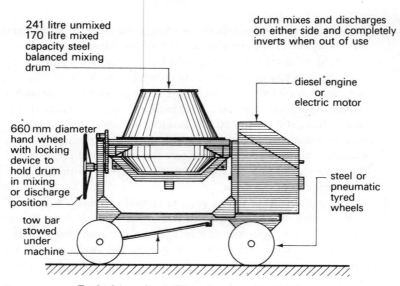

241 litre unmixed
170 litre mixed
capacity steel
balanced mixing
drum

drum mixes and discharges
on either side and completely
inverts when out of use

diesel engine
or
electric motor

660 mm diameter
hand wheel
with locking
device to
hold drum
in mixing
or discharge
position

steel or
pneumatic
tyred
wheels

tow bar
stowed
under
machine

Typical (one bag) tilting drum concrete mixer

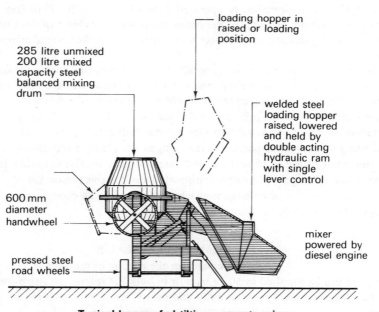

loading hopper in
raised or loading
position

285 litre unmixed
200 litre mixed
capacity steel
balanced mixing
drum

welded steel
loading hopper
raised, lowered
and held by
double acting
hydraulic ram
with single
lever control

600 mm
diameter
handwheel

mixer
powered by
diesel engine

pressed steel
road wheels

Typical hopper fed tilting concrete mixer

**Fig. V.33 Typical tilting drum mixers (Liner Concrete
Machinery Co Ltd)**

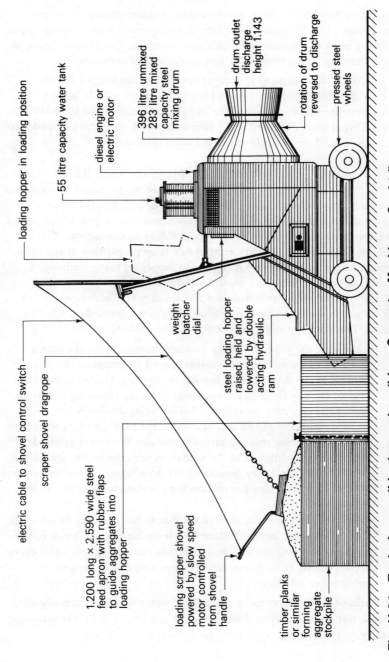

electric cable to shovel control switch

scraper shovel dragrope

1.200 long × 2.590 wide steel feed apron with rubber flaps to guide aggregates into loading hopper

loading scraper shovel powered by slow speed motor controlled from shovel handle

timber planks or similar forming aggregate stockpile

weight batcher dial

steel loading hopper raised, held and lowered by double acting hydraulic ram

loading hopper in loading position

55 litre capacity water tank

diesel engine or electric motor

396 litre unmixed 283 litre mixed capacity steel mixing drum

drum outlet discharge height 1.143

rotation of drum reversed to discharge

pressed steel wheels

Fig. V.34 Typical reversible drum mixer (Liner Concrete Machinery Co. Ltd)

legs with a bottom discharge outlet to the container. Storage capacities range from 12 to 50 tonnes. Silos can be incorporated into an on-site static batching plant or they can have their own weighing attachments. Some of the advantages of silo storage for large quantities of cement are:

1. Cost of bulk cement is cheaper per tonne than bagged cement.
2. Unloading is by direct pumping from delivery vehicle to silo.
3. Less site space is required for any given quantity to be stored on site.
4. First cement delivered is the first to be used since it is pumped into the top of the silo and extracted from the bottom.

READY MIXED CONCRETE

The popularity of ready mixed concrete has increased tremendously since 1968 when the British Ready Mixed Concrete Association laid down minimum standards for plant, equipment, personnel and quality control for all BRMCA approved depots. The ready mixed concrete industry consumes a large proportion of the total cement output of the United Kingdom in supplying many millions of cubic metres of concrete per annum to all parts of the country.

Ready mixed concrete is supplied to sites in specially designed truck mixers which are basically a mobile mixing drum mounted on a lorry chassis. Truck mixers can be employed in one of three ways:

1. Loaded at the depot with dry batched materials plus the correct quantity of water, the truck mixer is used to complete the mixing process at the depot before leaving for the site. During transportation to the site the mix is kept agitated by the revolving drum; on arrival the contents are remixed before being discharged.
2. Fully or partially mixed concrete is loaded into the truck mixer at the depot. During transportation to the site the mix is agitated by the drum revolving at 1 to 2 revolutions per minute. On arrival the mix is finally mixed by increasing the drum's revolutions to between 10 and 15 revolutions per minute for a few minutes before being discharged.
3. When the time taken to deliver the mix to the site may be unacceptable the mixing can take place on site by loading the truck mixer at the depot with dry batched materials and adding the water upon arrival on site before completing the mixing operation and subsequent discharge.

All forms of truck mixer carry a supply of water which is normally used to wash out the drum after discharging the concrete and before returning to the depot — see Fig. V.35 for typical truck mixer details.

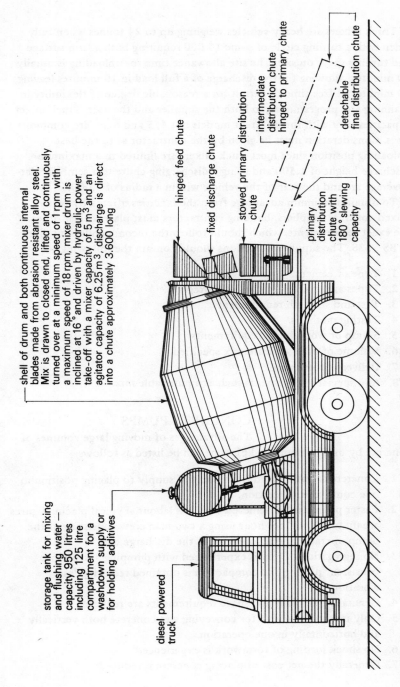

shell of drum and both continuous internal blades made from abrasion resistant alloy steel. Mix is drawn to closed end, lifted and continuously turned over at a minimum speed of 1 rpm with a maximum speed of 18 rpm, mixer drum is inclined at 16° and driven by hydraulic power take-off with a mixer capacity of 5 m³ and an agitator capacity of 6.25 m³, discharge is direct into a chute approximately 3,600 long

hinged feed chute

fixed discharge chute

stowed primary distribution chute

intermediate distribution chute hinged to primary chute

detachable final distribution chute

primary distribution chute with 180° slewing capacity

storage tank for mixing and flushing water — capacity 950 litres including 125 litre compartment for a washdown supply or for holding additives

diesel powered truck

Fig. V.35 Typical ready mix concrete truck details

Truck mixers are heavy vehicles weighing up to 24 tonnes when fully laden with a turning circle of some 15.000 requiring both a firm surface and turning space on site. The site allowance time for unloading is usually 30 minutes, allowing for the discharge of a full load in 10 minutes leaving 20 minutes of free time to permit for a reasonable degree of flexibility in planning and programming to both the supplier and the user. Truck mixer capacities vary with the different models but 4, 5 and 6 m^3 are common sizes. Consideration must be given by the contractor as to the best unloading position since most truck mixers are limited to a maximum discharge height of 1.500 and using a discharging chute to a semi-circular coverage around the rear of the vehicle within a radius of 3.000.

To obtain maximum advantage from the facilities offered by ready mixed concrete suppliers, building contractors must place a clear order of the exact requirements, which should follow the recommendations given in BS 5328. The supply instructions should contain the following:

1. Type of cement.
2. Types and maximum sizes of aggregates.
3. Test and strength requirements.
4. Testing methods.
5. Slump or workability requirements.
6. Volume of each separate mix specified.
7. Delivery programme.
8. Any special requirements such as a pumpable mix.

CONCRETE PUMPS

The advantages of moving large volumes of concrete by using a pump and pipeline can be listed as follows:

1. Concrete is transported from point of supply to placing position in one continuous operation.
2. Faster pours can be achieved with less labour. Typical placing figures are up to 100 m^3 per hour using a two-man crew consisting of the pump operator and an operator at the discharge end.
3. No segregation of mix is experienced with pumping and a more consistent placing and compaction is obtained requiring less vibration.
4. Generally site plant and space requirements are reduced.
5. Only method available for conveying wet concrete both vertically and horizontally in one operation.
6. No shock loading of formwork is experienced.
7. Generally the net cost of placing concrete is reduced.

364

Against the above listed advantages must be set the following limitations:

1. Concrete supply must be consistent and regular, which can usually be achieved by well-planned and organised deliveries of ready mixed concrete. It should be noted that under ideal conditions the discharge rate of each truck mixer can be in the order of 10 minutes.

2. Concrete mix must be properly designed and controlled since not all concrete mixes are pumpable. The concrete is pumped under high pressure which can cause bleeding and segregation of the mix; therefore the mix must be properly designed to avoid these problems as well as having good cohesive, plasticity and self-lubricating properties to enable it to be pumped through the system without excessive pressure and without causing blockages.

3. More formwork will be required to receive the high output of the pump to make its use an economic proposition.

Most pumps used today are of the twin-cylinder hydraulically driven design either as a trailer pump or lorry-mounted pump using a small bore (100 mm diameter) pipeline capable of pumping concrete 85.000 vertically and 200.000 horizontally although these figures will vary with the actual pump used — see Fig. V.36 for typical example. The delivery pipes are usually of rigid seamless steel in 3.000 lengths except where flexibility is required as on booms and at the delivery end. Large radius bends of up to 1.000 radius giving 22½°, 45° and 90° turning are available to give flexible layout patterns. Generally small diameter pipes of 75 and 100 mm are used for vertical pumping whereas larger diameters of up to 150 mm are used for horizontal pumping. If a concrete mix with large aggregates is to be pumped the pipe diameter should be at least three or four times the maximum aggregate size.

The time required on site to set up a pump is approximately 30 to 45 minutes. The pump operator will require a supply of water and grout for the initial coating of the pipeline, this usually requires about two or three bags of cement. A hard standing should be provided for the pump with adequate access and turning space for the attendant ready mixed concrete vehicles. The output of a concrete pump will be affected by the distance the concrete is to be pumped, therefore the pump should be positioned so that it is as close to the discharge point as is practicable. Pours should be planned so that they progress backwards towards the pump, removing the redundant pipe lengths as the work proceeds.

Generally if the volume of concrete to be placed is sufficient to warrant hiring a pump and operators it will result in an easier, quicker and usually cheaper operation than placing the concrete by the traditional method of

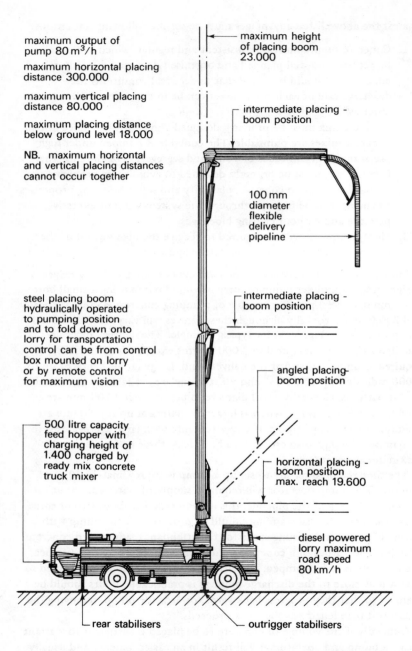

maximum output of pump 80 m³/h

maximum horizontal placing distance 300.000

maximum vertical placing distance 80.000

maximum placing distance below ground level 18.000

NB. maximum horizontal and vertical placing distances cannot occur together

maximum height of placing boom 23.000

intermediate placing - boom position

100 mm diameter flexible delivery pipeline

steel placing boom hydraulically operated to pumping position and to fold down onto lorry for transportation control can be from control box mounted on lorry or by remote control for maximum vision

intermediate placing - boom position

angled placing boom position

500 litre capacity feed hopper with charging height of 1.400 charged by ready mix concrete truck mixer

horizontal placing - boom position max. reach 19.600

diesel powered lorry maximum road speed 80 km/h

rear stabilisers

outrigger stabilisers

Fig. V.36 Typical lorry mounted concrete pump (Schwing)

crane and skip with typical outputs of 15 to 20 m^3 per hour as opposed to the 60 to 100 m^3 per hour output of the concrete pump. Concrete pumping and placing demands a certain amount of skill and experience and for this reason most pumps in use are hired out and operated by specialist contractors.

Bibliography

Relevant BS — British Standards Institution.

Relevant CP — British Standards Institution.

Building Regulations — HMSO.

Relevant BRE Digests — HMSO.

Relevant Advisory Leaflets — DOE.

DOE Construction Issues 1–17 — DOE.

R. Barry. *The Construction of Buildings.* Crosby Lockwood & Sons Ltd.

Mitchells Building Construction Series. B. T. Batsford Ltd.

W. B. McKay. *Building Construction*, Vols. 1 to 4. Longman.

Specification. The Architectural Press.

A. J. Elder. *A. J. Guide to the Building Regulations.* The Architectural Press.

Construction Safety. The National Federation of Building Trades Employers.

BSP Pocket Book. The British Steel Piling Co. Ltd.

W. Whitaker. *The Design of Piled Foundations.* Pergamon Press.

A. S. West. *Piling Practice.* Butterworths.

R. Holmes. *Introduction to Civil Engineering Construction.* College of Estate Management.

Lighting for Building Sites. The Electricity Council.

G. N. Smith. *Elements of Soil Mechanics for Civil and Mining Engineers.* Crosby Lockwood & Sons Ltd.

Application of Mastic Asphalt — Mastic Asphalt Council and Employers Federation.

Relevant A. J. Handbooks. The Architectural Press.
Relevant manufacturers' catalogues contained in the Barbour Index and
    Building Products Index Libraries.

Index

O

Open caissons, 117, 119, 121
Operatives, xi
Outlet units, 34-5

P

Pad foundations, 153-4, 164
Pavings, 285-8
Percussion bored piles, 216, 218-9
Perimeter trench, 78-80, 86-7
Pile caps, 224-6
Pile framing, 85
Piled foundations, 169, 203-26
    caps, 224-6
    classification, 203-4
    contracts, 226
    displacement, 205-16
    downdrag, 204-5
    driving, 214-6
    end-bearing, 204
    friction, 204
    replacement, 216-22
    testing, 222-4
Piling helmets, 215-6
Piling rigs, 207-9, 211, 215
Pinning, 234
Pipe jacking, 100-3
    pipes, 103
Pipes, 245-7
    cast iron, 245, 252
    clay, 125, 245, 247-8
    glaze ware, 122, 245, 247-8
    perforated, 122
    pitch fibre, 125, 246-7
    porous, 125
    UPVC, 246-7, 253
Plant, 291-367
    backactors, 321, 323-4
    bulldozers, 312, 314-5
    cartridge hammers, 300, 302-4
    choice, 291-6
    compressors, 298, 300-1
    concrete mixers, 358-61
    concrete pumps, 364-7
    crane skips, 350, 353
    cranes, 337-57
    draglines, 321, 325
    dumpers, 330-1
    electric hand tools, 297-9
    face shovels, 321-2
    forklift trucks, 330, 333
    graders, 316
    hoists, 332, 334-5
    lorries, 329-30
    multi-purpose excavators, 326-7
    pneumatic tools, 298, 300-1

power floats, 304-6
pumps, 305. 307-9
rollers, 308, 310-11
scrapers, 313, 316-7
skimmers, 318, 320-1
tractor shovel, 318-9
trenchers, 326, 328
vibrators, 304
wire ropes, 350, 354
Plastic failure, 164, 168
Pneumatic caissons, 120-1
Pneumatic tools, 298, 300-1
Portland cement, 147-8
Power floats, 304-6
Precast concrete piles, 205
Precast concrete retaining walls,
    179, 182
Precast concrete soakaways, 269
Preformed concrete piles, 205-8
Pressure bulbs, 165
'Prestcore' pile, 206, 222-3
Pretest method of underpinning, 229
Private sewers, 257-8
Profile Board, 6
Protective clothing, 56
Protective screens, 53-5
Pumps 305, 307-9
Pusher arm, 63-4
'Pynford' stooling, 231, 234-5

Q

Quantity surveyor, x

R

Radiant heaters, 57
Raft foundations, 143, 146, 153,
    155-6, 164
Rainwater drainage, 252-5
Raking struts, 89
Rankine's formula, 84
Rapid hardening cement, 148
Ready mixed concrete, 362-4
Reinforced concrete foundations,
    152-8
    blinding, 156
    pad, 153-4
    rafts, 153, 155
    strip, 153-4
Replacement piles, 216-22
Resin grouts, 130
Retaining walls, 174-83
    cantilever, 177, 179-80, 182
    counterfort, 179, 181
    crib, 179, 182-3
    earth pressures, 175
    mass, 177-8